Wild Flowers of The United States

Volume Six   *Part Two of Three Parts*

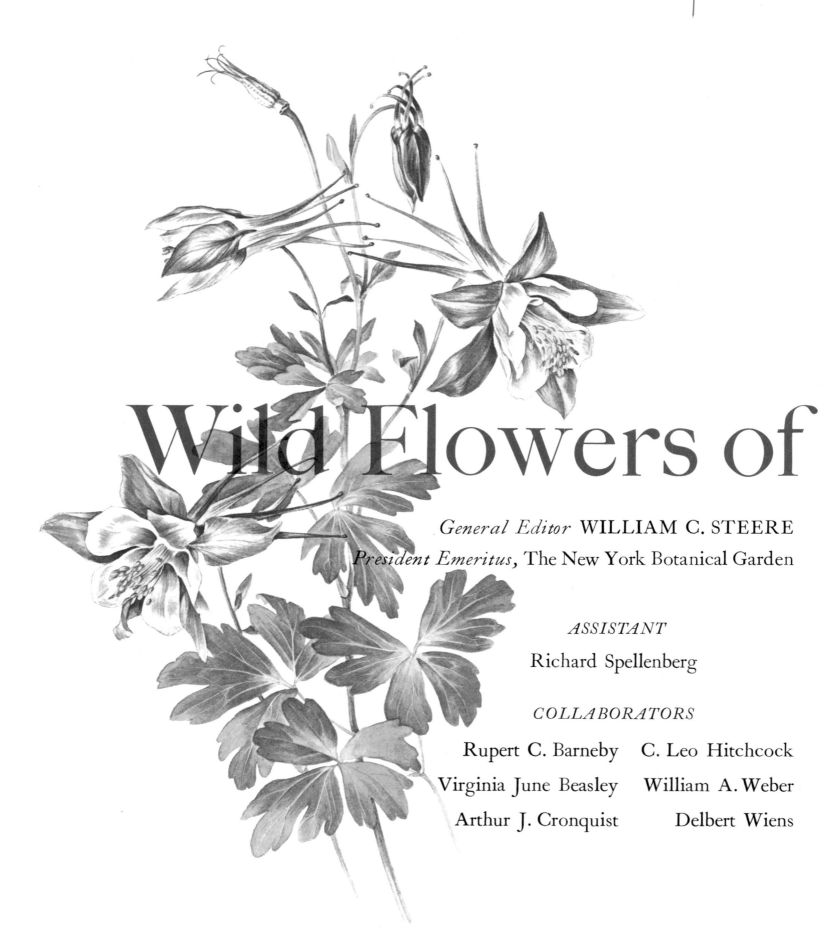

Wild Flowers of

General Editor WILLIAM C. STEERE
President Emeritus, The New York Botanical Garden

ASSISTANT

Richard Spellenberg

COLLABORATORS

Rupert C. Barneby   C. Leo Hitchcock

Virginia June Beasley   William A. Weber

Arthur J. Cronquist   Delbert Wiens

Publication of THE NEW YORK BOTANICAL GARDEN

Harold William Rickett

The New York Botanical Garden

The United States

Volume Six *Part Two of Three Parts*

THE CENTRAL MOUNTAINS AND PLAINS

FROM NORTH DAKOTA TO OKLAHOMA
AND WEST TO THE CASCADE MOUNTAINS
AND THE SIERRA NEVADA

McGRAW-HILL BOOK COMPANY · NEW YORK

WILD FLOWERS OF THE UNITED STATES:
VOLUME 6: THE CENTRAL MOUNTAINS
AND PLAINS

To DIARMUID C. RUSSELL,
to whose searching and imaginative
mind we attribute the original concept
of this series of books: and to his friends
DAVID and PEGGY ROCKEFELLER
who, inspired by his initiative, helped
this series to its conclusion

Already published
Volume 1: The Northeastern States
Volume 2: The Southeastern States
Volume 3: Texas
Volume 4: The Southwestern States
Volume 5: The Northwestern States
Volume 6: The Central Mountains and Plains

To be published
Complete index for the six volumes

Printed in England by
W. S. COWELL LTD, BUTTER MARKET, IPSWICH

Library of Congress Catalog Card Number 66–17920
First Edition 07–052643–5

CONTENTS

GROUP VII

SEPALS four or five. Petals four or five, radially symmetric, separate. Stamens as many as the petals or twice as many. Styles (or stigmas) generally more than one. Leaves various. Exceptions: petals are lacking in some species of the pink family; slightly bilateral in symmetry in some species of the saxifrage and parsley families. The calyx in some species of the parsley family is scarcely visible and may have no lobes or teeth. A few species of the pink family have a single style, and some have from two to fifteen stamens.

I. *Plants with no leaves divided, cleft, or lobed.*

   A. Styles from one to five, on one ovary; leaves paired: pink family.

   B. Styles from three to five, on as many separate or almost separate ovaries; succulent plants (except *Penthorum*): live-forever family.

   C. Styles five, on one ovary; leaves borne singly: flax family.

   D. Styles three, on one ovary; leaves at the ground, the blades covered with sticky hairs: sundew family.

   E. Styles two; ovary inferior; flowers small: species of *Hydrocotyle* and *Eryngium* in the parsley family.

   F. Styles none; four stigmas: *Parnassia* in the saxifrage family.

II. *Plants with at least some leaves divided, cleft, or lobed.*

   A. Styles two, on two partly separate ovaries; stamens five or ten: saxifrage family.

   B. Styles three, on one ovary; a conspicuous circle of hairs at the base of the petals: passion-flower family.

   C. Styles five, on one ovary; leaves with three notched segments at the tip of the stalk: wood-sorrel family.

   D. Styles from two to six, on one ovary; leaves divided into broad, pointed segments; flowers small, white or greenish: ginseng family.

   E. Styles two, on an inferior ovary; flowers yellow, white, pink, or reddish, mostly in compound umbels: parsley family.

THE PINK FAMILY (CARYOPHYLLACEAE)

A characteristic of the *Caryophyllaceae* is the disposition of their flowers in cymes: for this type of inflorescence the reader is referred to the Glossary and the Introduction; it is easily seen in some of the photographs and drawings on the following pages; but in others it disguises itself as an apparent head or umbel, or the flowers are borne singly. The flower-parts are generally in fours or fives, the stamens in most species being as many as the sepals or twice as many (from two to fifteen in some genera). Petals are lacking in a number of species. The ovary bears from one to five styles. The ovules – rudiment of seeds – are all attached to a central stalk which rises from the floor of the single cavity in the ovary but is not attached at the top. The leaves are generally narrow and paired.

This is a large family, chiefly of northern regions. In it are found both small weeds with minute flowers and larger plants with showy flowers. A number of species are valued in our gardens and greenhouses: carnations, pinks, baby's-breath, sandworts, campions, and others. Some of the weedy kinds are troublesome; some have proved fatal to cattle.

The two principal groups below have been separated by some botanists as two families; but the distinction is not clear enough.

Guide to Genera of Caryophyllaceae

I. *Genera whose sepals are joined to form a tube, cup, or bladder.*
See also *Scopulophila* under II.

A. Some of these have two styles on the ovary (or one style cleft in two): *Gypsophila* (flowers very many, very small, white, in large cymes); *Dianthus* (flowers white, pink, or red, in close cymes surrounded by bracts; generally only one in a cyme open; or they may be borne singly); *Saponaria* (petals pink and white, or red; calyx tubular, with twenty veins, or ovate and five-ribbed); *Achyronychia* (stems prostrate; flowers minute, white, in dense clusters; from ten to fifteen stamens but only five fertile).

B. Other genera of group I have from three to six styles: *Agrostemma* (flowers red; calyx-lobes narrow, longer than the petals); *Lychnis* (styles commonly five; petals mostly white, notched); *Silene* (styles commonly three; petals of many species cleft or lobed, white, pink, or red).

II. *Genera whose sepals are separate or nearly so. Flowers mostly small, white.*

A. Plants with petals deeply cleft, two-lobed: *Stellaria* (styles commonly three); *Cerastium* (styles commonly five).

B. Plants whose petals may be shallowly notched or not at all: *Spergularia* (leaves with evident stipules; petals white or pink; commonly three styles; from two to seven stamens); *Spergula* (leaves in circles, with evident stipules; petals white; commonly five styles; five or ten stamens); *Sagina* (petals present or absent; five styles); *Paronychia* (plants small, prostrate or spreading; one style); *Scleranthus* (leaves awl-like; flowers minute; two styles); *Scopulophila* (sepals joined at the base; one style cleft into three); *Holosteum* (petals irregularly toothed; mostly three styles; flowers in umbels); *Arenaria* (commonly three styles; petals white, with or without a shallow notch, not lobed or cleft; plants commonly forming mats or cushions — but some species not so).

GYPSOPHILA

One cultivated species of *Gypsophila* is occasionally found growing wild throughout our range. Baby's-breath, *G. paniculata* (to 4 feet), is much branched, with lanceolate or narrower leaves up to 4 inches long, smooth, with a bloom. The numerous flowers are small, white. Blooming in summer.

DIANTHUS

Several species of *Dianthus* are familiar in gardens: Sweet-William, *D. barbatus*; garden pinks, *D. plumarius*; and — under glass — carnations, *D. caryophyllus*. We have no native species but two Old-World species are established in the United States.

DEPTFORD PINK, D. ARMERIA (up to 3 feet), has narrow leaves standing close to the stem, to 4 inches long. Several flowers are crowded at the tip among narrow bracts; usually only one open at a time. The spreading blades of the petals are pink or red, with pale spots near their base. June to August: in fields and waste ground in Kansas, Washington, Idaho, and Montana, and probably elsewhere. *Plate 89.*

Maiden pink, *D. deltoides*, is likewise in scattered places in our range, at least in western Montana. It has single flowers at the stem-tips, or two or three in an open cluster. The petals may be pink, rose, or white.

SAPONARIA

Two common weeds from the Old World represent the genus *Saponaria* in our range. They have commonly lanceolate leaves. The flowers have a tubular calyx and notched petals. The capsule opens at the tip, forming four teeth.

The name is derived from *sapo*, "soap"; an extract from either of these species forms a lather with water. This is due to poisonous substances named saponins.

BOUNCING-BET, S. OFFICINALIS (1–3 feet), forms
  large colonies of leafy stems, with numerous pink or white flowers in close clusters in the axils. The petals have a stalk within the calyx and a blade which tends to bend back; there are two narrow teeth where blade and stalk meet. The five teeth of the calyx are generally partly joined so as to form two lobes.

July to September: widespread in the eastern states; in our range mostly in Washington and Oregon. *Plate 89.* This was formerly cultivated, but is rarely seen in gardens now except as a weed, curiously, since it is rather pretty.

Cowherb or Cow Cockie, *S. vaccaria*, carries its flowers in a cyme at the tip of the stem. The calyx has five angles. The petals are pink or pale red, and lack the teeth at the base of the blade. These differences have been considered by many botanists sufficient to place this species in a genus by itself, as *Vaccaria segetalis*. It is common throughout our range, in old fields and waste ground, etc. *Plate 96.*

AGROSTEMMA

One species of *Agrostemma* is a weed on waste land and roadsides through much of North America and throughout our range; less common in Idaho and Montana than elsewhere.

CORN COCKLE, A. GITHAGO (to 4 feet), has a white-
  hairy stem bearing narrow, hairy leaves 2–5 inches long. The flowers are several at tips of stems. The petals are red. The calyx has five long teeth which project between and beyond the petals; they continue five of the ten strong ribs in the tube of the calyx. Ten stamens; five styles. June and July. This European plant has been known as troublesome in grainfields ("corn" in England being mostly wheat). *Plate 89.*

ACHYRONYCHIA

Our only species of *Achyronychia*, *A. cooperi*, is found in our southwestern corner and on the southern edge of the Great Basin. It is a desert plant, with prostrate stems, spatula-like leaves $\frac{1}{5}$–$\frac{2}{5}$ inch long, in pairs with the two in each pair unequal. The tiny flowers are in dense clusters in the axils, with white sepals, no petals, from ten to fifteen stamens but only five with pollen, and one style cleft into two branches.

CAMPIONS* (LYCHNIS)

The ovary of *Lychnis* is usually characterized by having five styles, and this is commonly used to distinguish the genus from *Silene*; but the number in *Lychnis* actually varies from three to six, and in *Silene* it is three or four. Other characteristics of *Lychnis* must be taken into consideration.† The petals of both genera are notched or cleft, and there are generally two small projections inside at the base of the blade (where it meets the stalk). The seed-pod splits at the tip into generally five teeth (which may each be finally cleft into two).

L. ALBA (2–4 feet) has lanceolate leaves, the lowest
  stalked. The flowers are in cymes with leafy bracts. Pistils and stamens are on different plants. The calyx of the pistillate flowers may have about ten veins, that of the staminate about twenty; but there is great variation. The petals are white, their appendages forming a prominent circle just where the corolla emerges from the calyx. The pistillate calyx soon becomes "inflated" – ovate; the staminate remains narrowly elliptic.

June to August: widely distributed throughout our area (except perhaps in Oklahoma). *Plate 89.* Both pistillate and staminate flowers are shown. This has been often confused with *Silene noctiflora*, which,

*Species of *Silene* are also called campions.
†In my opinion, the two genera cannot be clearly separated.

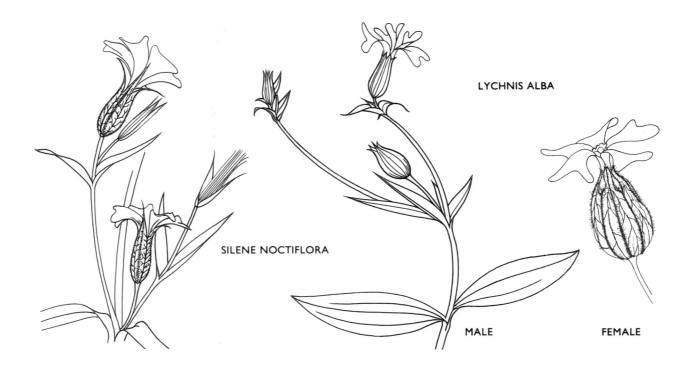

however, has stamens and pistils together in the flowers, a differently veined calyx, and narrower bracts.

Mullein-pink or rose campion, *L. coronaria*, may be found west of the Rockies, but is much commoner east and west of our range. It has small flowers with intensely magenta-red petals, at the tips of the unbranched stems (16–40 inches tall). The plant is gray-woolly. The calyx has ten ribs and five teeth.

L. APETALA (2–10 inches) commonly forms tufts of narrow, downy leaves not more than 1½ inches long. There are from one to three flowers on a stem. They droop while in the bud, gradually straightening as they open. The calyx is much inflated; it is pale, commonly with ten purple or dark green ribs (alternate ribs not running all the way up), and five very short teeth. In spite of the name, which means "without petals," petals are present; but on many plants they do not emerge from the calyx. When they appear, they are seen to have small pink or mauve blades.

July and August: in alpine and arctic regions around the world in high latitudes and southward along the summits of the Rocky Mountains to Colorado. *Plate 89. L. kingii*, in the high mountains of Utah, Colorado, and Wyoming, differs in having the flowers erect from the first, and a calyx not so greatly inflated.

L. DRUMMONDII (8–20 inches) is certainly on the borderline between *Lychnis* and *Silene*. It has five styles (at least typically). The basal leaves form a rosette; their blades are lanceolate, elliptic, or wider in the outer half, tapering to slender stalks. Stem-leaves are very narrow. The stem has glandular hairs directed downward. The flowers are in a narrow cyme, the petals with white or pink blades about ⅛ inch long; the calyx tubular.

June to August: in mountains from Canada to southeastern Oregon, southern Nevada, Colorado; and in South Dakota and Nebraska.

CAMPIONS (SILENE)

For the distinction – or lack of distinction – between *Silene* and *Lychnis*, see the description of *Lychnis*. The two genera merge together through such species as *L. drummondii* and *S. parryi*.

The five sepals of *Silene* are joined to form a tube, which in many species enlarges to form a sort of bladder around the fruit, a capsule. The five petals have long, stalk-like bases; the blades are generally showy, spreading at right angles; they mostly have small,

scalelike appendages just where stalk and blade merge. There are ten stamens. The ovary is on a short stalk. The capsule opens at the end, splitting into usually six teeth. The leaves are in pairs or circles. Many species have sticky stems.

We have many more species of *Silene* than of *Lychnis*: twenty-nine. They form a varied group, with petals of various colors, some notched or cleft, some four-lobed; some with calyx much inflated in fruit;

PLATE 89

Agrostemma githago   *Elbert*

Silene cucubalus   *Elbert*

Saponaria officinalis   *Johnson*

Lychnis alba (female)   *Johnson*

Lychnis apetala   *W. Weber*

Dianthus armeria   *Gottscho*

Lychnis apetala   *Andersen*

Lychnis alba (male)   *Gottscho*

many native western species and some widespread weedy species from the Old World. In general the flowers have ten stamens, three styles, five petals, and a calyx with ten conspicuous veins; but there are exceptions to all these statements. Most species have stamens and pistil in the same flower.

The groups in which I have placed our species are not clearly separated; and how can one tell at sight whether a plant belongs to an American or an Old-World species? However, they will serve, if carefully used, to eliminate certain species from a particular gathering. For example, if one picks up a plant with inflated calyx in Oregon, he needs to look only under I A and C; if in Kansas, only under I A and B; and to identify a plant with calyx not inflated in the fruiting stage, all of group I can be passed over.

I. *Species with calyx enlarged – inflated – around the seed-pod.*
   A. Weedy Old-World species with calyx greatly inflated. Most of these are more abundant to the east of our range. Their occurrence in our area is spotty.

BLADDER CAMPION, S. CUCUBALUS (to 40 inches), has the lower leaves joined in pairs around the stem. The inflorescence is a clear example of a cyme (and in fact formed the model for the drawing illustrating this in the Glossary). The petals are white, two-lobed. At maturity the calyx is almost a globe, tinted pinkish-brown, its veins emitting many small and indistinct branches.

June to August: in waste places in Kansas, Colorado, and Oregon, and probably elsewhere. *Plate 89. S. cserei* is similar; the leaves are thicker and the inflorescence narrower. In North Dakota; and reported, perhaps erroneously, in Montana. *S. conoidea* (to 32 inches) has a hairy calyx with from twenty-five to thirty veins. The stem is downy, the hairs pointing downward. The petals range from white to purplish, shallowly or not at all notched. In South Dakota and from the West Coast to Idaho.

NIGHT-FLOWERING CATCHFLY, S. NOCTIFLORA (to 2 feet), is hairy and sticky throughout. The petals are white or pink. The calyx has ten veins mostly with side veins in a pinnate arrangement; the calyx-teeth are slender.

June to December: in waste ground throughout our area.

   B. Species, with inflated calyx, native east of our range. These are limited in our area to the plains east of the Rockies.

STARRY CAMPION, S. STELLATA (16–40 inches) is easily recognized among the other species in Kansas and Oklahoma by its corolla: the blades of the white petals are cleft into a number of narrow lobes, forming the "star." The leaves are in circles of four. July to September. *Plate 90.*

Snowy campion, *S. nivea* (about 1 foot), has lanceolate leaves, few flowers, and white petals which are slightly notched. In South Dakota.

   C. Western species, with moderately inflated calyx. These are not found east of the Rocky Mountains.

S. DOUGLASII forms tufts or mats, the stems bending up from a prostrate base, 16 inches long or longer. The plants are finely and densely downy. The leaves are narrow, or wider towards the end, 1–3 inches long and up to ½ inch wide; the basal leaves long-stalked. The petals are cream or greenish, pink, or purplish-tinged, generally two-lobed, with a prominent tooth on each side.

May to July: on plains with sagebrush and on mountain slopes from Washington to California and eastward to western Montana and Utah.

S. PARRYI (to 16 inches, or taller) has erect stems, downy and to some extent glandular. The leaves are mostly at the base, widest at or near the end, 1–3 inches long. The petals are white, greenish, or purplish-tinged, two-lobed about half the length of the blade, with a prominent tooth on each side which may make the blades seem four-lobed.

July and August: in mountains from Washington to Idaho, northwestern Wyoming, and the Rocky Mountains. *Plate 90.*

S. suksdorfii (to 6 inches) is an alpine species of the Cascade and Wenatchee Mountains in Washington and Oregon. The petals are two-lobed and have a tooth on each side; white or greenish or lavender-tinged. The leaves are mostly less than an inch long. June to August.

S. petersonii (to 6 inches) has been found only in south-central Utah. Stems densely downy and glandular. Leaves 1–1½ inches. Flowers droop; petals pink or rose-purple, the blades irregularly toothed and shallowly lobed. July and August. *S. clokeyi* is similar. Possibly in our extreme southwestern corner.

II. *Species whose calyx is not inflated.*
   These are mostly native western species, some with narrow ranges. The first two, our only red-flowered species, however, are eastern and limited in our range to Oklahoma and Kansas. Several others are Old-World species now found throughout our area, but not abundantly.

FIRE-PINK, S. VIRGINICA, has slender, hairy stems 8–24 inches long, bearing thin, smooth leaves. The flowers have deep red blades, lobed at the end, with two points which may curve inward.

PLATE 90

Silene stellata   *Johnson*

Silene menziesii   *Scribner*

Silene scouleri   *Hesselberg*

Silene antirrhina   *Horne*

Silene virginica   *V. Richard*

Silene acaulis   *Rhein*

Stellaria media   *Rickett*

Silene parryi   *Korling*

April to June: in open woods and on slopes in Oklahoma. *Plate 90*. Royal catchfly, *S. regia*, 2–4 feet tall, has finely downy leaves. The petals are bright red, scarcely notched. June to August: in dry woods and on prairies in Kansas and Oklahoma.

MOSS-PINK, S. ACAULIS, is one of those high-latitude, "circumpolar" species found around the world in the far north and extending southward along high mountain ranges. In our range it is found in the Cascade Mountains, in Idaho and Nevada, and through the Rocky Mountains. It forms cushions, the stems mostly an inch or two tall, and narrow leaves less than $\frac{1}{2}$ inch long, which remain attached long after they wither. The petals are pink or lavender, rarely white.

June to August: in moist places at high altitudes. *Plate 90*. Superficially the plants resemble some of the high-mountain species of phlox; but these have joined petals.

GARDEN CATCHFLY or NONE-SO-PRETTY, S. ARMERIA (to 2 feet), has been grown in gardens and may be found growing in waste land, flowering in June and July. It is generally smooth. The leaves have no stalks and tend to surround the stem at their base. The lavender-pink flowers are in compact clusters (cymes) at the tips of branches.

S. dichotoma is widespread throughout the country but not common in our range. The name means "forked" and refers to the two branches at the tip of the stem along which the flowers grow in what seems to be a one-sided spike (really a kind of cyme); there may be similar branches from the axils. The flowers are generally white, less commonly pink. May to July: in North Dakota and Montana and probably elsewhere.

SLEEPY CATCHFLY, S. ANTIRRHINA (8–32 inches), has stems marked by sticky bands between the leaves; on these, small insects are held. The leaves are narrow, meeting around the stem at their base. The small white or pink flowers are in cymes at the tips of the stem and branches.

May to August: in fields and on prairies and waste land throughout. *Plate 90*.

The following three species have four appendages at the base of the blade of the petal, instead of the two in most other species.

S. OREGANA (1–2 feet) has two or three pairs of leaves near the base and from one to three pairs higher on the stem, all $1\frac{1}{2}$–3 inches long, tending to be widest between middle and tip. The calyx is glandular, tapering at each end and marked by ten ribs which may be purplish. The pinkish petals are four-lobed at the end; the lobes may be again lobed or forked, the final parts being very narrow.

June to August: from sagebrush and pine to the high eastern slopes of the Cascade Mountains in Washington, southward to northeastern California, southeastern Washington and eastern Oregon, and eastward to western Montana, northwestern Wyoming, and northeastern Nevada.

S. scaposa, in eastern Oregon, central Idaho, and northern Nevada, in similar in aspect. The petals have four nearly equal lobes or may be unlobed. Uncommon.

S. spaldingii, from eastern Washington to western Montana, is woolly and rather sticky, with many flowers in a compact, leafy cyme. The blades of the petals are very short, white. Not often seen.

S. MENZIESII is low, rather matted, with many narrow leaves 1–4 inches long. The flowers are in a leafy cyme, with a white corolla not more than $\frac{1}{2}$ inch long; the petals are two-lobed, and may have teeth at the sides.

May to August: from the Rocky Mountains westward throughout our range. *Plate 90*.

S. seelyi, found on the Wenatchee Mountains in Washington, is similar, but with leaves less than an inch long, and purplish petals.

S. SCOULERI (to 3 feet) is densely downy all over. The basal leaves are up to 6 inches long; those above successively smaller. The numerous flowers are in small, close clusters which together form a sort of "interrupted spike"; i.e. interrupted by short lengths of bare stem. The corolla ranges from greenish-white to purplish, with two or four lobes or teeth.

June to August: in open woodland and on prairies from Washington to California, eastward to western Montana, thence southward through the Rocky Mountains. *Plate 90*.

S. occidentalis, a Californian species, in our range in the northeastern corner of that state, is more glandular; the lower leaves are not more than an inch long; the petals are flesh-colored or rose, almost equally four-lobed. June and July.

S. nuda, on the eastern slope of the Sierra Nevada and in south-central Oregon, has basal leaves 2–8 inches long, their stalks about equaling the blades. There are one or two pairs of leaves on the stem. The petals are pink, cleft. May and June: with sagebrush and pine.

S. sargentii has a tuft of narrow basal leaves up to an inch long, and one or two pairs of leaves on the stem. The flowers are few — perhaps only one; the petals have two-lobed blades only about $\frac{1}{8}$ inch long, from whitish to rose-purple; generally with a small tooth on each side. Rocky places high in the Sierra Nevada and in western Nevada.

S. montana (6–18 inches), on the eastern slope of the Sierra Nevada and northward to Crater Lake in Oregon, has basal leaves 1–3 inches long, narrow or wider towards the tip; from two to four pairs on the stem. Petals white tinged with pink or purple, the blades about $\frac{1}{4}$ inch long, cleft into four narrow lobes. June to August.

S. *verecunda* (4–12 inches) ranges from California to southwestern Utah, with sagebrush and piñon-juniper forest. The leaves are widest between middle and tip. The flowers are in a tall narrow inflorescence. The petals are greenish-white, pink, or rose, the blades about $\frac{1}{4}$ inch long, two-lobed. June to August.

S. REPENS is generally matted, with the stems at first trailing then growing erect, 4–8 inches tall. The leaves are mostly narrow, 1–2 inches long, and mostly grow in tufts; there are also a few pairs on each stem. The flowers are in several stalked clusters – or single – in the axils of bracts, forming a narrow, somewhat raceme-like inflorescence. The petals range from white to rose or purple, the two-lobed blades less than $\frac{1}{3}$ inch long.

July and August: mostly on high rock slopes in central Idaho, northwestern Wyoming, and western Montana; also in the high mountains of Alaska, Europe, and Asia.

CHICKWEEDS (STELLARIA)

Chickweeds growing in moist places are likely to be *Stellaria*; those of dry places, *Cerastium*; but there are exceptions. The petals of both genera are forked or two-lobed (or lacking); there are generally five in *Stellaria*, but they vary in number. The stamens are commonly twice as many. The ovary generally has three or four styles. The seed-pod opens at the tip, forming twice as many teeth as the number of styles.

The name *Stellaria* comes from *stella*, "star," and refers to the flowers. Some species have been commonly called starworts.

I. *Species with flowers borne singly in the axils.*
    In some of these there may also be a few flowers in a cyme at the tip of the stem (see *S. nitens*).
    Most of these have at least some leaves stalked. Only the first two are found in our area east of the Rocky Mountains.
    See also *S. calycantha* under II.

COMMON CHICKWEED, S. MEDIA, is a widespread weed troublesome especially in lawns. The stems spread on the ground, bearing leaves with ovate blades up to an inch long, mostly on short stalks. The petals are slightly shorter than the sepals, and very deeply cleft so that there are apparently about ten; or there may be none. Throughout the area. *Plate 90.* Some slight usefulness may be found for this weed: chicks do indeed like it and it is often fed to canaries and other caged birds.

S. *crassifolia* may have erect stems, or they may bend up from a horizontal base, forming mats. The leaves are lanceolate, all without stalks. The petals about equal the sepals, up to $\frac{1}{8}$ inch long. July and August: mostly in moist soil from Idaho and Montana southward to Colorado; and in North Dakota.

S. *simcoei* has downy stems, commonly matted. The leaves have ovate or lanceolate blades. There are four or five sepals; petals much shorter or lacking; eight or ten stamens. Generally at high altitudes from Washington to Idaho and Montana, along streams and in meadows, flowering from July to September. S. *crispa* is commonly matted, smooth, the leaves with ovate or lanceolate blades which have a minutely crisped margin. Petals are generally lacking. Mostly at lower altitudes, in moist places, from Washington to Idaho and Montana; May to August. S. *obtusa* forms mats of smooth stems and ovate leaves. The flowers are on very slender stalks up to an inch long. Four or five sepals, no petals, eight or ten stamens. Along streams and in meadows in the Cascade Mountains of Washington and Oregon, the Blue Mountains of southeastern Washington and adjacent Oregon, and through the Rockies to Colorado. S. *nitens* has erect, threadlike stems (to 8 inches), the leaves on the lower half. The lowest leaves have a tiny ovate blade on a stalk about as long; the leaves above are narrow, without stalks. The flowers may be in the axils or in terminal cymes. Petals are shorter than the sepals, the blades cleft almost into two. April to June: in open places from Washington to California and eastward to western Montana, Idaho, and Utah.

II. *Species with flowers in cymes at the tips of stems.*
     There may also be a few single flowers in the axils, or additional cymes (see *S. nitens* under I).
     Leaves lack stalks. Petals are generally present.
     These are found mostly from the Cascades and the Sierra Nevada to and including the Rockies; three extend eastward in the plains.

S. JAMESIANA has weak stems which may be erect, up to 16 inches tall, downy-glandular. The leaves are narrow or lanceolate, 1–4 inches long. The flowers are numerous, in cymes at the tips and from the axils. Petals up to $\frac{2}{5}$ inch long.

May to July: in woods and alpine meadows and on rocky slopes from Washington to the Sierra Nevada in California and eastward through Idaho and Utah to Wyoming and Colorado. *Plate 91.*

S. americana is generally less than 6 inches tall. Leaves glandular-downy, ovate or lanceolate, to $1\frac{1}{4}$ inches. Flowers few. July and August: at high altitudes on rocks in Montana.

S. umbellata is widespread through our range as far east as (and including) the Rockies. The cymes have small, papery bracts. Sepals less than $\frac{1}{8}$ inch; petals generally lacking. Leaves oblong or narrowly lanceolate, $\frac{1}{2}$–1 inch long, smooth; the margins may be crisped. July and August: mostly in moist soil.

STITCHWORT, S. LONGIFOLIA, has stems up to 2 feet long, generally angling upward. The leaves are narrowly lanceolate, $\frac{3}{5}$–$1\frac{1}{2}$ inches long. The petals are up to $\frac{1}{4}$ inch long, about equaling the sepals. There are cymes from the axils as well as at the tips of stems.

May to August: on streams, in meadows, and in other moist places throughout our range from the Rockies westward, and in North Dakota and Kansas. *Plate 91*. The English name refers to the sharp pains known as stitches, for which these plants were once thought to be remedial. Perhaps this is another example of the doctrine of signatures, which taught that the Creator "signed" plants to show what they were good for; the needle-like leaves pointed a remedy for pains that suggest a needle-stab. Compare *Goodyera*, *Aristolochia*. *S. longipes* is so similar as almost to defy

identification with ordinary equipment. The leaves lack the minute roughness on their edges which is characteristic of leaves of *S. longifolia* (but visible only with high magnification). The cymes are less leafy, the bracts smaller, papery. Flower-stalks are longer: to 3 inches. A very variable species, widespread in the Rockies and eastward in North Dakota. *Plate 91*.

S. graminea is more common east and west of our area, but does occur in it, as an occasional weed. It is weak-stemmed and narrow-leaved, like the preceding two species. The leaves are fringed with hairs at their base. The flowers are on long stalks in terminal cymes. The sepals are prominently fringed with short hairs. The petals are up to $\frac{1}{4}$ inch. Mostly from Washington to Idaho, and in Colorado. *Plate 91*.

S. CALYCANTHA may form mats, with prostrate stems; or these may grow upward. The leaves are ovate or narrowly or broadly lanceolate, to 2 inches long. The plants are smooth. The flowers are both in the axils and in terminal leafy-bracted cymes. Petals vary greatly, from twice as long as the sepals to none.

May to August: around the world at high latitudes and southward to California, Utah, and Wyoming. *Plate 91*. On the basis of the differences in leaf-shape, disposition of flowers, etc. a number of varieties have been named.

CHICKWEEDS (CERASTIUM)

Chickweeds of the genus *Cerastium* have five (rarely four) two-lobed or notched, white petals, generally ten stamens, and an ovary bearing five (or four or three) styles. They are small plants, much like *Stellaria*; some are downy or sticky; they are more commonly found in dry places than *Stellaria*. The ovary forms a capsule, which opens at the tip, forming twice as many teeth as there were styles.

MOUSE-EAR CHICKWEED, C. VULGATUM, owes part of its English name to its small downy leaves. This is a familiar pest in lawns and gardens, its stems spreading and dropping seeds. The flowers are in compact clusters at the tips of the stems. Petals are about as long as sepals, notched rather than cleft. March to August: naturalized throughout North America; from the Old World. *Plate 91*. *C. nutans* is sticky-hairy with narrower leaves. April to June: on moist and dry banks and woodland throughout our area at lower altitudes. *Nutans* means "nodding," which is botanical jargon for "drooping, turned downward." In this species it refers to the seed-pod.

C. VISCOSUM is distinguished by its abundant gland-

tipped hairs, which are responsible for its sticky (viscous) character. The flowers are in tight little clusters at the upturned tips of forking stems. Petals are small — about $\frac{1}{5}$ inch, the same as sepals; or they may be lacking. In waste places and fields. *Plate 91*.

C. ARVENSE has trailing stems which may form mats up to 16 inches across; they are smooth or downy and glandular. The flowering stems rise erect, to 20 inches, bearing narrow leaves up to $1\frac{1}{2}$ inches long, often with bunches of smaller leaves in the axils. The flowers are in clusters of generally more than five. The petals are about $\frac{1}{2}$ inch long, deeply lobed.

February to August: on rocky hillsides and high mountain meadows from Canada to California, Colorado, and South Dakota. *Plate 91*. This is the handsomest species of *Cerastium*. It is also the most variable: many varieties have been named, differing in hairs, glands, and other details; these have by some been treated as distinct species.

C. beeringianum is similar, with leaves oblong and blunt. July and August: high in the Rocky Mountains in Washington, California, Idaho, and Utah, and from Montana to Colorado.

PLATE 91

Cerastium viscosum *McDowell*

Cerastium vulgatum *Scribner*

Stellaria graminea *Rickett*

Spergularia marina *Mackintosh*

Stellaria calycantha *McDowell*

Cerastium arvense *Korling*

Stellaria longifolia *Beesley*

Stellaria longipes *Scribner*

Stellaria jamesiana *Korling*

SAND-SPURREYS (SPERGULARIA)

The sand-spurreys are small plants with mostly spreading or prostrate stems, narrow leaves, and pink or white flowers in leafy cymes at the ends of the stems. Stipules are quite evident, though small. There are five sepals; five petals generally shorter than the sepals, not notched or lobed; generally from seven to ten stamens in our species, except the first; three styles. The seed-pod splits into three parts.

Most species grow in salt or alkaline soil, a number being coastal. We have five.

S. MARINA is somewhat glandular-downy. Stems are more or less erect, up to 14 inches long; leaves $\frac{2}{5}$–$1\frac{1}{2}$ inch, about $\frac{1}{25}$ inch wide. Petals white or pink; sepals about $\frac{1}{8}$ inch long. From two to five stamens.

May to August: chiefly, as its name indicates, a coastal species, but found also inland in brackish, moist places and in alkaline soil eastward to the Rocky Mountains. *Plate 91*. From the Old World.

S. RUBRA has prostrate stems up to a foot long. The leaves are generally in bunches, $\frac{1}{5}$–$\frac{3}{5}$ inch long. The petals are pink; sepals $\frac{1}{8}$ inch, glandular-downy.

April to October: an abundant weed in gardens and waste places through most of western North America. *Plate 92*. From Europe.

The following two species also have glandular-downy sepals. *S. diandra*: Stems slender, prostrate or spreading, to 6 inches long. Leaves not in bunches, $\frac{2}{5}$–$\frac{4}{5}$ inches. Petals pink. April to July: along the Snake and Columbia Rivers. *S. atrosperma*: Stems erect or spreading. Leaves not in bunches. Petals white or pink. April to July: only in Carson Valley, Nevada.

S. media: Smooth or sparsely downy, rather succulent, with stems up to a foot long. Leaves commonly in bunches. Sepals smooth; petals white. April to July: north-central Colorado.

SPURREY (SPERGULA)

One species of *Spergula* is found in our range.

S. ARVENSIS is distinguished from other small *Caryophyllaceae* by the disposition of its leaves in circles; they are about 1–2 inches long, very narrow, at intervals of 2–3 inches on the stem; the stems may reach a height of 2 feet. The flowers are in a terminal cyme; the stalks generally turn down as the seed-pod develops. There are generally five sepals, five white petals, ten (or less commonly five) stamens, and five styles. The pod splits into five parts. March to October: commoner west and east of our range.

PEARLWORTS (SAGINA)

The pearlworts are small plants with threadlike leaves and tiny flowers. Our species have five sepals and five white petals, generally ten stamens, five styles. The capsule splits into five parts.

S. SAGINOIDES forms mats of smooth stems and leaves. The stems are threadlike, up to 2 inches long; the leaves very narrow, $\frac{1}{5}$–$\frac{3}{5}$ inch long. The petals are shorter than the sepals ($\frac{1}{2}$–1 inch long). The flowers may be single at the tips of stems.

May to September: in moist soil, mud flats etc., around the world and southward through the mountains in our area and elsewhere.

S. decumbens is erect or nearly so, the threadlike stems up to 6 inches tall. March to August: in sandy fields in Kansas and Oklahoma. *S. occidentalis* may grow up to 8 inches tall. The calyx may be glandular-downy. The petals are about equal to the sepals (about $\frac{1}{10}$ inch). May to August: mostly west of our range, but has been found eastward to Idaho in moist soil.

THE WHITLOW-WORTS (PARONYCHIA)

An affliction of the finger-nails was, long ago, known as whitlow, and these little plants were supposed to provide a cure, because of their scaly surface (compare *Draba verna*). They are small plants with minute flowers; five sepals joined at the base; no petals; five stamens; one style. The fruit contains one seed. The leaves are rather awl-shaped, with transparent stipules.

I.   *Species whose leaves are elliptic or spatula-like.*

P. PULVINATA forms dense cushions. The flowering

PLATE 92

Arenaria lanuginosa   *D. Richards*

Spergularia rubra   *Korling*

Arenaria macrophylla   *Scribner*

Paronychia jamesii   *Scribner*

Paronychia pulvinata   *Redfield*

Arenaria lateriflora   *Johnson*

Paronychia sessiliflora   *Stockert*

stems rise only 2 inches, the flowers being amongst the leaves. The leaves do not exceed $\frac{1}{4}$ inch. In high mountains in Utah, Wyoming, and Colorado. *Plate 92*.

   P. canadensis is very slender, erect, bushy-branched, 4–16 inches tall, smooth. An eastern species found in Kansas. *P. fastigiata* is similar but downy; the sepals are ribbed. In southeastern Kansas.

II.   *Species whose leaves are narrow, even needle-like.*

P. SESSILIFLORA forms dense tufts, and mats up to 8
   inches across and 2 inches thick. The flowering stems are mostly $\frac{1}{2}$–$1\frac{1}{2}$ inches tall (or up to 6 inches);

usually bearing a single flower. June to August: on dry hills and in valleys in grassland, sagebrush, etc. from Canada southward to Nebraska, Colorado, and Utah. *Plate 92*.

   P. depressa has prostrate stems up to 7 inches long, forming mats, rarely more than $2\frac{1}{2}$ inches above ground. The flowers are in clusters among the leaves. On dry hills and plains from south Dakota to Wyoming, Nebraska, and Colorado.

   P. jamesii is similar, 4–12 inches tall. The cymes are few-flowered. On dry plains and hills from Nebraska to Colorado and Oklahoma. *Plate 92*. *P. virginica*, with open, forking cymes, is found in Oklahoma.

SCLERANTHUS

   The European knawel, *Scleranthus annuus*, is occasionally found as a weed in Washington and Idaho. Its stems are prostrate or spread upward, to 6

inches long. They bear awl-shaped leaves less than an inch long. The minute flowers are in clusters in the forks of the stems and the axils. They have no petals.

SCOPULOPHILA

   The only species of *Scopulophila*, *S. rixfordii*, is in eastern California and adjacent Nevada. It has stems 2–8 inches tall, bearing narrow leaves widest

near the tip, $\frac{1}{5}$–$\frac{3}{5}$ inch long. The flowers are in small clusters in the axils. There are no petals. Five fertile stamens alternate with five sterile ones.

HOLOSTEUM

   Jagged-chickweed, *H. umbellatum*, is an Old-World species established in eastern Washington and Oregon, and in Idaho, also in Kansas and probably elsewhere. It somewhat resembles both *Stellaria* and

Cerastium but has its flowers in a (false) umbel. It is pale, about a foot tall, with leaves about an inch long, mostly near the ground. The flowers are tiny, the petals white, not cleft but minutely toothed.

SANDWORTS (ARENARIA)

   The name sandwort is not really appropriate to all the species of *Arenaria*, which are numerous and found in many kinds of situations around the world. However, most of their preference is for sandy, rocky, gravelly, or in general dry places; and since the botanical name is from *arena*, "sand," the corresponding English name may be used for all of them.

   This is a large group of small plants, so many alike in aspect that they are difficult to identify without – or even with – recourse to technical detail. Attention must be given to the manner of growth, the exact dimensions of leaves, the position of flowers, the length of petals and sepals. Twenty-seven species are found in our range. Geographical distribution is helpful to a minor degree.

   The leaves lack stalks and stipules. The flowers are small, with five separate sepals and five white petals which may be notched – or there may be none;

ten stamens; generally three styles. The capsule splits into three or six parts.

I.   *Species with leaves mostly $\frac{1}{8}$ inch wide or wider, not needle-like.*

   The flowers are borne singly in the axils or in small cymes at the tips of stems and branches.

   These species extend westward from Colorado through the Great Basin; some also northward and eastward.

A. MACROPHYLLA may grow in loose mats, with
   stems erect or bending upward, 2–10 inches long. The leaves are narrowly elliptic or lanceolate, sharp-pointed, $\frac{2}{5}$–$2\frac{1}{2}$ inches long, $\frac{1}{8}$–$\frac{3}{5}$ inch wide. The flowers may be single or up to five in cymes. Sepals are $\frac{1}{8}$–$\frac{1}{4}$ inch long, petals longer or shorter.

   May to August: in woods and meadows and on

rocky slopes in mountains throughout our range. *Plate 92.*

A. LATERIFLORA is generally erect (2–16 inches), with narrowly elliptic leaves (or they may be wider towards their tip) generally blunt, even roundish at the tip, $\frac{2}{5}$–$1\frac{1}{2}$ inches long, $\frac{1}{8}$–$\frac{1}{2}$ inch wide. The stems and branches are tipped with few-flowered cymes; there may be additional cymes from the axils. Sepals about $\frac{1}{8}$ inch, petals about $\frac{1}{4}$ inch.

May to August: in moist woods, meadows, and open slopes in mountains from Washington to California and in the Rocky Mountains from Montana to Colorado; and eastward. *Plate 92.*

A. LANUGINOSA has reclining or leaning stems up to 4 feet long, with narrowly elliptic, sharp-pointed leaves up to an inch long. Flowers are borne singly from the axils. The petals are commonly shorter than the sepals, or lacking.

May to August: in damp woods, shady ditches, etc. in southern Utah and Colorado; and eastward. *Plate 92.*

A. SERPYLLIFOLIA is roughish-downy and may be glandular. The stems are erect or nearly so (4–12 inches), with ovate or lanceolate leaves $\frac{1}{8}$–$\frac{1}{3}$ inch long, from $\frac{1}{15}$–$\frac{1}{6}$ inch wide, sharp-pointed. The flowers are in open cymes, the bracts like the leaves. Sepals about $\frac{1}{8}$ inch long; petals shorter. In many kinds of places through much of North America, and in the Old World. *Plate 93. Serpyllum* is an old name for thyme, with which leaves of this species were compared.

A. CONFUSA has many stems, which are prostrate or bend upwards, 8–20 inches long, with lanceolate leaves $\frac{1}{5}$–$\frac{4}{5}$ inch long, about $\frac{1}{8}$ inch wide. Flowers are many; sepals about $\frac{1}{8}$ inch long, petals a little less.

II. *Species with needle-like leaves.*
See also *A. serpyllifolia, A. lanuginosa* under I.

A. Plants which form mats or cushions, the flowering stems rarely more than 6 inches tall, bearing open cymes or single flowers. The capsule opens by three teeth.
These are all found in Colorado and, except one, in the Great Basin; and most to Oregon.

A. ROSSII forms cushions 2–6 inches across; the flowering branches turn up to a height of $1\frac{1}{2}$ inches. Leaves are about $\frac{1}{4}$ inch long. The flowers are generally single at the tips of the branches. The sepals are about $\frac{1}{8}$ inch long; the petals about the same (lacking in one variety).

July and August: in gravelly soil high in the mountains in Washington, Idaho, perhaps northeastern Oregon; and from Montana to Colorado.

A. RUBELLA forms a cushion up to 4 inches across. The plants are finely glandular-downy, or the leaves may be smooth. The flowering stems are 1–6 inches tall, each with several flowers. Sepals are $\frac{1}{8}$–$\frac{1}{6}$ inch long; petals about the same.

June to August: slopes and meadows and gravelly stream-banks high in the mountains from Washington to California and eastward to the Rocky Mountains. *Plate 93.* Smooth plants like *A. rubella,* growing in gravelly soil in high mountains from southern Nevada to Colorado, have been named *A. filiorum.*

A. OBTUSILOBA has trailing, loosely or densely matted stems, the mats up to 16 inches across. Flowering stems, mostly with one flower, are $\frac{1}{2}$–2 inches tall. Leaves are up to $\frac{2}{5}$ inch long, not so sharp-pointed as those of other species in this group. Sepals about $\frac{1}{5}$ inch long; petals longer.

June to September: in meadows and rocky places high in the mountains from Washington to Oregon, Idaho, and the Rocky Mountains. *Plate 93. A. nuttallii,* from Washington through the Sierra Nevada and eastward to the Rockies, is similar in aspect, with generally seven or more flowers in the cymes. The flowering stems are up to 4 inches tall. From hills with sagebrush to alpine slopes, flowering from May to August.

B. Plants which do not form mats or cushions, at most with trailing stems.
1. Plants with flowers in open cymes (compare 2 and see *A. congesta*); the flowering stems over 4 inches tall; most leaves over $\frac{2}{5}$ inch long; bunches of small leaves not commonly present in the axils.

a. Plants west of the plains (compare b).

A. KINGII forms tufts of leaves, the stems 4–12 inches tall, with leaves mostly at the base and rather soft, $\frac{4}{5}$–$1\frac{1}{2}$ inches long or longer.

June to August: from hills with sagebrush to alpine slopes from southeastern Oregon southward on the eastern slope of the Sierra Nevada and eastward through southern Idaho to western Wyoming and Utah. *Plate 93.*

A. fendleri is similar. The sepals are narrow rather than ovate, and the stems glandular-downy. On plains and high on the mountains in Wyoming and possibly adjacent Nebraska, and Colorado. *Plate 93. A. eastwoodiae* also is similar, either smooth or glandular, with almost all leaves at the base of the stems. In dry stony places in the deserts of eastern Utah and western Colorado. *A. stenomeres* also is similar to *A. kingii.* The petals are very narrow (*steno-*). Known only in the Meadow Valley Range in Lincoln Co., Nevada.

A. CAPILLARIS forms loose mats up to 8 inches across, the flowering stems rising as tall as 1 foot. The basal leaves are rather soft, mostly $1-1\frac{1}{2}$ inches long. The flowers are few in small cymes. The sepals are $\frac{1}{8}-\frac{1}{6}$ inch long, the petals much longer.

June to August: from plains to high rocky slopes in Washington and Oregon, Montana, and northern Nevada. *Plate 93*. *A. aculeata* is similar, with shorter basal leaves and usually no more than two pairs above, generally about $\frac{1}{4}$ inch long. The sepals have a broad margin and are generally purplish. In similar places from northeastern Oregon to western Montana, Utah, Nevada, and California. *A. pumicola* also resembles *A. capillaris*, with sepals like those of *A. aculeata*. In sand from central Oregon to the southern Sierra Nevada. *A. aberrans* may perhaps be found in southern Utah. It has leaves less than an inch long, and a generally grasslike appearance, *Plate 93*.

A. macradenia has prostrate branches, or nearly so; the flowering stems 8–16 inches tall, usually bearing many pairs of leaves; leaves short, awl-like, 1–2 inches long. May to July: on dry slopes in the southern Sierra Nevada and southern California.

b. Plants growing in the plains, and mostly also westward. See also *A. fendleri* under a.

A. STRICTA has usually several stems, erect or bending upward, 4–12 inches tall, tending to be glandular-downy. The rather stiff leaves are $\frac{1}{8}-\frac{3}{4}$ inch long, and may have bunches of small leaves in their axils. The sepals are lanceolate, about $\frac{1}{8}$ inch long; the petals commonly longer.

April to July: widespread in lowlands through much of North America. *Plate 94*. The plants illustrated are a variety with stiffer stems.

A. patula has softer leaves, without bunches in the axils. This is found in our range in Kansas and Oklahoma.

2.   Plants with flowers in compact cymes, like heads.

A. HOOKERI forms cushions up to 6 inches across. The flowering stems are mostly $1-2\frac{1}{2}$ inches tall, some up to 6 inches.

June and July: in sandy and rocky places with sagebrush and on the lower mountains of the eastern slope of the Rocky Mountains from central Montana to Nebraska and Colorado, and westward in Utah. *Plate 94*.

A. CONGESTA has its name from the crowded or "congested" flowers; but some plants have more open clusters. The plants form mats 2–6 inches across. The flowering stems are leafy, 6–16 inches tall. There are bunches of small leaves in the lower axils.

June to August: from sagebrush to alpine slopes throughout our range west of the plains. *Plate 94*.

A. FRANKLINII may have prostrate stems, or they may spread; they are covered with old leaves, withered but still attached. Flowering stems are generally $1\frac{1}{2}-2\frac{1}{2}$ inches tall. The numerous leaves, $\frac{2}{5}-\frac{4}{5}$ inch long, have spreading sharp tips.

May and June: on dunes, and slopes with sagebrush, from central Washington to central and southeastern Oregon, central Idaho, and northwestern Nevada. *Plate 94*.

THE LIVE-FOREVER FAMILY (CRASSULACEAE)

With one exception, the *Crassulaceae* are succulent plants, their leaves undivided and unlobed. The sepals and petals are mostly in fours or fives, the stamens generally twice as many. There are four or five pistils, in many species partly joined, which form a group of pods (follicles). The flowers are in cymes; particularly in the kind of cyme that consists of several radiating branches, the flowers along their upper sides. In many species, however, the cyme is "condensed" by the shortening of its branches, and may be taken for head, spike, or raceme.

Several species are called live-forever. The succulent leaves are reservoirs of water, protected from evaporation, so that detached parts or even entire plants can remain alive without access to water. Many species are decorative, being cultivated especially in "rock gardens": species of *Crassula, Sedum, Sempervivum*, and such southern genera as *Bryophyllum*.

STONECROPS (SEDUM)

The stonecrops are succulent, growing mostly on rocks and gravel. Generally the underground stems form sterile branches which bear compact rosettes of leaves; the flowering branches are erect or nearly so. The flowers are in cymes at the tips of these branches; the branches widely spreading with flowers along their

PLATE 93

Arenaria obtusiloba   *Scribner*

Arenaria fendleri   *Rickett*

Arenaria aberrans   *Stockert*

Arenaria kingii   *Korling*

Arenaria serpyllifolia   *Korling*

Arenaria rubella   *Scribner*

Arenaria capillaris   *Spurr*

length, or rather compact so as to appear like a head or raceme. There are four or five sepals, petals, and pistils, generally twice as many stamens. Stamens and pistils may be in different flowers. Petals and pistils are mostly joined at their base. The pistils become small follicles.

We have sixteen species of these small plants. Identification depends upon careful attention to details.

I. *Species whose pistillate flowers are of other colors than yellow.*

The staminate flowers may be yellow, or of a color like that of the pistillate. See also *S. obtusatum* under II.

ROSEROOT, S. ROSEA (1–12 inches), has many flattish leaves, usually wider towards the tip, up to an inch long and $\frac{3}{5}$ inch wide. The flowers are crowded in a headlike cluster at the tip of each stem. Sepals and petals commonly number four, but on many plants there are five of each. The stamens project slightly. The petals are commonly purple in bud, becoming a deep rose-crimson or even red or pink when open. Stamens and pistils are commonly on different plants.

June to August: on rocks, moist slopes, and tundra from arctic regions to the Sierra Nevada and eastward to Montana and Colorado, at high altitudes. *Plate 94.* Commonly miscalled *S. roseum*; but *Rosea*, an old name, is a substantive, not subject to change of gender. The broken stem is said to emit the odor of roses. In some northern races the staminate flowers are yellow. In the western part of our area the leaves may be finely toothed; in the Rocky Mountains they commonly lack teeth and the plants have even been separated as a distinct species with the name *S. integrifolium*; under which name they appear in volume 4. The species has been often confused with the following.

QUEEN'S-CROWN, S. RHODANTHUM (1–12 inches), has rather narrow leaves, flattish, $\frac{2}{5}$–$1\frac{1}{5}$ inches long. The flowers may be in several clusters in the axils of the uppermost leaves, or all at the tip in what seems to be a head (really a condensed cyme); in any arrangement the flowers are accompanied by leaflike bracts. The petals are pink or white, narrow and sharp-pointed. The stamens do not project.

July and August: in moist ground, generally at lower altitudes than the preceding species but also found with it on tundra, etc., from southeastern Montana to Colorado and Utah. *Plate 94.*

S. cockerellii (to 8 inches) may extend from New Mexico into Colorado. It forms rosettes of small leaves at ground level, besides the flattish leaves on the stem, less than an inch long. The flowers are on three branches which spread from the tip. The petals are white with a faint pinkish tinge. In rocky and mossy places.

The following four species are eastern, limited in our range to Kansas and Oklahoma.

S. PULCHELLUM (up to 18 inches) has very narrow leaves, many as thick as they are wide, up to an inch long. The flowers are on several branches spreading from the tip of each stem, the first to open being at the point where the branches start. The petals are white or pink. May to July: on rocks and thin soil. *Plate 95.*

S. ternatum has creeping stems from which rise erect flowering branches up to a foot tall. In spite of the name, the leaves are not generally in threes; there are about six at the base of each erect stem, with broad blades. The flowers are on about three spreading branches; they are white. April to June: on damp rocks, mossy banks, etc.

S. telephium has escaped from cultivation. The ovate, toothed leaves are mostly in pairs. The flowers are crowded in a broad, headlike cluster at the tip of the stem; they may be red (such plants being sometimes separated as *S. purpureum*) or yellowish. On roadsides and the edges of fields.

II. *Species with yellow flowers.*
See also *S. telephium* under I.

S. STENOPETALUM (2–8 inches) has numerous rosettes of leaves. The leaves on the flowering stems are borne singly, narrow, ridged underneath. The upper leaves remain attached at flowering time, and generally have small bulblike bodies in their axils. The flowers are in a compact cyme; they too may be replaced by bulbs.

May to August: in grassland and sagebrush, also under pine and even to almost alpine heights from Washington to California and eastward to Montana. *Plate 94.* This has often been called *S. douglasii*, a later name and therefore illegitimate. It has also been quite generally confused with *S. lanceolatum* (as in this series, regrettably, in volume 5).

S. LANCEOLATUM (2–12 inches), like the preceding species, has numerous basal rosettes. The leaves on the stems are borne singly; they vary greatly in shape, from narrow to ovate, and in thickness; they are not ridged underneath. They may fall as the flowers open. The flowers are in a compact cyme. The small pods (follicles) stand erect.

June to August: in open places usually on rocks or gravelly soil from sea level to nearly alpine altitudes from Canada to California and eastward to South Dakota, Nebraska, and Colorado. *Plate 95.* This has generally passed as *S. stenopetalum.*

S. LEIBERGII (3–5 inches) has very short, very thick basal leaves, almost like grains of rice; those

PLATE 94

Arenaria hookeri *Roberts*

Sedum rhodanthum *Roberts*

Sedum rosea *Korling*

Sedum stenopetalum *Winthers*

Arenaria congesta *Korling*

Arenaria franklinii *Spurr*

Arenaria stricta *Horst*

above are rather narrower and up to an inch long, but are usually fallen before flowers open. The flowers are on widely spreading branches which may be curved downward. The pods spread apart.

May to July: on mossy rocks and gravelly hill-sides mostly in the cañons of southeastern Washington, northern Oregon, and western Idaho. *Plate 95.*

S. nuttallianum (up to 6 inches) has branching stems along which the flowers are seated. The leaves are about $\frac{1}{4}$ inch long, borne singly. The petals and sepals are almost equal. The pods diverge widely. April to July: in dry soil in Kansas and Oklahoma.

Wallpepper, *S. acre*, has been found in Kansas and Montana. It forms mats of prostrate stems, the flowering branches up to 4 inches tall, bearing leaves about $\frac{1}{4}$ inch long. A cultivated species. *S. sarmentosum*, from eastern Asia, has escaped from cultivation in the eastern states and has been found in Kansas. It has creeping stems, leaves in groups of two or three, and a cyme of several spreading branches, with a flower at the point of origin and flowers on the branches.

S. DEBILE has its name from its prostrate stems (*debilis*, "weak"). The flowers are on stems that bend up, 2–5 inches tall. The leaves are in basal rosettes, and in pairs on the stems. They are ovate with the broader end out, or almost round. The cymes are rather loose. The petals are light yellow. The follicles stand erect.

June to August: on rock ledges, gravel bars, and alpine ridges and slopes from southeastern Oregon and central Idaho to Nevada, Utah, and western Wyoming. *Plate 95.*

S. obtusatum, a species of the high Sierra Nevada, may reach western Nevada. The leaves are spatula-like, $\frac{2}{5}$–$\frac{4}{5}$ inch long. Petals are lemon-yellow, cream, or pink with cream margins, joined about one-fourth of their length. June to August. *S. divergens*, farther north high in the Cascade Mountains, may possibly be in the extreme west of our range. It has leaves mostly paired on the flowering stems, which rise from prostrate, rooted stems. The petals are yellow, not joined. The follicles spread apart. *S. oreganum*, also of the Cascades, is in our area in central Washington. Its leaves are borne singly, generally overlapping, widest at and near the tip. The branches of the cyme spread slightly. The petals are pinkish in age. The plant is smooth with a bloom. June to August.

TILLAEA

One species of *Tillaea* is found in our area.

PIGMY-WEED, T. AQUATICA, is about 2 inches tall, the threadlike stems matted, with green or reddish, narrow, succulent leaves $\frac{1}{4}$–1 inch long. The flowers are in the axils. They have three or four minute sepals, the same number of pink petals, and as many stamens and pistils. The pistils form follicles. April to August: on mud flats and dried pools, scattered in our range; reported in Washington and Oregon (mostly west of the Cascade Mountains), California, Nevada, Utah, Wyoming, and Colorado.

PENTHORUM

One species of *Penthorum* is in our range.

DITCH-STONECROP, P. SEDOIDES (2–3 feet), is not succulent (indeed some botanists have removed it from the *Crassulaceae*). The leaves are lanceolate, toothed, 2–4 inches long, borne singly. The flowers are on the spreading branches of a cyme. They very rarely have petals; five sepals, partly joined; ten stamens; five pistils joined in their lower half, forming a five-horned capsule.

July to October: in moist soil from North Dakota to Oklahoma. *Plate 95.*

THE SAXIFRAGE FAMILY (SAXIFRAGACEAE)

Most of our species of *Saxifragaceae* are small herbaceous plants, many with long-stalked leaves at the base of the flowering stem. The flowers have mostly five sepals, five petals, and five or ten stamens. These are seated on or near the rim of a "floral tube" (flower-base) which is not distinct from the joined base of the calyx; it may be cup- or saucer-shaped. The ovary is generally partly inferior, i.e. its surface joined to the tube around it through its lower part. It generally tapers up into two beaks, which may each be terminated by a style and stigma, or by a stigma

PLATE 95

Sedum pulchellum   *Bowen*

Sedum lanceolatum   *Niehaus*

Sedum debile   *Dilley*

Saxifraga ferruginea   *Spurr*

Sedum leibergii   *George*

Penthorum sedoides   *Rickett*

Saxifraga rhomboidea   *Korling*

Saxifraga occidentalis   *Rickett*

without a true style. In some genera there may be three or four or more parts of the pistil.

Some botanists place hydrangeas, mock orange, currants, and gooseberries in this family.

Since these are all shrubs, their proper classification does not concern us here. There are also a few shrubby species in the *Saxifragaceae* proper, omitted from our treatment.

Guide to Genera of Saxifragaceae

I.   *Genera with five petals and ten stamens.*

A. Plants whose petals are not lobed, cleft, or divided; two styles: *Saxifraga* (petals white or yellow or in one species red, longer than the sepals); *Tiarella* (petals white, very narrow, leaves three-lobed); *Telesonix* (petals pink or red, short; leaves on the stem and at the base).

B. Plants whose petals are lobed, cleft, or divided: *Lithophragma* (three styles; petals deeply cleft or divided generally into narrow segments; leaves lobed, cleft, or divided); *Tellima* (two styles; petals generally turning pink, deeply cleft, bent back). *Mitella* (see under II).

II. *Genera with five or fewer petals or none and five or fewer stamens.*

A. Plants with cleft or divided petals: *Mitella* (petals longer than the sepals); *Elmera* (petals no longer than the sepals).

B. Plants whose petals are not cleft or divided; mostly two styles: *Conimitella* (flowers few, small, in a simple raceme); *Bolandra* (petals very narrow, red; conspicuous stipules on the stem-leaves); *Heuchera* (flowers small, in a raceme or branched inflorescence, white or pink; leaves of most species hairy); *Boykinia* (leaves on the stem like those at the base but with large stipules; petals much larger than the calyx-lobes); *Sullivantia* (petals slightly longer than the calyx-lobes; basal leaf-blades sharply cut into sharp-toothed lobes); *Suksdorfia* (petals twice as long as the calyx-lobes, white or violet; leaves cleft and lobed, not toothed; stem-leaves with stipules or enlarged stalk); *Lepuropetalon* (matted plants; flowers minute, borne singly in the axils; three styles); *Leptarrhena* (flowers many, crowded at the tip of the stem; leaves elliptic or oval, leathery, blunt-toothed).

C. Plants with four sepals, no petals, four stamens; stems creeping: *Chrysosplenium*.

D. Plants with unlobed and undivided leaves, mostly at the base (one on the stem in some species); petals large, veined; four stigmas, no styles: *Parnassia*.

THE SAXIFRAGES (SAXIFRAGA)

The saxifrages constitute a large genus of small plants, many at home in the far north and at high altitudes. The flowers are in cymes, which may resemble racemes. The sepals and petals number five. The petals are white, those of some species with yellow or purplish spots. There are ten stamens. The pistil commonly consists of two parts, each with its style, joined at the base and to a varying degree joined with the base of the flower so as to be partly inferior.

The name, from the Latin, means "rock-breaking," and has been attributed to the general occurrence of the genus on rocks; but in medieval times it was used by the herbalists for the treatment of the disease called "stone."

I.   *Species whose leaves are all at the base of the stem. The plants do not form tufts.*

S. FERRUGINEA (4–24 inches) has basal leaves 1–6 inches long, stalked, the blade with blunt teeth.

The flowering stems are glandular-downy. The calyx is deeply cleft, with lobes bent down. The petals are white (rarely purplish), up to $\frac{1}{3}$ inch long. The flowers may be replaced by small bulbs.

June to August: from Washington to northwestern California and eastward to Idaho and western Montana. *Plate 95*.

S. stellaria, found in our range only on Mt. Evans, Colorado, is similar, with smaller, less toothed leaves. In the inflorescence almost all the axils contain minute bulbs instead of flowers. *S. bryophora*, in the high Sierra Nevada, is similar, with petals not more than $\frac{1}{8}$ inch long, and leaves generally without teeth.

S. OCCIDENTALIS (2–12 inches) has downy-glandular, reddish stems. The leaves are stalked, with ovate or elliptic blades up to $2\frac{1}{2}$ inches long, coarsely toothed. The flowers are on more or less spreading branches. The white petals are $\frac{1}{8}$ inch long, commonly with two yellow spots at the base.

PLATE 96

Saxifraga oppositifolia *Mary Ferguson*

Saxifraga flagellaris *Scribner*

Saxifraga oregana *Scribner*

Saxifraga aprica *Niehaus*

Saxifraga mertensiana *Mansfield*

Saponaria vaccaria *Scribner*

Saxifraga odontoloma *Korling*

Saxifraga lyallii *Korling*

April to August: on moist banks and meadows up to rocky slopes at high altitudes in Washington and northern Oregon and eastward to Idaho, northeastern Nevada, Montana, and northern Wyoming. *Plate 95.*

S. nidifica has smooth, ovate leaf-blades, with or without small teeth. The inflorescence is narrow. In moist places in the Sierra Nevada and southern Oregon.

S. OREGANA (1–4 feet) is glandular-hairy in the upper parts, with yellow, pink or purple glands. The leaves are 2¼–14 inches long, with blades narrow but wider towards the tip and more or less toothed, on a flattish-winged, short stalk. The calyx-lobes are usually bent down. The petals are white; one or more may be lacking.

April to July: in bogs and on stream-banks and wet meadows from Washington to the Sierra Nevada and Idaho and Montana, and southward to Wyoming and Colorado. *Plate 96.*

S. RHOMBOIDEA (2–12 inches) has, in its upper parts, whitish hairs tipped with a reddish or yellowish gland. The leaf-blades are triangular or nearly so, ½–2 inches long, toothed, on a broad, flattish stalk. The inflorescence is headlike or more open. The petals are white or cream.

May to August: in moist places from plains with sagebrush to alpine meadows, from central Idaho and west-central Utah to the Rocky Mountains. *Plate 95.*

S. INTEGRIFOLIA (4–16 inches) has elliptic or lanceolate or ovate leaf-blades, mostly ½–1½ inches long, with or without a short stalk; mostly without teeth. The flowers are in a loose or compact cyme. The petals are white (or greenish or yellowish).

March to July: on prairies and grassy slopes, wet banks, and high meadows from Washington to California and eastward to Idaho, western Montana, and Nevada. *Plate 97.*

S. texana sends up a leafless flowering stem (to 8 inches) from a small corm. The elliptic or lanceolate leaf-blades taper to long stalks. The flowers are in a cluster at first compact, later opening. The five petals are white or pink. In our range only in Oklahoma and Kansas. *S. virginiensis*, an eastern species, is also found in Oklahoma. It has a basal rosette of toothed leaves with scarcely any stalks. The stem rises a foot or more, with many branches in the upper part, each ending in a cluster of white flowers. The plant tends to be downy.

S. aprica has basal leaves almost without stalks, rather broad, with or without teeth. The inflorescence is headlike. The plant may be reddish. The petals are white, the seed-pods red. In moist gravelly and stony places in the Sierra Nevada, western Nevada, and southern Oregon. *Plate 96.*

S. ODONTOLOMA (6–24 inches) has coarsely toothed, roundish leaf-blades up to 3 inches across, on very long stalks. The stem has, in its upper parts, hairs tipped with yellowish or purplish glands. The petals are white, and unequal.

July to September: in moist places at various altitudes from Canada to California and through the Rocky Mountains. *Plate 96.* This has been generally known as *S. arguta*.

S. lyallii (2–12 inches) may form small mats. The leaf-blades are wedge-shaped or fan-shaped, ⅕–2 inches long and nearly as broad, toothed, tapering to slender stalks. The flowers are in a slender raceme. The calyx-lobes are bent back. The petals are white (or pink in age). July and August: in wet places at high altitudes in northern Washington, northern Idaho, and western Montana. *Plate 96.*

S. mertensiana (6–16 inches) has roundish leaf-blades which are coarsely toothed, or lobed and the lobes toothed. The leaf-stalks are up to four times as long as the blades, with stipules that sheathe the stem. The flowers are in an open, branched inflorescence. The petals are white. Some flowers are commonly replaced by small pink bulbs. April to August: on wet banks and along streams from the Cascade Mountains to northwestern Montana, central Idaho, and northeastern Oregon, and from central California to Utah. *Plate 96.*

S. foliolosa is a very rare alpine species, in Colorado. The leaves are less than ½ inch long, with a few teeth at the tip. The flowers are replaced by small green bulbs.

II.   *Species with leaves on the flowering stems.*
      Generally these are smaller than those in the basal rosette. They may be confined to the lower part of the stem.

S. FLAGELLARIS is named for its whiplike runners (*flagella*, "whips") up to 4 inches long, which form buds and new stems at their tips. The flowering stems (⅗–5 inches) have overlapping leaves. The petals are yellow.

July and August: around the world in high latitudes, southward to Montana, northeastern Utah, and Colorado. *Plate 96.*

S. serpyllifolia is also yellow-flowered, the petals orange below the middle, up to ⅓ inch long. The flowering stems (1–2½ inches) have from one to five narrow, short leaves; the basal rosettes are succulent. July and August: on rock slopes in northeastern Utah and adjacent Wyoming and from Montana to Colorado. *Plate 97.* Often known as *S. chrysantha*.

S. oppositifolia (½–2 inches) forms tufts or cushions up to 8 inches across, commonly reddish-tinged, with pretty rose-red flowers. The leaves may be 1–2 inches long, paired. At high altitudes on rocks in the

PLATE 97

Saxifraga debilis *On*

Saxifraga integrifolia *Happy*

Saxifraga serpyllifolia *Blecher*

Saxifraga cernua *Blecher*

Saxifraga adscendens *Korling*

Saxifraga bronchialis *Korling*

Saxifraga caespitosa *Thompson*

Saxifraga tolmiei *Weisser*

Cascade and Wallowa Mountains of Washington and Oregon and in Idaho, Montana, and Wyoming. *Plate 96.*

S. debilis forms tufts up to 3 inches across, generally glandular-downy. Flowering stems to 4 inches. Leaves mostly basal, their blades lobed, to $\frac{1}{2}$ inch wide. Flowers few, the petals white, pink-veined. July and August: on damp rocks in the Cascades of Washington, the Blue and Wallowa Mountains of Oregon, the Sierra Nevada, and the Rockies from Montana to Utah and Colorado. *Plate 97. S. cernua* (to 8 inches) is similar. There are commonly small bulbs in the axils and even in place of flowers. In moist rock crevices, on stream-banks, etc. around the world at high latitudes and southward to northern Washington, northern Nevada, through the Rockies, and to South Dakota. *Plate 97.*

S. ADSCENDENS ($\frac{3}{5}$–4 inches) has most leaves in a rosette at the base, without teeth or with three or five teeth or lobes at the tip, tapering to a stalk-like base. The stem-leaves are similar. The plants are glandular-downy. The petals are white, two or three times as long as the calyx.

July and August: in rock crevices and on gravelly meadows from northern Washington to central Idaho and northeastern Oregon and Utah and through the Rocky Mountains to Colorado. *Plate 97.*

S. caespitosa is similar but forms tufts; the stems up to 6 inches tall; the leaves with up to seven lobes. April to September; from sea level to alpine heights in Washington and the Columbia River Gorge and from Montana and central Idaho to Utah, northeastern Nevada, and Colorado. *Plate 97.*

S. BRONCHIALIS forms tufts or cushions up to a foot across, with stiff, crowded, narrow leaves, less than an inch long, some widest at the tip, with a small spine at the tip. The flowers are in a flattish cluster. The petals are white, spotted with crimson above the middle, with yellow below.

June to August: from sea level to alpine heights from Washington to northern Oregon and Idaho, and through the Rocky Mountains. *Plate 97.*

S. tolmiei (1–3 inches) forms mats of sterile branches. The flowers are one or a few in a loose inflorescence. The petals are white, not spotted. The stamens have broad, almost petal-like stalks. July and August: in mountain meadows and rock crevices and on moist rock slopes from the Cascade Mountains to Idaho and Montana. *Plate 97.*

S. hirculus is a rare species of high mountain bogs in Colorado. It has basal leaves up to two inches long, slender-stalked, without teeth, the blades spatula-like. The flowers, borne singly, are yellow. Flower-stalk and calyx bear rusty hairs.

TIARELLA

One species of *Tiarella* is found in our range.

T. TRIFOLIATA (8–24 inches) has basal leaves with broad blades on long stalks; in one subspecies they are divided into three wedge-shaped segments, the end one about $\frac{1}{2}$ inch long, the side ones shorter and commonly lobed or cleft, all scalloped or coarsely toothed at the end; in another subspecies they are undivided, up to 3 inches long and 5 inches wide, deeply five-lobed and scalloped or toothed; the latter is illustrated. (These two are quite generally treated as two species, the second named *T. unifoliata*. In volume 5

the wrong name was adopted.) The flowers are on short stalks in small, widely separated clusters along the erect stems, making it a sort of branched raceme. The calyx and stalks are glandular, as is the main stem. The petals are very narrow, white. The ten stamens are in two lengths. The ovary bears two quite long beaks on which are the threadlike styles. The seed-pod opens along the beaks, breaking into two unequal parts.

May to August: in moist woods on stream-banks from Alaska to California and eastward to Idaho and Montana, and northeastern Oregon. *Plate 98.*

TELESONIX

There is one species of *Telesonix*.

T. JAMESII (2–6 inches) is generally glandular-downy, the stems tending to be reddish. The leaves are mostly at the base, with roundish, shallowly lobed or scalloped and toothed blades indented at the base, on slender stalks; leaves above are much smaller. The flowers are clustered, at intervals, in the axils of bracts.

They are showy, with rose-red petals about $\frac{1}{8}$ inch long (about the length of the calyx or longer). Ten stamens. The ovary tapers into two styles; it is partly united with the surrounding flower-base.

July and August: in moist rock crevices and on rock slopes from eastern Idaho and Montana to Wyoming, eastern Utah, southern Nevada, and South Dakota and Colorado. *Plate 98.*

PLATE 98

Beaupré

Lithophragma parviflorum

Mitella stauropetala   *Dye*

Mitella nuda   *Rhein*

Mitella nuda   *D. Richards*

Telesonix jamesii   *Roberts*

Tellima grandiflora   *Johnson*

Tiarella trifoliata   *Spurr*

Lithophragma bulbiferum *Frost*

Lithophragma parviflorum   *Korling*

LITHOPHRAGMA

The principal leaves of *Lithophragma* are at the base of the erect flowering stem; their blades are mostly palmately cleft or divided; the stalks are long. The leaves above are smaller and their lobes and segments generally narrower. The flowers are in a cluster at and near the tip of the stem; they may be replaced by small bulbs. The flower-base is cup-shaped with five sepals. There are five white or pink petals, generally lobed or cleft, and ten stamens. The ovary has three styles. The capsule splits into three.

L. BULBIFERUM (2–12 inches) is glandular-downy.

The blades of the basal leaves are generally divided into five wedge-shaped segments $\frac{1}{5}$–$1\frac{3}{5}$ inches broad. There are about five leaves on the stem, with bulbs in the axils. The plant is commonly reddish. From two to five flowers mostly make up the inflorescence, their petals cleft into three or more usually five.

March to July: on grassy hillsides and in sagebrush and forest from Canada to California and eastward to North and South Dakota and Colorado. *Plate 98*. *L. glabrum* is very similar (considered by some to include *L. bulbiferum* as a variety). It generally has only two stem-leaves, and no little bulbs in their axils. The inflorescence is more contracted, not so flat. In similar environments from eastern Washington and northeastern Oregon to northwestern Montana. *L. brevilobum* is also similar. The leaves are deeply three-lobed. No bulbs. In northeastern California. In this group is also *L. rupicola*. The stems are rough with minute bristles. The raceme may have from eight to twenty flowers, with petals about $\frac{1}{8}$ inch long. May to July: in moist places with sagebrush, juniper, or pine in northeastern California and southern Oregon.

L. TENELLUM (4–12 inches) is glandular-downy with yellow-tipped hairs. The basal blades are $\frac{1}{5}$–$\frac{3}{5}$ inch wide, roundish, divided into three segments which are deeply three-lobed, or three- or five-lobed, or merely coarsely scalloped. Usually two or three stem-leaves. From five to ten flowers; the petals with three principal lobes and two or four much smaller.

April to June: with sagebrush and pine on the eastern side of the Cascade Mountains in Washington and Oregon and eastward to Montana and Wyoming; and in Nevada and Colorado.

L. PARVIFLORUM (2–20 inches) is densely glandular-downy and commonly reddish. The basal leaves have three or more usually five segments, these further cleft and lobed. Two or three stem-leaves. Petals generally cleft into three; on some plants into five.

March to June: on prairies and in grassland, sagebrush, and forest from Canada to California and eastward to South Dakota and Colorado. *Plate 98*. *L. trifoliatum* is similar. The calyx is three times as long as wide. The petals have three lobes. March and April: on dry slopes in northeastern California.

TELLIMA

There is only one species of *Tellima*.

FRINGE-CUPS, T. GRANDIFLORA (up to 3 feet), is hairy and glandular. The basal leaves have stalks 2–8 inches long, bearing roundish, lobed and toothed blades indented at the base, 1–3 inches across. There are from one to three much smaller, short-stalked leaves on the stem. The flowers are in tall, rather one-sided, spike-like racemes. The five petals, delicately fringed, are responsible for the English name. There are ten stamens, and a two-horned pistil. The seed-pod (capsule) splits along the beaks.

April to July: along streams and in woods from Alaska to California and eastward to northeastern Washington and northern Idaho, and the Columbia River Gorge. *Plate 98*.

MITREWORTS (MITELLA)

The petals of *Mitella* are decorative and distinctive (as seen through a magnifier); they have narrow stalks with blades cleft or divided generally into narrow parts. There are five sepals and five petals, and five stamens in all but one, which has ten. The ovary is joined with the surrounding flower-base over about three-fourths of its surface (thus being partly inferior). It has no true styles, the two stigmas being seated on the two beaks. The flowers are in a slim raceme. The leaves are all or mostly at the base of the stem, with roundish or ovate blades, variously scalloped and toothed, on long stalks. The stems are generally glandular-downy.

The two-beaked pod suggested a bishop's mitre.

I. *Species whose petals are pinnately divided.*

M. NUDA (1–8 inches) differs from all our other

PLATE 99

Johnson

Mitella pentandra

Mitella trifida   *Spurr*

Mitella pentandra   *Spurr*

Heuchera nivalis   *Scribner*

Mitella breweri   *On*

Heuchera cylindrica   *George*

Heuchera richardsonii   *Johnson*

Mitella caulescens   *Scribner*

Heuchera bracteata   *D. Richards*

species in having ten stamens. The petals are green-ish-yellow; the segments commonly nine (but vary-ing). From three to twelve flowers make a raceme. The leaf-blades are scalloped, rarely more than an inch across.

May to August: in damp woods and bogs from Canada southward to northwestern Washington and eastward to North Dakota and the Atlantic. *Plate 98.*

M. PENTANDRA (4–12 inches) is distinguished by having each stamen opposite the center of a petal; in all our other five-staminate species, the stamen is opposite the gap between two petals. The petals are like those of *M. nuda*. The leaf-blades are ovate, toothed.

June to August: in moist woods and on mountain meadows from Canada southward to Colorado and the Great Basin. *Plate 99.*

M. BREWERI (6–12 inches) has round, indistinctly lobed and toothed or scalloped leaf-blades up to 3 inches across. The yellowish petals have mostly seven segments. The flower-base is saucer-shaped. There are from twenty to sixty flowers in the raceme.

May to August: on wooded and open slopes at medium and high altitudes from the Cascade Moun-tains to Idaho and Montana. *Plate 99. M. caulescens* (4–16 inches) has several leaves on the flowering stem, smaller and shorter-stalked than those at the base. The leaf-blades are mostly five-lobed, finely scalloped or toothed. There are up to twenty-five flowers in a raceme. The greenish petals may have up to nine seg-ments. April to June: in woods and wet meadows from the Cascades to Montana. *Plate 99.*

II. *Species whose petals are cleft or divided otherwise than pinnately.*

M. TRIFIDA (6–14 inches) has leaves whose blades are roundish, indistinctly lobed, up to 2½ inches across. The calyx-lobes are white. The petals, also white, or tinged with purple, are scarcely longer than the calyx-lobes, and much narrower; the blade is cleft into three pointed lobes at the end.

May to July: in forests and on mountain slopes from the Cascades to the Rockies. *Plate 99. M. diversi-folia* (6–20 inches) has basal leaves with blades mostly 1–2 inches long, ovate, deeply indented at the base, shallowly lobed but not toothed. There may be a leaf (very rarely two) on the flowering stem. The raceme contains from eight to thirty-five flowers. The white petals are cleft at the end into three or less commonly five narrow parallel lobes. May to July: in the Cascade Mountains of southern Washington and Oregon, barely in our range.

M. STAUROPETALA (up to 20 inches) may have pur-plish-tinged leaves, their blades 1–3 inches across, not quite as long, lobed and scalloped. The racemes have flowers all on one side and close to-gether, from ten to thirty-five. The petals are white or purplish, generally cleft into three threadlike lobes. The calyx-lobes are the same color, broad and petal-like.

May and June: in woods from extreme eastern Washington and northeastern and central Oregon to the Rocky Mountains in Montana and southward to Utah and Colorado. *Plate 98.*

ELMERA

There is but one species of *Elmera*.

E. RACEMOSA (4–10 inches) has round-bladed, downy, long-stalked leaves; the blades are 1–2 inches wide, the length less; there are many shallow lobes with scalloped edges. Most leaves are at the base of the stem, with generally two or three smaller leaves above. The flowers are in a tall, narrow raceme. The calyx-lobes are yellowish. The small white petals (no longer than the calyx-lobes) are cleft into from three to seven lobes, all on a narrow stalk. There are five stamens. The ovary is joined with the floral tube only a short distance; it tapers up into two beaks, at the ends of which are the short, thick styles.

June to August: only in the Wenatchee Moun-tains and surrounding central Washington. *Plate 100.*

CONIMITELLA

The genus *Conimitella* has only one species.

C. WILLIAMSII (8–24 inches) has leaves something like those of *Mitella*, at the base of the flowering stem, and small flowers in a slender raceme. The leaf-blades are rather leathery, commonly purplish on the under surface, ⅖–1⅗ inches broad, shallowly scal-loped, and fringed with stiff hairs. The flowers have five sepals, and five petals with an unlobed blade which tapers to a stalk, overall about ⅕ inch long. The partly inferior ovary has two beaks, a stigma on each.

June and July: in rock crevices, on moist cliffs, and on open mountain slopes in Montana, Idaho, and northwestern Wyoming.

BOLANDRA

We have one species of *Bolandra*.

B. OREGANA (6–24 inches) has leaves at the base and
on the stem with lobed and toothed blades 1–3
inches wide, on stalks up to 6 inches long. The flowers
are on few branches. The calyx-lobes are reddish, as
are the narrow petals. There are five of each and five
stamens shorter than the petals. The pistil consists of
two parts joined only near their base, tapering up to
the stigmas.

May and June: on moist mossy rocks from the
Columbia River Gorge eastward along the Snake
River and its tributaries in southeastern Washington,
northeastern Oregon, and adjacent Idaho.

THE ALUMROOTS (HEUCHERA)

The leaves of *Heuchera* are mostly at the base of
the stem; they are long-stalked, with roundish, lobed
or scalloped or toothed blades. There may be a few
leaves on the flowering stem. The small flowers are in
clusters at intervals along the stem, forming a sort of
raceme. The flower has a tubular or cup-shaped base,
on the rim of which are seated the five sepals and five
petals, all very small. There are five stamens, and a
pistil with two beaks, its sides partly or wholly joined
with the flower-base (and therefore to some degree inferior). The capsule splits along the beaks.

The genus is easy to recognize, but to identify
the species requires close study of the small parts of
the flowers; a magnifier is essential.

These are mostly plants of moist rock ledges and
ravines, not very decorative. One species, however,
has given rise to the coral-bells of gardens.

I. *Species whose stamens, as seen from the side of the
flower, project beyond sepals and petals.*

H. RICHARDSONII (12–16 inches) has flowers which
are oblique at the end of the perianth; i.e. the upper side is longer than the lower. These flowers are the
largest in our species – up to $\frac{2}{5}$ inch long. The stem
and leaf-stalks are shaggy-hairy; also the veins on the
under side of the leaf-blades. The petals are slender
and greenish.

May to July: on prairies and in dry woods from
Montana and North Dakota to Colorado and Kansas
(and perhaps Oklahoma). *Plate 99.*

H. americana is an eastern species found in Oklahoma. The stem and the stalks and blades of the leaves
are mostly smooth. The flowers are about $\frac{1}{4}$ inch long.
The petals are commonly reddish. The inflorescence is
nearly cylindric. April to June: in woods and on rocks.

H. BRACTEATA (4–16 inches) has its flowers on one
side of the stem in a rather dense cluster resembling a spike or head; they are greenish. The stem and
leaves are commonly glandular-downy.

June to August: on foothills and mountains in
Wyoming and Colorado. *Plate 99.*

H. GLABRA (6–24 inches) is mostly smooth, glandular-downy in places. The numerous flowers
occupy a large, open inflorescence. The white petals
are from twice to four times as long as the calyx-lobes,
with slender stalks.

June to August: on stream-banks and in moist
rock crevices in eastern Washington. *H. micrantha*,
from the Cascades to eastern Washington, northeastern Oregon, and adjacent Idaho, is very similar,
differing chiefly in the presence of long soft hairs on
leaf-stalks and the stem of the inflorescence, also on
the flower-base and calyx. May to August: *Plate 100.*

H. rubescens has small leaves, the blades not more
than an inch across, the stalks 2–3 inches long. In one
variety the floral tube is plainly oblique, as in *H.
richardsonii*. The calyx is pink and hairy. The hairiness
of leaves and stem varies greatly in different varieties.
May to July: in dry rocky places, up to high altitudes,
from the Sierra Nevada to Utah, extreme southeastern
Oregon, southwestern Idaho, and Colorado. *Plate 100.*

H. versicolor grows in southern Utah; its leaf-
blades may reach 3 inches in diameter. The flowering
stems may be a foot tall, commonly bearing several
small leaves. The flowers are crowded; the sepals
pink.

II. *Species whose stamens do not project beyond the perianth.*

H. GROSSULARIIFOLIA (6–32 inches) is smooth or
glandular-downy; the leaf-margins are toothed,
with stiff hairs at the points. The flowers are tightly
crowded. The petals are white, from shorter than the
sepals to half again as long.

May to August: on grassy hillsides and rocky
walls of cañons, and high on rock slopes from northeastern Oregon to Idaho and southwestern Montana;
and in the Columbia River Gorge.

H. CYLINDRICA (4–36 inches) has leaf-blades varying
from smooth to glandular-downy or stiff-hairy.
The inflorescence is at first dense, finally open but with
short flower-stalks. The calyx is cream or greenish-

yellow. The petals are much shorter than the calyx-lobes; perhaps lacking, or up to five.

April to August: on rocky soil and slopes and cliffs from Canada to northeastern California, central Montana, and central Nevada. *Plate 99.*

H. PARVIFOLIA (6–24 inches) is commonly glandular-downy all over (some plants almost smooth). The flowers are at first tightly crowded. The petals are white, longer than the calyx-lobes, with a narrow stalk; the flowers are about $\frac{1}{6}$ inch long.

June to August: on gravel and rock slopes and cliffs in the Rocky Mountains and westward to Idaho and Nevada. *Plate 100.*

H. nivalis (4–8 inches) has flowers in a narrow inflorescence like a spike. The flowers are not more than $\frac{1}{10}$ inch long, but wider than long, greenish or yellowish. The leaves are glandular-downy and stiffly

hairy. On high mountains in Colorado. *Plate 99. H. hallii* (4–12 inches), also in the mountains of Colorado, is glandular-downy or smooth. The leaf-blades are not wider than $1\frac{1}{5}$ inches, fringed with hairs and bristly-toothed. The inflorescence is narrow, the flowers from greenish-white to pink-and-yellow. *Plate 100.*

H. chlorantha (16–40 inches) is a species of western Washington and Oregon, entering our range on the eastern slopes of the Cascade Mountains in Oregon. The lower part of the stem and the leaf-stalks are densely soft-hairy; above there may be whitish gland-tipped hairs. The flowers are greenish or cream; petals may be lacking. May to August.

H. duranii (6–12 inches) on rocky hillsides in Mono County, California, and western Nevada, has leaf-blades less than an inch wide, on stalks up to 2 inches. The flowers are yellowish, with some pink, to $\frac{1}{10}$ inch long. July and August.

BOYKINIA

One species of *Boykinia* grows in our range.

B. MAJOR (1–3 feet) has leaves on the stems as well as at the base. They have roundish, lobed and toothed blades up to 8 inches across; the lower are on stalks up to 8 inches long. There are also large, leaflike stipules at the base of at least the upper leaves. The flowers are

in flattish clusters. They have five sepals, five white petals, five short stamens. The ovary is partly joined to the surrounding floral tube; it tapers upward into two beaklike styles.

June to September: in meadows and moist rocky places from northeastern Oregon to Idaho and western Montana. *Plate 100.*

SULLIVANTIA

The leaves of *Sullivantia* have sharply lobed and toothed, roundish blades, on long stalks. They are both at the ground and on the stem. The small flowers are in a branched inflorescence. The calyx has five lobes; there are five white petals; and five stamens. The pistil is of the type usual in this family, with two beaks, each bearing a stigma. The ovary is partly joined to the surrounding floral tube, and is therefore partly inferior. The capsule splits inside the beaks.

William Starling Sullivant was a specialist on mosses, in the middle of the nineteenth century.

S. PURPUSII (8–12 inches) has leaf-blades about an inch long and somewhat wider, on stalks 2–4 inches long. The inflorescence is widely branched and glandular. The petals are about $\frac{1}{8}$ inch long.

July and August: on wet rocks, in Colorado.

S. oregana (2–8 inches) is smooth or nearly so except for some purple-tipped hairs in the inflorescence. The leaf-blades are up to 4 inches wide. There are from one to three leaves on the flowering stem. May to August: on moist cliffs in the Columbia River Gorge.

SUKSDORFIA

There are only two species of *Suksdorfia.*

The branches of the inflorescence all rise to nearly the same level, so that the cluster is nearly flat. The flowers are of the type usual in this family: five sepals, five petals (a little longer than the sepals); five stamens; and a two-beaked pistil, the ovary partly inferior, and each beak bearing a stigma. The capsule splits along the inner sides of the beaks.

Wilhelm Nikolaus Suksdorf was a noted collector and student of northwestern plants in the late nineteenth and early twentieth centuries.

S. RANUNCULIFOLIA (4–14 inches) has a glandular-downy stem. At and near the base are several leaves with rather succulent roundish blades about $1–1\frac{1}{2}$ inches wide on long stalks; the lobes of the blade are broad, and again lobed, the lobes roundish, or

PLATE 100

Elmera racemosa *Fries*

Heuchera rubescens *Korling*

Boykinia major *Korling*

Suksdorfia ranunculifolia *Thompson*

Heuchera micrantha *Davisson*

Suksdorfia violacea *Thompson*

Heuchera parvifolia *W. Weber*

Heuchera hallii *Roberts*

merely scalloped. The petals are white, or purplish-tinged at their base, about ⅛ inch long.

May to August: on wet, mossy rocks on foothills and high in mountains mostly along the eastern side of the Cascade Mountains to California and eastward to Montana and northeastern Oregon. *Plate 100.*

S. VIOLACEA (4–8 inches) has basal leaves with blades

½–1 inch wide; they are usually withered before flowers open. The flowers are few. The petals are commonly violet, rarely almost white, ¼–⅓ inch long.

March to June: in crevices and on cliffs, mossy banks, and sandy places from northeastern Washington to northwestern Montana and southward along the Cascade Mountains to the Columbia River Gorge. *Plate 100.*

LEPUROPETALON

The one species of *Lepuropetalon* is a plant of the southeastern coastal plain, reaching our area in Oklahoma. *L. spathulatum* forms small mats or patches,

with leaf-blades only about ¼ inch long, and minute flowers in their axils. The petals are white. There are five sepals, five petals, ten stamens, three styles.

LEPTARRHENA

The one species of *Leptarrhena* crosses our area.

L. PYROLIFOLIA has short-stalked basal leaves with elliptic, toothed blades 1–6 inches long (perhaps recalling those of *Pyrola*, shinleaf). There are a few much smaller leaves on the flowering stem. The flowers are at the tip of the stem, in a cluster which at first suggests a head but later opens to reveal many short

branches. The calyx has five minute lobes; the five petals are about twice as long; ten stamens; and two pistils joined at the base, each tapering into a beak which bears a stigma. These pistils develop into a pair of follicles.

June to August: from the Cascade Mountains of Washington and Oregon to northern Idaho and western Montana.

CHRYSOSPLENIUM

One species of *Chrysosplenium* is in our range.

C. TETRANDRUM is a small plant with creeping stems up to 6 inches long, the tips bending up and bearing the flowers in a leafy cluster, about 4 inches tall. The leaves are near the beginning of the stems, aside from those in the inflorescence. Their blades are roundish, up to ½ inch wide, deeply scalloped (i.e. shallowly lobed). The flowers are about ⅛ inch across,

greenish, lacking petals, the calyx with four lobes. There are four stamens, alternating with glands. The ovary is partly inferior, with two short styles.

June: in rock crevices and on wet banks around the world in the far north; in our range in northern Washington and through the Rocky Mountains to Colorado. This has been called golden-saxifrage or golden-carpet; but these names belong to European species with yellow-green leaves or sepals.

GRASS-OF-PARNASSUS (PARNASSIA)

Grass-of-Parnassus is not a grass, not even grass-like; and it was not found on Mount Parnassus. The name is a translation of *Gramen Parnassi*, applied to *P. palustris* by the Flemish herbalist Mathias de Lobel, in the sixteenth century; *gramen* at that time was used for many herbaceous plants, not only grasses. The *Parnassi* part must be a sort of dedication to the Muses (much as we honor botanists in such names as *P. kotzebuei*). Another name is white liverwort; the same species was used medicinally for liverish ailments.

The flowers are large for this family. There are five calyx-lobes. The five petals are white or cream with green veins. There are five pollen-bearing sta-

mens, and, alternating with them, five sterile "staminodes." The ovary is joined only at its base with the short, conical flower-base. It bears four stigmas with almost no styles. The fruit is a capsule.

Because of many differences between *Parnassia* and the rest of the family, some botanists have created a separate family for the genus.

Except one arctic species, our plants are 4–12 inches tall. There are several leaves at the base of each stem, and in some species a smaller one, without a stalk, halfway up. One flower is borne at the tip of the stem. Flowering is mainly from July to September (depending on altitude).

FRINGED PARNASSIA, P. FIMBRIATA, has its names from the petals, which are beautifully fringed on the lower half of their edges. The sterile stamens are lobed scales which in some varieties bear knob-tipped "fingers." The leaf-blades may be broader than long and indented at the base.

In bogs and wet meadows and by streams from the Cascade Mountains and the Sierra Nevada to Montana, Wyoming, and Colorado. *Plate 101*.

P. PARVIFLORA has smaller (*parvi-*) flowers, the petals not over $\frac{2}{5}$ inch. The sterile stamens are small scales like hands with from five to nine fingers. The leaves have ovate or elliptic blades, up to 1 inch long. The leaf on the stem does not send basal lobes around the stem.

In bogs and wet meadows and on stream-banks in northern Idaho, Montana, and South Dakota. *Plate 101*.

P. PALUSTRIS has petals up to $\frac{1}{2}$ inch long with up to thirteen veins. The sterile stamens resemble those of *P. parviflora* but usually have more fingers.

The stem-leaf has lobes around the stem.

Along streams in the mountains and up to the tundra, around the world in northern latitudes, in our range through the Rocky Mountains and westward to Utah, southern Nevada, and California. *Plate 101*. A variable species; the original *Gramen Parnassi*.

P. KOTZEBUEI grows only 2–3 inches tall. The flowering stems generally have no leaf above the base. The leaf-blades are less than an inch long, on stalks not much if any longer. The petals, to $\frac{1}{3}$ inch long, have no more than three veins. The sterile stamen may be only a narrow or two-lobed scale, or it may be like a small hand with about five fingers, knob-tipped.

On arctic tundra around the world and in Montana and Wyoming, northeastern Nevada, and northern Washington. *Plate 101*.

P. GLAUCA is an eastern species, in our range in North and South Dakota. The foliage is bluish-green ("glaucous"), some leaves up to 3 inches long; the stem may have one leaf. The sterile stamens are deeply cleft into three segments. *Plates 101, 102*.

THE SUNDEW FAMILY (DROSERACEAE)

The *Droseraceae* are represented in our area only by the genus *Drosera*.

SUNDEWS (DROSERA)

The sundews are plants of bogs and the like, and so are not abundant in our range. They are insect-catching plants. Their small leaves, at ground level, bear hairs with sticky, glandular tips, to which small insects adhere; and hairs around the victim bend over until it is covered by the glands. These exude a digestive material which causes the decomposition of the insect body; and some of the products of this digestion may be absorbed by the leaf, thus rendering the plant to some extent independent of the usual sources of nitrogenous or other nutrients (commonly lacking or scarce in bogs).

The flowers are in a false raceme at the curved tip of the leafless stem. They have five sepals, five white or pink petals, about five stamens, and three styles, cleft so that they seem to be six.

D. ROTUNDIFOLIA (2–10 inches) is named for the round leaf-blades, which have slender hairy stalks. The blades are less than $\frac{1}{2}$ inch long, but may be broader.

June to September: from Canada southward to the Sierra Nevada (possibly reaching western Nevada), Idaho, Montana, and North Dakota. *Plate 101*. *D. anglica* has been reported in the Sierra Nevada and Idaho. It has leaf-blades up to 2 inches long but not more than $\frac{1}{5}$ inch wide, tapering to the stalk; these leaves tend to stand erect or nearly so. *Plate 101*.

THE FLAX FAMILY (LINACEAE)

Flax plants are slender, commonly with unbranched stems, and have small, narrow leaves. The flowers have five overlapping sepals, five petals, five stamens, and a pistil with several styles (most commonly three or five) which may be partly joined. The fruit is a small roundish capsule.

All but one of our species are in *Linum*.

FLAX (LINUM)

The characteristics of *Linum* are those described for the family. The petals may be blue or yellow. We have a group of western yellow-flowered species; and a few from the East are within our eastern boundaries. Two conspicuous blue-flowered species are found practically throughout the country.

The name *Linum* is classical Latin for "flax." Almost the same name existed in Greek and in the old Teutonic. We see it also in the words linen, linseed, and even lingerie; and the fiber is still called line in some parts of England. The value of flax for cloth, thread, cord, oil has been recognized since prehistoric times. With this plant, which is often seen in this country growing wild, are associated a number of native species, with no English names unless we call them all wild flax.

I.   *Blue-flowered species.*
       These are found throughout our range.

FLAX, L. USITATISSIMUM (1–3 feet), is the cultivated species. It has many lanceolate leaves commonly more than an inch long, with three main veins. The petals are $\frac{2}{5}-\frac{3}{5}$ inch long. The inner sepals are fringed with minute hairs.

February to November: in waste land and on roadsides. *Plate 102.*

L. LEWISII (4–30 inches) has densely leafy stems. The narrow leaves have one main vein. The petals are $\frac{1}{2}$–1 inch long. The inner sepals are not fringed.

May to September: usually on dry soil, from plains to high ridges. *Plate 102.* Closely related to the European *L. perenne*, and by many botanists placed in that species as a subspecies. True *L. perenne* may be found as an escape from gardens. It is not so tall as *L. lewisii* but more branched.

II.   *Yellow-flowered or copper-color-flowered species.*

     A. Species with several styles, not joined.

L. KINGII is our most widespread species of this group. It is smooth, with narrow leaves very crowded, especially near the ground. The stalks of the stamens are broad towards that base.

June and July: in rocky and sandy soils from eastern Nevada through Utah to southeastern Idaho, southwestern Wyoming, and western Colorado. *Plate 102.*

Two eastern species belong in this group. *L. virginianum* is found in Kansas. It grows up to 3 feet tall, with several flowers on wiry spreading stalks. Petals about $\frac{1}{4}$ inch, sepals about $\frac{1}{8}$ inch. In dry woods. *L. striatum*, also up to 3 feet tall, is in Oklahoma. It is distinguished by narrow wings running down the stem from the edges of the leaves. Petals about $\frac{1}{4}$ inch, sepals about $\frac{1}{15}-\frac{1}{10}$ inch. In damp woods and swamps.

     B. Species with several styles joined at least at the base (commonly up almost to their tips).

1.   Two species both east and west of the Rocky Mountains.

L. RIGIDUM (4–20 inches) has copper-colored or deep yellow petals, many with a reddish center; they range from $\frac{1}{2}$ inch to nearly 1 inch long. The sepals are toothed. Leaves are very narrow.

April to June: on prairies, especially in rocky places, from western Montana to northern Utah and Colorado and from North Dakota to Oklahoma. *Plate 102. L. puberulum* is closely related and occupies part of the same country. It has crowded, almost needle-like leaves. The flowers are coppery-yellow with a hint of blue, and dark reddish in the center. Petals are about $\frac{1}{2}$ inch long. May to July: from southeastern California to southeastern Wyoming and Colorado and perhaps Oklahoma.

2.   Four species west of the mountains.

L. ARISTATUM (8–16 inches) has bushy, branching, prominently angled stems with few and small leaves. The plant is whitish. The petals are $\frac{1}{2}$ inch long. Sepals are narrow and tapering.

May to September: in sandy soil in southeastern Utah and southwestern Colorado. *L. australe* is closely related. It is less bushy, more leafy, with petals less than $\frac{1}{2}$ inch long. From southern Nevada to Colorado and southeastern Wyoming; and in western Montana. Perhaps better treated as a variety.

L. DIGYNUM (2–16 inches) has at least its lower leaves in pairs. They are elliptic, up to an inch long, with one vein. The sepals are unequal, the outer toothed. The petals are about $\frac{1}{8}$ inch long. There are two (*di-*) styles.

May to July: in meadows and on prairies from the Sierra Nevada northward through Oregon and Washington.

L. subteres (8–12 inches) is whitish with a bloom. The leaves are crowded near the ground and on the larger branches, rather thick and succulent, widest at their tips. Petals about $\frac{1}{2}$ inch. In sandy places. Utah, southern Nevada.

3.   Five species in our area east of the mountains (most also ranging southward).

PLATE 101

Parnassia fimbriata *Scribner*

Parnassia parviflora *Hesselberg*

Parnassia fimbriata *Korling*

Drosera rotundifolia *Justice*

Drosera anglica *Scribner*

Parnassia palustris *Johnson*

Parnassia parviflora *Green*

Parnassia kotzebuei *Scribner*

Parnassia glauca *Gottscho*

L. COMPACTUM (4–8 inches) has many leaves near the base which are early lost; the upper ones remaining. The sepals are gland-toothed, the inner much shorter. Petals about $\frac{1}{8}$ inch long.

June to August: on dry plains from North Dakota and eastern Montana to eastern Wyoming, Kansas, and Colorado. The flower color is much like that of some forms of *L. rigidum (Plate 102)*, and it is possible that these two are closely related. *L. sulcatum* (to nearly 3 feet) has a sharply angled or winged stem. Sepals toothed. Petals light yellow, commonly more than $\frac{1}{2}$ inch long. Styles joined only near the base.

June to October: prairies, North Dakota, Kansas, and Oklahoma. *Plate 102*. *L. hudsonioides* (4–10 inches) has been reported in Kansas. It also has an angled stem, with short stiff hairs. The leaves are not more than $\frac{1}{3}$ inch long, very narrow. The sepals have a short spinelike tip. *L. imbricatum* is similar, and may have been confused with *L. hudsonioides* in Kansas and Oklahoma. It is hairier; the flower-stalks do not exceed $\frac{1}{4}$ inch; the petals no more than $\frac{1}{3}$ inch. *L. medium* (to 3 feet), from the eastern states, reaches Oklahoma. The branches are all near the top, and stiff. In general like *L. virginianum*.

HESPEROLINON

One species of *Hesperolinon, H. micranthum*, is barely in our range in northeastern California and southern Oregon. Its petals vary from whitish to rose, and have two small lobes on their stalks; about $\frac{1}{4}$ inch long. May to July: on wooded or open slopes and ridges, commonly in brush.

THE PASSION-FLOWER FAMILY (PASSIFLORACEAE)

The *Passifloraceae* are represented in the United States only by the genus *Passiflora*.

PASSION-FLOWERS (PASSIFLORA)

The passion-flowers are plants mainly of the southern and eastern United States. Two species enter Kansas and Oklahoma. The flowers are remarkable for the fringe of narrow, hairlike parts just within the perianth. In the center are five stamens, their stalks joined, and a stalked pistil with three styles projecting sideways, each with a knoblike stigma. The early explorers saw in this curious flower a divine representation of the passion of Jesus: the fringe was the crown of thorns; the stamens, the five wounds; the styles with their stigmas, the nails. The ten parts of the perianth (five sepals, five petals, generally much alike) were the ten apostles (Peter and Judas excluded).

The plants are mostly vines, climbing by means of tendrils (identified with the scourges); their leaves are mostly palmately lobed or cleft into three.

Our species may flower from June to September.

MAYPOPS, P. INCARNATA, may have a stem up to 25 feet long. The lobes of the leaf are sharp-pointed. The perianth is lavender, about 2 inches across; the fringe, nearly an inch long, is purple and pink. The yellow berry is edible. In thickets or trailing on open ground. *Plate 103*.

P. lutea is smaller, the stem up to 10 feet. The lobes of the leaf are blunt. The perianth is greenish-yellow. The fringe is partly yellow. The berry is purple. Thickets, edges of woods. *Plate 103*.

THE WOOD-SORREL FAMILY (OXALIDACEAE)

The *Oxalidaceae* are represented in this country by one genus.

THE WOOD-SORRELS (OXALIS)

The wood-sorrels (which do not all grow in woods) are small plants with leaves mostly divided palmately into three heart-shaped segments. The flowers have five sepals, five petals, ten stamens, and a pistil with five styles. The ovary becomes a narrow seed-pod, which in most species splits open explosively, scattering the seeds.

There are about 800 species, mostly in Africa

PLATE 102

Oxalis repens
Roberts

Parnassia glauca
Rickett

Linum lewisii
Korling

Oxalis stricta
Johnson

Linum rigidum
Koch

Linum usitatissimum
Rickett

Linum sulcatum
Horst

Oxalis grayi
Hesselberg

Linum kingii
Korling

and North America. The most abundant species in our range came from the Old World.

The name *Oxalis* comes from a Greek word meaning "sharp," referring to the sharp taste of the leaves. This is due to an acid, which has received the name oxalic acid. It is poisonous in any large quantity; but the leaves of *O. acetosella* have long been used in salads and soups.

I.   *Species with yellow flowers.*

     A. Common Old-World weeds of waste ground, lawns, etc. throughout the country. Their names are hopelessly confused, scarcely two authors applying them to the same species.

O. REPENS has creeping (*repens*) or trailing stems which root. The flowers are on stalks rising from the axils; they are about ½ inch across. The stalks of the seed-pods, several in a sort of umbel, turn down, the pods standing erect at their tips. *Plate 102*. The correct name is *O. corniculata*, but this has been so commonly used for *O. stricta* that it has become a source of confusion; accordingly the above name, though illegitimate, is retained here for convenience.

O. stricta has also been called *O. europaea*, and perhaps, since *O. dillenii* has been confused with *O. stricta*, we should reject the name *O. stricta* and use the substitute *O. europaea*. To avoid going to extremes, the correct name is here retained. *O. stricta* has erect or less commonly trailing stems up to 18 inches tall. The flowers are in small groups at the ends of stems growing from the axils. The leaves lack stipules. The stalks of the seed-pods do not turn down. *Plate 102*.

O. dillenii, often miscalled *O. stricta*, has stems spreading and bending up; the hairs point up along the stem. Stipules are present. The flowers resemble those of *O. stricta*, but the stalks of the seed-pods turn down as in *O. repens*.

O. PILOSA has downy or hairy ("pilose") stems which sprawl on the ground, bending up at the ends. The leaf-blades also are hairy. Petals are ½–1 inch long. The seed-pods are on turned-down stalks as in *O. repens*.

Through the year as climate permits: from California along our southern boundary. *Plate 103*.

II.   *Species with flower-colors other than yellow.*
     Both the following species grow from bulbs.

O. VIOLACEA has leaves colored on the under surface; a breath of wind across a field of these plants turns it suddenly from green to crimson or violet. There are several flowers to a stem, the petals purple or violet.

May and June: in fields and on prairies from North Dakota to Oklahoma and Colorado. *Plate 103*.

O. grayi is another species commoner south of our boundary, but found in the south of the Intermountain Region. The four or more leaf-segments are very narrow, generally notched. The petals are pink. July and August, in woods. *Plate 102*.

O. OREGANA grows from the rhizome, all leaves being at ground level. The leaf-stalks have brown hairs; the blades may be nearly two inches across. Flowering stems are 2–6 inches tall, each with one white or pink flower.

April to September: in woods on the eastern slope of the Cascade Mountains, and westward and southward. *Plate 103*.

THE GINSENG FAMILY (ARALIACEAE)

The *Araliaceae* are represented in our area by two genera, one of which is limited to our easternmost states. The family is characterized by divided leaves and small white or greenish flowers in close inflorescences. There are five sepals (scarcely evident), five petals, five stamens, and an inferior ovary bearing two or more styles and one ovule in each of five chambers.

PANAX

Two species of *Panax* are within our eastern limits. Dwarf ginseng or ground-nut, *P. trifolius*, is up to 8 inches tall. There are three leaves, each divided palmately into three or five rather narrow segments. The flowers are in a single umbel at the tip. They have two styles. The fruit is flattish, dry when mature. April to June: in moist woods and openings from North Dakota to Oklahoma, and eastward. *Plate 103*. Ginseng, *P. quinquefolius*, has three or four leaves divided generally into five (*quinque*) broad segments. The flowers are small, greenish-white, in a small umbel overtopped by the large leaves. They have two styles. The fruit is flattish, dry when mature. June and July: in cool woods from North Dakota to Oklahoma, and

PLATE 103

Passiflora incarnata   *Johnson*

Panax trifolius   *Horne*

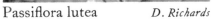

Passiflora lutea   *D. Richards*

Panax quinquefolius   *Justice*

Oxalis pilosa   *White*

Oxalis oregana   *Cole*

Oxalis violacea   *Johnson*

eastward. *Plate 103*. Because of its supposed medicinal virtues, the plant has become almost extinct; having been rooted up and sold, mostly to the Chinese.

The supposition may be due largely to the forked root, which may be thought to resemble a man. Our physicians have found no sovereign virtues in the plant.

ARALIA

The leaves of *Aralia* are large, the blades divided first into three and these segments again divided; at first sight a single leaf may seem to be a stem or branch bearing several leaves. The ovary bears five or six styles. The fruit is a purplish-black berry.

WILD SARSAPARILLA, A. NUDICAULIS (8–16 inches), has a single leaf growing from a rhizome, and a single leafless flowering stem beside it; the leaf is the taller. Its three segments are divided pinnately (or some apparently palmately). The flowers are in several umbels (from two to seven on one stem), on stalks radiating from the tip; these look rather like heads because of the shortness of many flower-stalks ($\frac{1}{5}$–$\frac{4}{5}$ inch).

May and June: in woods from northeastern Washington to Montana, thence southward to Colorado. *Plate 104*.

AMERICAN SPIKENARD, A. RACEMOSA (2–10 feet), has a branched stem which bears several leaves, divided twice pinnately. The final segments are generally indented at the base and taper to sharp points. The flowers are in many umbels borne in a tall ("racemose") branched inflorescence.

June to August: mainly in woods and thickets in the eastern states, westward through Texas to Utah. *Plate 104*. The roots are aromatic, which may account for the English name. True spikenard or nard is an ointment prepared from an Indian plant. *Plate 104*.

THE PARSLEY FAMILY (UMBELLIFERAE)

The *Umbelliferae* get their name from the disposition of their flowers (in almost all genera) in umbels (*umbella*, "umbrella"). The stalks in an umbel correspond to the ribs of an umbrella, generally radiating from the tip of a stem; these are called rays.

Most umbels in this family are compound; that is, the rays bear not single flowers but secondary umbels, in which the radiating members are the stalks of individual flowers. In many genera these flower-stalks are very short, so that the secondary umbel is a head; in some genera the same applies to the rays, so that the entire umbel is a head.

The rays may be associated with bracts at their base, which form a circle called an involucre. There are commonly bracts at the base of the secondary umbels also; in the following pages these are termed bractlets.

The flowers themselves are generally small. The calyx of many genera is barely visible, merely a rim or a circle of minute teeth; in others it forms relatively conspicuous teeth. There are five petals, five stamens, and two styles rising from an inferior ovary (the base of the style may be expanded to form what may be mistaken for an

ovary). The fruit consists of two parts, each containing one seed, and splitting apart at maturity; the face of each part (i.e. the surface not joined to the other part) bears typically five ribs, variously adorned with "wings" (membranes or flanges).

Between the ribs and in other parts of the fruit there may be oil-tubes; but these are not generally visible on the surface.

The leaves are divided in almost all genera; and the division may be complex and impossible to describe without the introduction of additional technical terms. The segments referred to in the following pages are the "final" segments formed by the division. One characteristic feature of the leaves is their stalk, which is generally expanded ("dilated") into a sheath which embraces the stem. The leaves are borne singly, with few exceptions; but in many genera are crowded at ground level.

Because of the large number of genera and species* and their general similarity, identification may be very difficult – and not only for the amateur. The foregoing detailed description,

*One hundred and eighty-two species in fifty-one genera in our area.

with the introduction of a special vocabulary, was written with this in mind. The reader must be prepared to measure the final leaf-segments, to count the rays of the umbel, to look for involucre and bractlets, and to study the features of the fruits if these can be found. It must be borne in mind (as with other families) that the stated measurements express a range, which may not be valid for all individuals; a number of umbels or leaves should be compared.

Guide to Genera of Umbelliferae

I. *Plants with all or most leaves at or near the ground.*
    In many species the leaves are at the summit of a short leafless stem. Above them is the stalk of the umbel.

    A. Genera with fruits (mostly flattish) winged at their edges: *Cymopterus* (rays less than an inch long; flower-stalks short, the secondary umbels like heads); *Pseudocymopterus* (leaf-segments threadlike or lanceolate; rays up to 2 inches; calyx-teeth ovate); *Pteryxia* (mostly forming tufts; rays very unequal; bractlets equal to or longer than the flowers; petals yellow or white); *Lomatium* (rays 1–8 inches, mostly unequal; flowers yellow, white, or reddish); *Oreoxis* (stems in tufts, to 6 inches; rays short, the umbel compact; flowers yellow or whitish; fruit with corky ribs and wings; high altitudes); *Orogenia* (dwarf; leaf-segments narrow, without teeth or lobes; fruit plump, with thick corky wings at the edges; flowers white, in heads); *Aletes* (rays nearly equal, up to 1⅕ inches; flower-stalks very short, the yellow flowers in heads; calyx-lobes triangular; fruit with corky wings).

    B. Genera with fruits lacking wings, but ribbed: *Podistera* (tufts and cushions; rays and flower-stalks short or lacking, the flowers in a head; petals greenish- or orange-yellow; high altitudes); *Rhysopterus* (flowers white; fruit seven-ribbed; leaves short and broad; only southeastern Oregon); *Tauschia* (to 2 feet tall; leaf-segments lobed or sharply toothed; rays to 2 inches; flowers yellow; fruit ribbed; only in south-central Washington); *Harbouria* (flowers yellow; fruit flattish, ribbed).

Guide continued on page 312

CYMOPTERUS

The leaves of *Cymopterus* are at or near the ground, the stem (below the stalk of the umbel) being very short. The blades are much divided, cleft, and lobed, the final parts small. The styles lack the bulblike base common in the family. The fruit is oblong or ovate, flattish, with wings at the sides and in some species also on the faces.

The number of rays cited in the following descriptions refers only to those that bear flowers; there may also be sterile rays not further mentioned here.

We have twenty-six species, most of them commoner in the drier parts of the area, especially in Utah and Nevada. Some are restricted to small ranges.

I. *Species with yellow flowers.*
    See also under II B, *C. purpureus, rosei.*

    The first three have no involucre; the last three have no individual flower-stalks, so that the rays end in heads rather than secondary umbels. Bractlets are present in all, equal to or longer than the flowers.

C. LONGIPES (to 14 inches) has twice pinnately divided leaves, the segments pinnately lobed; they are rather succulent, with a slight bloom. There are from three to eight rays, up to ⅖ inch long. Flower-stalks are about ⅓ inch.

April to July: on dry hills and in dry valleys from western Wyoming to Utah and Colorado. *Plate 104.*

C. duchesnensis (to 10 inches): Segments widest and toothed at the end. From six to ten rays, ½–1½ inches. Flower-stalks to ⅙ inch. Uintah Basin, northeastern Utah.

C. humboldtensis (to 4 inches): Leaves gray-green. From two to four rays, less than ⅕ inch. Flower-stalks about ¹⁄₁₂ inch. Southern Idaho, northeastern Nevada.

C. glaucus (to 6 inches): Pale blue-green; final segments small. Involucre of several narrow bracts. From one to four very unequal rays up to an inch long. Flower-stalks to ⅓ inch. Central Idaho, western Montana.

C. FENDLERI (to 1 foot) has leaves divided once or twice pinnately. The involucre is a low sheath, on some plants with up to three narrow bracts. There are from three to five rays up to an inch long. The bractlets are narrow or ovate, leaflike. The flowers have no stalks, thus forming heads.

CYMOPTERUS

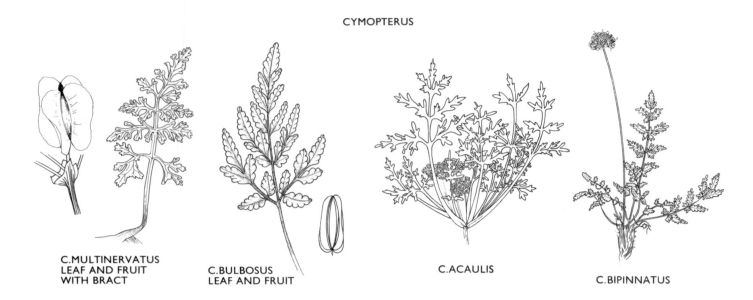

C.MULTINERVATUS
LEAF AND FRUIT
WITH BRACT

C.BULBOSUS
LEAF AND FRUIT

C.ACAULIS

C.BIPINNATUS

May and June: in gravelly places in Utah. *Plate 104.*

C. newberryi (to 8 inches): Involucre as in *C. fendleri*. Rays $\frac{1}{5}$–$1\frac{1}{5}$ inches. Bractlets narrow, leaflike. Southern Utah. *C. basalticus* (to 5 inches): Involucre lacking or of one or two narrow bracts. From seven to fourteen rays up to $\frac{3}{4}$ inch. Flowers yellow or reddish. Eastern Nevada, western Utah.

II.   *Species with flowers rarely yellow.*
        See also under I, *C. basalticus*; under B, *C. purpureus.*

A. Plants with white flowers. See also under B, *C. montanus, globosus, nivalis, ripleyi.*
        Except in the first of group A, an involucre is lacking (or rarely present but inconspicuous in another). Except as noted, there are not more than ten rays, these up to $\frac{2}{5}$ inch long. Bractlets are narrow, commonly (but not in all) about equal to the flowers.

C. CINERARIUS (up to 3 inches) lacks rays and flower-stalks, so that all the flowers form one head. The involucre is relatively conspicuous, consisting of partly joined bracts many of which may be toothed at the end. Bractlets are not evident.
        June and July: in open high places in eastern California and adjacent Nevada. *Plate 104.*

C. ACAULIS (to 1 foot) has from three to five rays, bearing secondary umbels of flowers with very short stalks ($\frac{1}{20}$ inch), and so more like heads.
        April and May: on dry flats and hillsides from eastern Oregon to Montana and Colorado. *Plate 104.*

C. BIPINNATUS (to 10 inches) has gray-green, rather roughish leaves; their segments may be crowded.

The flower-stalks are up to $\frac{1}{8}$ inch long. There are up to fifteen rays, up to $2\frac{1}{2}$ inches long.
        May to July: in open places from foothills to above timberline from eastern Oregon and northwestern Utah to southwestern Wyoming and western Montana.

C. corrugatus (to 4 inches) has rather succulent or leathery leaves. There are up to ten rays $\frac{1}{12}$–$\frac{2}{5}$ inch long. The flower-stalks are up to $\frac{1}{2}$ inch long. The bractlets are whitish, shorter than the flowers. Western Nevada, southeastern Oregon. *C. aboriginum* (to 14 inches): Leaves gray-green, minutely hairy. Segments narrow. From three to ten rays up to $\frac{4}{5}$ inch long. Flower-stalks $\frac{1}{8}$–$\frac{1}{3}$ inch. An involucre of a few narrow bracts may be present. Death Valley region and adjacent Nevada.

C. coulteri (to 4 inches): Leaves succulent or leathery. Rays unequal, up to $\frac{2}{5}$ inch. Bractlets reddish, longer than the flowers. Western Utah. *C. minimus* (to 3 inches): From two to four rays up to $\frac{1}{4}$ inch. Flower-stalks to $\frac{1}{8}$ inch. Western Utah. *C. ibapensis* (to 8 inches): Segments well separated. From five to ten rays $\frac{1}{5}$–$\frac{4}{5}$ inch long. Flower-stalks to $\frac{1}{3}$ inch. Bractlets few, inconspicuous, equaling the flowers. Eastern Nevada, western Utah.

B. Species with reddish, pink, or white flowers; rarely yellow.
        See also *C. basalticus* under I.

1.   An involucre is present only in the first four of these.

C. MONTANUS (to 1 foot) has pale, rather succulent leaves, roughish on edges and veins. The involucre is silvery with green ribs. From five to ten rays. Flower-stalks very short. The flowers are white or reddish.

PLATE 104

Cymopterus longipes   *Rose*

Cymopterus bulbosus   *W. Weber*

Aralia nudicaulis   *Johnson*

Cymopterus acaulis   *Stockert*

Cymopterus fendleri   *Finzel*

Aralia racemosa   *Justice*

Cymopterus cinerarius   *Buckalew*

Cymopterus montanus   *Morris*

March to May: on dry plains from South Dakota and Wyoming to Colorado and Oklahoma. *Plate 104.*

C. bulbosus (2–14 inches): Involucre a low sheath or of whitish bracts. Bractlets similar, equal to or longer than the flowers. From three to eight rays. Flower-stalks $\frac{1}{8}$–$\frac{1}{2}$ inch. Flowers reddish. Southwestern Wyoming and central Colorado. *Plate 104. C. purpurascens* (1–6 inches): Involucre of conspicuous white bracts, generally joined below their middle. From three to five rays up to $\frac{2}{5}$ inch. Flower-stalks up to $\frac{1}{8}$ inch. Umbels compact. Flowers reddish. Southeastern California, Utah, Nevada, and southern Idaho. *Plate 105. C. multinervatus* (2–9 inches): Flower-stalks very short. From one to five rays up to an inch. Involucre a low sheath or a purplish lobed cup or one or two conspicuous bracts. Flowers reddish. Southern Utah, southern Nevada.

2.   The remaining species lack an involucre.

C. GLOBOSUS (1–9 inches) has rather leathery leaves with a bloom. Rays and flower-stalks are lacking, the inflorescence being a flattish ("discoid") mass. The flowers are white or red.

April and May: mostly on sandy soil from California to western Utah. *C. ripleyi* (4–6 inches), on sand-dunes in southern Nevada, has leaves divided and redivided into three – not pinnately. Inflorescence and flowers as in *C. globosus.*

C. PURPUREUS (4–20 inches) has leaves divided first into three, then pinnately. The final segments have spine-tipped teeth. There are up to twelve rays $\frac{1}{2}$–2 inches long; flower-stalks are $\frac{1}{6}$–$\frac{1}{2}$ inch long. Flowers are red* or yellow.

May and June: southwestern and northeastern Utah and southwestern Colorado. *C. jonesii* is similar. Bractlets as long as the flowers. Wings of the fruit inflated at the base and several times as wide as the central part. Southwestern Utah and adjacent Nevada.

C. nivalis (2–6 inches): Leaves divided pinnately, the segments well separated, rough-downy. Flowers white or pink. From central Idaho to Northeastern Nevada. *C. planosus* (4–12 inches): Leaves rather succulent, pale, twice pinnate, the segments well separated. Flowers reddish. Northwestern Colorado. *Plate 105. C. rosei* (3–6 inches): Leaves rather leathery, the segments well separated and with or without toothed lobes. Flowers reddish or yellow. South-central Utah.

PSEUDOCYMOPTERUS

One species of *Pseudocymopterus* is found in our range.

P. MONTANUS (1–3 feet) may have a short leafy stem.

The leaves are pinnately divided, the final segments from threadlike to lanceolate. The inflorescence consists of from five to twenty-five mostly unequal rays $\frac{1}{8}$–2 inches long. There are several bractlets up to $\frac{1}{3}$ inch long. The flower-stalks are short (to $\frac{1}{5}$ inch).

The flowers are yellow or reddish. The fruit has spongy wings on the edges.

May to October: in pine woods mostly at high altitudes in southern Wyoming and western Utah. *Plate 105.* The proper disposition of this species has puzzled many botanists. It has been placed in *Cymopterus*, in *Lomatium*, in *Thaspium*, in *Ligusticum*, and in other genera, acquiring in the process some twenty-four names!

PTERYXIA

The differences between *Pteryxia* and *Cymopterus* are slight; and indeed the two genera, with *Pseudocymopterus*, have been united in a recent treatment. In general *Pteryxia* forms low tufts; some species with short leafy stems. The final segments of the leaves are narrow. The rays of the umbel are unequal. The bractlets, usually all on one side, are equal to or longer than the flowers. All these characteristics are shared among the three genera, but the combination perhaps enables us to distinguish *Pteryxia*, as a rather "unnatural" genus. All our species have yellow flowers; the first may have white flowers.

P. TEREBINTHINA (4–24 inches) has leaves divided finally into segments up to $\frac{1}{6}$ inch long and $\frac{1}{25}$

inch wide. There are from seven to twenty-four unequal rays $\frac{1}{5}$–3 inches long. Flower-stalks are from almost nothing to $\frac{1}{3}$ inch. The wings of the fruit are wavy.

April to July: in dry sandy and rocky places from eastern Washington to California and eastward to Montana, Wyoming, and northern Colorado. *Plate 105.*

---

*Classical *purpureus* was a color derived from a Mediterranean shellfish; it was close to what we call crimson. Translated as "purple," it retained that meaning until modern times, when the word came to mean a quite different color – except to botanists, who persisted in the classical usage, but used "purple" more loosely for a number of reddish tints. In these *Umbelliferae* no flowers are purple in the usual modern sense – in fact not even in the classical sense. The flowers of *Cymopterus* and other genera named *purpureus* and described in botanical works as "purple" are mostly close to the color of *C. planosus* shown on *Plate 105.*

PLATE 105

Pseudocymopterus montanus   *Johnson*

Cymopterus purpurascens   *Thorne*

Pteryxia petraea   *Korling*

Pteryxia hendersoni   *Roberts*

Pseudocymopterus montanus   *Rickett*

Cymopterus planosus   *W. Weber*

Pteryxia terebinthina   *Thompson*

P. petraea (6–18 inches) has leaves with a narrow outline, the final segments up to $\frac{1}{3}$ inch long. Not more than seven rays, very unequal, $\frac{1}{25}$–25 inches long. Wings of the fruit flat. May and June: from southeastern Oregon and southern Idaho to California and central Nevada. *Plate 105.*

P. HENDERSONI (2–16 inches) has no leafy stem. The
   leaves are twice pinnately divided, with the final segments up to $\frac{1}{2}$ inch long and $\frac{1}{12}$ inch wide. There

may (rarely) be an involucre of one or two narrow bracts. There are from three to seven very unequal rays. The wings of the fruit are flat.

   June to August: from southern Idaho and eastern Nevada to Montana and Colorado. *Plate 105.*
   P. anisata (4–12 inches) is similar. The final leaf-segments may run together, thus making them lobes of a larger segment. From six to nine very unequal rays. Bractlets lanceolate, up to $\frac{3}{5}$ inch, much longer than the flowers. On dry hills in central Colorado.

LOMATIUM

The great genus *Lomatium* is one of those, unfortunately numerous in the West, with very many species distinguished by minor technicalities and thus almost unidentifiable by the amateur. In our area there are fifty-four species. While I cannot promise that the following treatment will enable anyone to identify any *Lomatium* he may find, yet it may place his specimen in a group. I can at least say that, to the best of my knowledge, all the species of the area are named and briefly described.

   The genus as a whole is characterized by the lack of an involucre – a circle of bracts – around the base of the umbel. The rays of the umbel bear secondary umbels, generally surrounded by a circle of bractlets; these may be helpful in identifying a plant. The rays of the umbel may be nearly equal in length or markedly unequal. The flattish fruits have "winged" edges and three ribs on each face. The leaves are generally much divided, mostly into three main segments which may be again divided into three, these segments divided pinnately (but see group II A). The shape and size of the "final segments" are helpful in identification, and where dimensions of segments are stated in the following pages, it is to these final segments that they apply.

   In classifying these numerous species, the attempt to separate them by easily visible features results in groups none too clearly distinguished. The reader must sometimes search several headings to name his plant. The geographical data may help, especially since many species are found only in a relatively small area. A number of these are desert plants.

   For the abbreviations used here, see page 1.

I.   *Species whose flowers are regularly of other colors than yellow (white except as noted).*
   A few species in group II may have reddish or reddish-tinged or white flowers. See *L. dissectum, macdougali, plummerae.*
   The rays are mostly unequal. The leaves are at or near the ground. The stem is mostly 4–12 inches tall.

A. Downy or hairy plants. The bractlets, though small, are easily seen.

L. MACROCARPUM (4–20 inches) has white or reddish flowers, rarely yellow. The bractlets are $\frac{1}{2}$–1 inch long, the secondary umbels being very compact, the flower-stalks very short. Leaf-segments $\frac{1}{3}$ inch. The fruits are $\frac{1}{2}$–1 inch long, narrow. Leaf-segments up to $\frac{1}{3}$ inch long, crowded.

   March to May: on dry hills and plains from Washington to North Dakota and southward to California, Nevada, Utah, and Wyoming. *Plate 106. L. nevadense:* Bractlets narrow, about the same length as the flowers. Fruit $\frac{1}{3}$ inch. Generally at high altitudes from Ore to Calif and Utah. *L. orientale* (to 16 inches): Leaf-segments narrow, to $\frac{1}{2}$ inch. Rays nearly equal. From Mont to e Colo, N D to Kan. *Plate 106. L. farinosum:* Leaf-segments up to 3 inches, not crowded. Fruit $\frac{1}{4}$ inch long. e Wash – w Mont. *L. ravenii:* Softly hairy. Leaf-segments $\frac{1}{4}$ inch. Flowers white or pink. Lassen Co., Calif.

B. Smooth plants. The bractlets are narrow, of various lengths, easily seen or inconspicuous. Plants mostly of Washington, Oregon, and Idaho, one in Montana.

L. GORMANI (4–6 inches) may have relatively few leaf-segments, nearly $\frac{1}{2}$ inch long, not close together; or, on some leaves, more numerous, smaller, more crowded segments. The bractlets are few, bristle-like, or none. The flower-stalks are very short (to $\frac{1}{8}$ inch) so that the umbel is like a head. Flowers are white, the stamens tipped with red.

   March to May: in open areas, commonly with sagebrush, from central Washington to Idaho and southward to northeastern California. *Plate 106.* One common name is pepper-and-salt; the white flowers dotted with red-tipped stamens. *L. geyeri* (6–24 inches): Similar. Up to twenty rays. Flower-stalks a little longer (to $\frac{1}{5}$ inch). Bractlets about as long as the flowers, joined. c Wash, Ida. *L. orogenioides* (to 16

PLATE 106

Lomatium nudicaule   *Korling*

Lomatium macrocarpum   *Dye*

Lomatium ambiguum   *Korling*

Lomatium simplex   *McRae*

Lomatium orientale   *Roberts*

Lomatium cuspidatum   *Spurr*

Lomatium gormani   *Lomax*

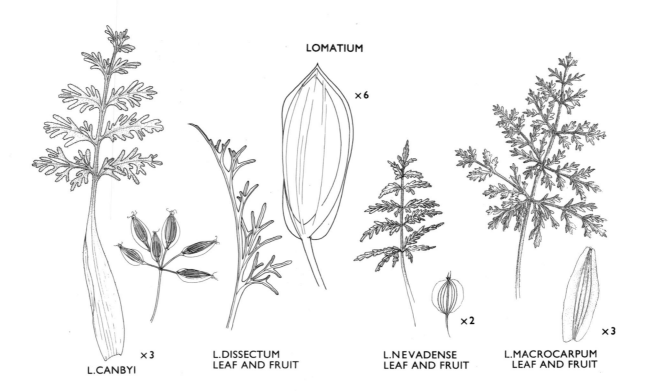

LOMATIUM

×6

×3
L.CANBYI

L.DISSECTUM
LEAF AND FRUIT

×2

L.NEVADENSE
LEAF AND FRUIT

×3

L.MACROCARPUM
LEAF AND FRUIT

inches): Leaf-segments few, threadlike, to 2 inches, widely spaced. Flower-stalks very short. Bractlets few, narrow, short. Fruit without marginal wing. e Wash, n Ida. *L. cusickii:* Leaf-segments few, narrow, $\frac{1}{2}$–$2\frac{1}{2}$ inches, widely spaced. Bractlets commonly broad-based and joined. Flowers white, cream, or reddish. Moderate and high altitudes, ne Ore to w Mont.

L. CANBYI (4–8 inches) is smooth with a bloom. The leaf-segments are many, small ($\frac{1}{5}$ inch), narrow, crowded. There are up to seventeen nearly equal rays. Bractlets are narrow, about equal to the flowers. The flower-stalks are $\frac{1}{3}$–$\frac{1}{2}$ inch long.

March and April: on open rocky places, commonly with sagebrush, from eastern Washington and western Idaho to northeastern California. *L. greenmanii* (to 4 inches): Leaf-segments to $\frac{1}{8}$ inch long, crowded. Rays few. Bractlets few, threadlike, very short. Flower-stalks very short. ne Ore. *L. minus:* Leaf-segments many, threadlike or broader, to $\frac{1}{8}$ inch, crowded. Flowers reddish. ne Ore. *L. cuspidatum* (to 20 inches): Leaf-segments many, crowded, to $\frac{1}{5}$ inch, lanceolate, sharp. Bractlets tending to lanceolate, or threadlike, shorter than the flowers. Flowers reddish. Fruit narrow-winged. c Wash. *Plate 106. L. tuberosum:* Leaf-segments similar, not so sharp. Very large, broad, bladeless, stalks sheathing the base. Up to eight rays. Bractlets inconspicuous. Flowers reddish, the stamens yellow-tipped. sc Wash.

II.   *Species with yellow flowers.*
         See also *L. macrocarpum* under I.

A. Plants whose leaf-segments are more than $\frac{2}{5}$ inch long (except perhaps near the tips of the leaves).
         See also *L. megarrhizum, L. dissectum, L. peckianum* under B.

1.   Three of these have relatively few leaf-segments, lanceolate or broader and not crowded together.

L. NUDICAULE (1–3 feet) has an overall blue-green color. The leaf-segments range from lanceolate to almost round, 1–$3\frac{1}{2}$ inches long; their tips may be toothed. From ten to twenty rays; no bractlets.

April to June: in dry, mostly open places from the Cascade Mountains and the Sierra Nevada to Idaho and Utah. *Plate 106.*

L. latilobum (to 7 inches): Leaf-segments lanceolate. Rays almost equal. Bractlets lanceolate or narrower, about $\frac{1}{5}$ inch. Flowers few. se Utah. *L. triternatum:* Two subspecies with ovate leaf-segments $\frac{1}{2}$–$2\frac{1}{2}$ inches. From ten to twenty-two nearly equal rays. Bractlets threadlike or lacking. Wash to Mont, s to Calif and Ida.

2.   The remaining nine species with leaf-segments more than $\frac{2}{5}$ inch long have narrow, even threadlike segments. Bractlets are lacking or minute in the first five.

L. AMBIGUUM (to 18 inches) has narrow leaf-segments up to 3 inches long. There are from five to seventeen rays. The fruit is narrow-winged.

PLATE 107

Lomatium leptocarpum   *Andersen*

Lomatium cous   *Wilson*

Lomatium dissectum   *Spurr*

Lomatium brandegei   *Spurr*

Lomatium dissectum   *McRae*

Lomatium triternatum   *Dye*

Lomatium grayi   *Frost*

Lomatium nuttallii   *Korling*

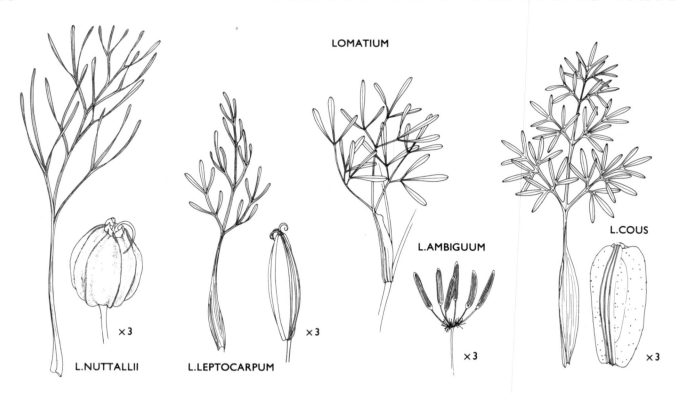

LOMATIUM

L.NUTTALLII   L.LEPTOCARPUM   L.AMBIGUUM   L.COUS

May to July: in rocky places from Washington and northeastern Oregon to western Montana, Wyoming, and the Wasatch Mountains of Utah. *Plate 106.*

L. triternatum (6–32 inches): Two subspecies with narrow segments up to 3 inches long. Bractlets threadlike. Cascade Mts and northern Sierra Nevada to the Rocky Mts. *Plate 107.*

L. LAEVIGATUM (10–16 inches) has leaf-segments up to $1\frac{1}{2}$ inches long. There are from nine to twenty rays.

April: in the Columbia River valley, in Washington and Oregon. *L. rollinsii* (to 20 inches): Leaf-segments to $1\frac{1}{5}$ inches. From four to eight rays. Bractlets minute, threadlike. e Ore, w Ida. *L. hamblenae* (to 14 inches); Leaf-segments $\frac{1}{5}$–1 inch. Bractlets few, short, narrow or lanceolate. From two to eight rays. c Wash.

L. NUTTALLII (to 17 inches) has leaf-segments $\frac{2}{5}$–2 inches long. There are from five to sixteen rays. The bractlets are narrow, equaling or longer than the flowers.

May to July: from eastern Nevada to southwestern Wyoming. *Plate 107. L. simplex* has leaf-segments 1–5 inches long, commonly densely downy on the under side. From c Wash and Ore to w Mont and sw Colo. *Plate 106.* Similar to *L. triternatum.*

L. LEPTOCARPUM (to 2 feet) has leaf-segments up to 2 inches long, threadlike or narrow. There are from four to fifteen rays. Bractlets about equal flowers.

May and June: from northern Idaho to north-western Colorado, and southwestward to northeastern California. *Plate 107.*

L. brandegei (to 2 feet) has leaf-segments $\frac{2}{5}$–$1\frac{3}{5}$ inches long. Bractlets mostly longer than the flowers. From ten to twenty-one nearly equal rays. c & nc Wash. *Plate 107.*

B. Yellow-flowered species with leaf-segments less than $\frac{2}{5}$ inch long. (There may be occasional longer segments, especially near the base of the main divisions.)

1. Seven of these have a leafy stem (short in some) above ground (below the stem that supports the umbel). They have narrow or even threadlike bractlets, leaf-segments also very narrow, numerous and crowded except as noted; rays not more than fifteen except as noted in one, generally unequal. Plants found mostly across the northern part of our area, one reaching Colorado, two in Nevada.

L. DISSECTUM (3–5 feet) may form a bushy clump.

The numerous leaf-segments are up to $\frac{1}{3}$ inch long, or, in a variety, to nearly 1 inch. The bractlets may be longer or shorter than the flowers. In one variety the flower-stalks are very short, the secondary umbels headlike. The flowers are yellow or reddish (both forms are illustrated).

April to July: in open rocky areas from the Cascade Mountains and the Sierra Nevada to Montana and Colorado. *Plate 107. L. salmoniflorum* (8–20 inches): Segments $\frac{1}{20}$–$\frac{1}{3}$ inch. Rays nearly equal. Bractlets few and short, or none. Flowers salmon-yellow. se Wash, ne Ore, w Ida. *L. sandbergii* (3–12 inches):

Leaf-sheaths with a conspicuous white margin. Segments $\frac{1}{10}$–$\frac{1}{6}$ inch. Bractlets as long as the flowers. n Ida, nw Mont.

L. THOMPSONII (20–40 inches) has leaf-segments $\frac{1}{3}$–$\frac{2}{5}$ inch long, not crowded. There are from thirteen to twenty-five rays. The bractlets are longer than the flowers.

June: north-central Washington. *Plate 108.* Originally described as a variety of *L. suksdorfii. L. idahoense* (8–16 inches): Segments oblong or narrower, $\frac{1}{20}$–$\frac{2}{5}$ inch, not crowded. From three to seven rays. No bractlets. c Ida. *L. circumdatum* (6–14 inches): Segments $\frac{1}{4}$–$\frac{2}{5}$ inch, not crowded. Bractlets conspicuous, longer than the flowers, ovate with the narrow end down. e Wash, se Ore, ne Nev, w Ida. (By some treated as identical with *L. cous*; see below.) *L. vaginatum* (9–18 inches): Roughish. Segments $\frac{1}{2}$–$\frac{1}{5}$ inch. Bractlets as in *L. circumdatum.* ec Ore to ne Calif.

2. The remaining yellow-flowered species have no leafy stem or a very short one; the leaves being at ground level or nearly so.

a. Seven of these have fairly obviously broader leaf-segments (crowded except as noted) than the remaining thirteen, whose segments are very narrow, even threadlike.

L. COUS (4–14 inches) has short, crowded, ovate or oblong segments up to $\frac{1}{5}$ inch long. There are up to twenty unequal rays. The bractlets are conspicuous, ovate or lanceolate with the narrower half down. Plants may be smooth or hairy.

April to July: in dry open places, generally among rocks, at various altitudes, from southeastern Washington and northeastern Oregon to western Montana and northern Wyoming, and southward to eastern Oregon and northern Nevada. *Plate 107.* Included here are plants, named *L. montanum,* differing only in having smooth fruits. *L. circumdatum,* placed above with the leafy-stemmed species, would also be included by some botanists (note the bractlets). *L. serpentinum* (10–12 inches): Segments lanceolate, to $\frac{1}{5}$ inch. Up to seventeen rays. Bractlets narrowly lanceolate, to $\frac{1}{5}$ inch. se Wash, e Ore, w Ida. *L. peckianum* (4–12 inches): Segments oblong or narrower, $\frac{1}{20}$–$\frac{1}{5}$ inch long. Not more than five rays. Bractlets few, inconspicuous, or none. Some plants roughish. s Ore, ne Calif, barely in our range. *L. plummerae* (6–14 inches): Segments oblong or narrower, $\frac{1}{8}$–$\frac{1}{3}$ inch. Up to twenty-five rays. Bractlets narrowly lanceolate, at least equal to the white or yellow flowers. n Sierra Nevada, w Nev. *L. oreganum* (to 3 inches): Segments oblong, $\frac{1}{12}$–$\frac{1}{8}$ inch. One fertile ray. Bractlets few, narrow, rather long. Plant softly hairy. High mountains, ne Ore. *L. minimum* ($\frac{2}{5}$–$1\frac{1}{2}$ inches): Segments from four to six pairs, distinct, $\frac{1}{10}$–

$\frac{2}{5}$ inch. Rays few. Bractlets leaflike, shorter than or equal to the flowers. Some plants roughish. sw Utah. *L. eastwoodae* (4–6 inches): Segments from five to seven pairs, lanceolate, $\frac{1}{12}$–$\frac{1}{6}$ inch. From four to six rays. Bractlets few, narrow, short. Around Grand Junction, Colorado.

b. The remaining thirteen species do not easily separate into small groups. All have narrow, even threadlike leaf-segments. The bractlets also are mostly very narrow, but not extremely inconspicuous or lacking. The rays range from one to thirty.

These species are here arranged in geographic groups, which are not mutually exclusive, but which will enable the reader, having gathered a plant in a known situation, to limit himself to relatively few names.
Oregon: *L. macdougali, hendersonii, watsonii, donnellii, frenchii, grayi.* Idaho: *L. hendersonii, juniperinum, grayi.* Wyoming: *L. grayi, macdougali, juniperinum, megarrhizum, foeniculaceum.* Nevada: *L. grayi.* Utah: *L. grayi, juniperinum, parryi, scabrum.* Colorado: *L. grayi, concinnum.* Montana: *L. foeniculaceum.* Oklahoma: *L. foeniculaceum, daucifolium.* South Dakota: *L. daucifolium.* Kansas: *L. daucifolium.* Nebraska: *L. daucifolium.* Washington: *L. grayi, watsonii.* California: *L. parryi.*

L. GRAYI (8–25 inches) has segments $\frac{1}{20}$–$\frac{2}{5}$ inch long, on some plants roughish. There are up to twenty-two rays. The threadlike bractlets are shorter than the flowers.

April and May: in dry rocky places at low and moderate altitudes from Washington to northern Idaho and southward to eastern Oregon, northeastern Nevada, Utah, southwestern Wyoming, and southwestern Colorado. *Plate 107. L. juniperinum* (6–10 inches): Segments to $\frac{1}{6}$ inch. Bractlets as long as the flowers. Plants finely downy. Utah, adjacent Ida and Wyo. *L. donnellii* (5–14 inches): Segments to $\frac{1}{3}$ inch. Up to thirty rays. Bractlets threadlike or lanceolate. c Ore. *L. hendersonii* (3–10 inches): Segments to $\frac{2}{5}$ inch. Five or six rays. Bractlets short, lanceolate. c Ore, sw Ida. Rare. *L. watsonii* (3–6 inches): Segments to $\frac{1}{5}$ inch. Rays from one to nine. Bractlets joined, equal to the flowers. Plants finely downy. sc Wash to ne Ore. *L. frenchii* (6–10 inches): similar. c Ore. *L. parryi* (8–16 inches): Segments to $\frac{2}{5}$ inch. Rays about fifteen, nearly equal. Bractlets equal to the flowers, some cleft. se Utah, se Calif.

L. concinnum (5–10 inches): Segments $\frac{1}{10}$–$\frac{2}{5}$ inch. Five or six fertile rays. Bractlets leaflike, ovate or lanceolate, at least as long as the flowers. sw Colo. *L. megarrhizum* (4–12 inches): Segments from two to five pairs, lobed, the lobes narrow, to $\frac{2}{5}$ inch; or unlobed, to 1 inch. Ten or eleven rays. sw Wyo. *L. scabrum* (4–14 inches): Segments to $\frac{1}{6}$ inch. Rays from seven to fourteen. Bractlets bristle-like, equal to or shorter than the flowers. Plants roughish. sw Utah.

L. FOENICULACEUM (4–20 inches) has crowded leaf-segments to $\frac{1}{6}$ inch long. There are from eight to twenty-four nearly equal rays. The joined bractlets equal the flowers. The plants may be softly hairy or smooth.

April to August: on dry open slopes from central and southeastern Oregon to Montana and southward to Nevada and Oklahoma. *Plate 108*. *L. macdougali:* Similar. Bractlets not joined. Flowers yellow or reddish. w Wyo, c Ore. *L. daucifolium:* Similar. Bractlets joined. Mostly smooth. SD to Okla.

OREOXIS

The leaves of *Oreoxis* are divided pinnately into narrow segments. The plants are small, forming tufts, growing at high altitudes (*ore-* is Greek for "mountain"). The umbels are compact, simulating heads, the rays few and short, the flower-stalks practically lacking. The fruits have corky wings on the ribs.

O. ALPINA ($\frac{1}{2}$–7 inches) may rarely have a narrow bract for an involucre. There are from three to six rays up to $\frac{1}{3}$ inch long. The bractlets are narrow, $\frac{1}{12}$–$\frac{1}{5}$ inch long. The flower-stalks are very short.

June to August: from Wyoming to Colorado and eastern Utah. *Plate 108*.

O. bakeri ($\frac{1}{12}$–5 inches) has leaf-segments up to $\frac{1}{3}$ inch. From three to eight rays, to $\frac{1}{5}$ inch long. No involucre. Bractlets commonly toothed at the tip. Flowers yellow or whitish. S Colorado, adjacent Utah.

O. humilis (1–6 inches) rarely has an involucre of a single bract. From three to nine rays $\frac{1}{12}$–$\frac{1}{5}$ inch long. Flowers yellow. Alpine, in the region of Pike's Peak, Colorado.

OROGENIA

One species of *Orogenia* is widespread in our area.

O. LINEARIFOLIA (2–6 inches) is smooth, with leaves divided into three and these segments commonly again divided into three, the final segments lanceolate or narrower, $\frac{1}{2}$–$2\frac{1}{2}$ inches long. There is no involucre; from one to four rays up to an inch long; one or more narrow bractlets up to $\frac{1}{8}$ inch long; white flowers in heads (their stalks very short); and a fruit nearly as thick as wide with prominent threadlike ribs, those on each side with broad corky wings.

March to May: on open slopes and ridges in foothills and at middle altitudes from southern Washington to western Montana and southward to eastern Oregon, Utah, and western Colorado, and probably in Nevada. *Plate 108*.

ALETES

Three species of *Aletes* are found in our range.

A. ACAULIS (2–14 inches) has lobed and spiny-toothed leaf-segments $\frac{1}{5}$–$\frac{2}{5}$ inch long. There is no involucre. There are from eight to fifteen nearly equal rays up to $1\frac{1}{5}$ inches long. Bractlets are narrow, up to $\frac{1}{8}$ inch long. The flower-stalks are so short that the secondary umbels are like heads. The flowers are yellow; the calyx-teeth relatively conspicuous, triangular. The fruit is $\frac{1}{6}$–$\frac{1}{3}$ inch long, with corky wings on edges and faces.

May to August: in mountains in Colorado and southward. *Plate 108*.

A. macdougali (2–10 inches) has the narrower leaf-segments commonly not lobed or toothed. The rays are from four to eight, $\frac{1}{8}$–$\frac{4}{5}$ inch long. April to June: in cañons and on mesas in southeastern Utah and southwestern Colorado. *Plate 108*.

A. humilis, 1–4 inches tall, the stalks of the umbels shorter than the leaves, with from four to six rays 1–2 inches long, and fruit inconspicuously ribbed, has been found only in Larimer County, Colorado.

PODISTERA

One species of *Podistera* grows in our southern states; another may be within our western limits.

P. EASTWOODAE forms tufts up to a foot tall, the leaves pinnately divided, often twice, the final segments ovate and variously cleft and lobed into narrow, sharp lobes about $\frac{1}{2}$ inch long. The rays of the umbel are short and flat, sometimes lacking. The flower-stalks are very short or lacking, so that the flowers form a head. The calyx-teeth are conspicuous;

PLATE 108

Aletes acaulis   *Scribner*

Lomatium thompsonii   *Spurr*

Aletes macdougali   *W. Weber*

Oreoxis alpina   *Korling*

Lomatium foeniculaceum   *Scribner*

Orogenia linearifolia   *Thompson*

Harbouria trachypleura   *Bohmfalk*

Podistera eastwoodae   *Ure*

the petals greenish-yellow. The fruit is slightly flattish, small, with threadlike ribs.

June and July: in high mountains in Utah and Colorado. *Plate 108.*

P. nevadensis forms cushions a foot across and only 1–3 inches thick. The leaves are divided once pinnately. Rays and flower-stalks are almost lacking, the whole inflorescence a head of orange-yellow flowers scarcely above the leaves. July: on alpine summits in the Sierra Nevada.

RHYSOPTERUS

One species of *Rhysopterus* is in our range. *R. plurijugus* (4–6 inches) is smooth, with slightly leathery leaves divided into three, the segments again divided into short ovate segments which run together and so are more properly named lobes. There are several rays $\frac{1}{5}$–$\frac{2}{5}$ inch long; no involucre; ovate bractlets; and white flowers on short stalks. The fruit is flattish with conspicuous corky ribs. The species has been found only in southeastern Oregon, growing in dry ground, flowering in May.

TAUSCHIA

One species is contributed by *Tauschia* to our area. *T. hooveri* (4–6 inches) is smooth, with a bloom. The leaves are divided pinnately into narrow segments $\frac{3}{5}$–$1\frac{2}{5}$ inches long (or some of these may be again divided). There is no involucre, and bractlets also are lacking. There are from three to seven unequal rays up to $\frac{2}{5}$ inch long. The flowers are white, the stamens tipped with red. The fruit is narrow, wider than thick, with threadlike ribs. February to April: with sagebrush in south-central Washington.

HARBOURIA

One species of *Harbouria* is in our range.

H. TRACHYPLEURA (3–20 inches) has a smooth stem except for some hairs just under the umbel. The leaves are pinnately divided into very narrow segments up to an inch long. There may be no involucre; or one or two inconspicuous bracts for an involucre. There are up to thirty rather short rays; several narrow, short bractlets; and yellow flowers on stalks so short they seem to be in a head. The fruit is flattish, with corky ribs.

May to July: at moderate altitudes from south of our boundary to northern Utah and southwestern Wyoming. *Plate 108.*

Guide to Genera of Umbelliferae

Continued from page 299

II. *Genera with leaves borne singly on the flowering stems.*

See also *Lomatium, Pteryxia, Rhysopterus*; some of their species have leaves carried up on short stems above ground.

A. Genera with yellow flowers. See also *Osmorhiza* under B. "Eastern," below, means in our range only in the eastern plains. *Bupleurum* (leaves undivided, without teeth, roundish or narrow; involucre of lanceolate bracts); *Pastinaca* (tall; leaves once pinnately divided into lobed and toothed segments; no involucre; no bractlets); *Foeniculum* (tall; leaf-segments threadlike; no involucre; fruit strongly ribbed); *Anethum* (similar; narrow wings on the ribs of the fruit); *Petro-* *selinum* (leaves finely divided; many rays; involucre of a few bracts, or lacking; a few narrow bractlets); *Taenidia* (leaf-segments short, broad, without teeth; eastern); *Thaspium* (leaf-segments large, toothed; no involucre; rays few; bractlets short, narrow; fruit with prominent wings; eastern); *Zizia* (like *Thaspium*; central flower of secondary umbel without stalk; fruit ribbed, not winged); *Polytaenia* (leaf-segments ovate, to slightly longer than 1 inch; no involucre; fruit with corky ribs at the sides; eastern); *Musineon* (leaves pinnately divided or cleft; involucre lacking or of one or two small bracts; fruit flattish with prominent sharp ribs); *Sanicula* (leaves broad; some flowers with stamens only; fruit densely bristly).

Guide continued on page 316

BUPLEURUM

The leaves of *Bupleurum* exemplify the relatively few genera of *Umbelliferae* with undivided leaves. Bractlets are ovate, joined at the base. The flowers are yellow or reddish; calyx-teeth are lacking. The fruit is slightly flattish, and has threadlike ribs.

B. AMERICANUM (2–20 inches) is smooth with a bloom. The leaves are long and narrow, those at the base of the stem up to 6 inches long, those on the stem few (or none), lanceolate. The involucre is several ovate or lanceolate, leaflike bracts up to $\frac{3}{5}$ inch long. There are up to fourteen unequal rays. The flowers are yellow or reddish, on stalks up to $\frac{1}{8}$ inch long.

July and August: on rock outcrops and dry meadows at all altitudes in Wyoming and Montana. *Plate 109.*

Hare's-ear, *B. rotundifolium*, is an immigrant from the Mediterranean region. The leaves are ovate or nearly round, many of them entirely surrounding the stem with their basal part. There is no involucre; from four to ten rays. The bractlets are two or three times as long as the yellow flowers. The fruit is purplish-brown. May and June: in fields and waste ground from South Dakota to Oklahoma. *Plate 109.*

PASTINACA

One species of *Pastinaca* is a common weed.

PARSNIP, P. SATIVA (1–5 feet), is our familiar vegetable, which has escaped from cultivation. The leaves are pinnately divided into lobed and toothed segments 2–4 inches long. The sheaths of the stem-leaves are conspicuous. An involucre is mostly lacking.

There are up to twenty-five rays. The flowers are on stalks $\frac{1}{5}$–$\frac{2}{5}$ inch long. The fruit is flat, with thin wings on the edges. On roadsides and waste ground throughout the country. *Pastinare* in Latin means "to dig"; a parsnip is something dug. The English name comes by way of Old French *passnaie* and Middle English *passenep*.

FOENICULUM

Fennel, *Foeniculum vulgare*, a heavy-scented culinary herb from the Mediterranean region, is found growing wild throughout the United States. Stem 3–7 feet tall, with leaves up to a foot long or more, the blades divided into many threadlike segments. Fruit almost as thick as wide, prominently ribbed. *Plate 109.* Various parts of the plant are used; the blanched leaves, called finocchio, are cooked or used in salads.

Another strong-scented herb sometimes found growing wild is dill, *Anethum graveolens*, 1–6 feet tall.

Leaves pinnately divided, the final segments threadlike. From ten to forty-five rays. No bracts or bractlets. Fruit flattish, with narrow wings on the ribs.

Parsley, *Petroselinum crispum*, may be found growing wild in the eastern states of our area. Its leaves are divided into many narrow segments. An involucre is generally lacking, but a few bracts may be present. There are from ten to twenty rays. There are a few (five or six) narrow bractlets. The fruit is flattish, with prominent ribs.

TAENIDIA

One species of *Taenidia* is within our eastern limits. *T. integerrima* (2–3 feet) may be known by its leaf-segments, ovate and lacking teeth or lobes. No involucre or bractlets. The fruit is oval, ribbed. May to July: in dry, open woodlands, on rocky hillsides in Kansas and Oklahoma. *Plate 109.*

MEADOW-PARSNIPS (THASPIUM)

The fruit of *Thaspium* has wings on its ribs. The leaves are undivided or, more commonly, divided into three segments which may be pinnately divided. The segments are ovate or lanceolate and toothed. There is no involucre. Rays are few. Bractlets are small and narrow. The fruit has several conspicuous wings.

T. TRIFOLIATUM (1–2 feet) has long-stalked basal
leaves with blades undivided or divided into three
segments 1–2 inches long. The stem-leaves are divided. One variety has yellow flowers, the other
reddish.

May to July: in woodlands from South Dakota
to Oklahoma. *Plate 109.*
T. *barbinode* (to 4 feet) has tufts of hairs ("beards,"
barbi-) at each node. The flowers are pale yellow or
cream. April to June: in Kansas and Oklahoma.

ZIZIA

One species of *Zizia* is common throughout the
Midwest and is found as far west as Oregon and Utah.
It may be mistaken for a thaspium, but differs in its
fruit, which is ribbed, not winged. A second species is
found on the plains.

GOLDEN ALEXANDERS, Z. APTERA (1–2 feet) has
basal leaves with a undivided, broad blade, commonly indented at the point of attachment to the long
stalk. The leaves on the stem are divided into three
lanceolate, coarsely toothed segments, which may be
lobed. The small yellow flowers are in close secondary
umbels, with a few narrow bractlets, at the ends of

wide-spreading rays which may be over an inch long.
There is no involucre. The fruit is oval, with threadlike ribs. The central flower (and the fruit) of each
secondary umbel has almost no stalk.
April to July: in moist meadows, along streams,
and in low damp ground generally from eastern
Washington to northeastern Nevada and eastward
throughout our range. *Plate 109.*
The more eastern species Z. *aurea* may be found
as far west as eastern Montana, Colorado, and Oklahoma. It differs in having all its leaves divided into
three, the middle segment commonly again divided
into three palmately or pinnately.

POLYTAENIA

One of the two species of the midwestern genus
Polytaenia is found within our eastern limits.

PRAIRIE-PARSLEY, P. NUTTALLII (to 3 feet), has
leaves divided palmately or pinnately and the
segments divided pinnately, the final segments being
ovate, a little more than an inch long, blunt; the uppermost leaves are only divided once, into three, and have

a conspicuous sheathing stalk. There is no involucre.
The yellow flowers are on short stalks at the ends of
the rather few rays; there are perhaps five very narrow
bractlets. The fruit is oval or nearly round, flattish,
with corky ribs and wings at the sides, threadlike ribs
on the faces.
April to June: on prairies and in woodlands from
North Dakota to Oklahoma.

MUSINEON

The stems of *Musineon* are clustered. The flowering stems overtop the leaves at maturity. An involucre
is generally lacking. Bractlets are present. Calyx-teeth
are ovate. The fruit is slightly flattish, ribbed.

M. DIVARICATUM (2–12 inches) has leaves near the
base, almost but not quite in pairs. They are pinnately cleft or divided, not more than 5 inches long,
bluish or whitish. The flowers are yellow. Up to
twenty nearly equal rays.
April to June: on open plains and slopes from
Canada southward to eastern Nevada, Idaho, Montana, and Nebraska. *Plate 109.*
M. *vaginatum* (6–12 inches) has leaves borne
singly along the flowering stem, divided first into

three, then pinnately. The flowers may be white or
yellowish. June and July: in rocky places in mountains
of Montana and Wyoming. Not well known.

M. TENUIFOLIUM (2–12 inches) has pinnately divided leaves, the final segments narrow and up
to an inch long. The stalk of the umbel is slightly hairy
at its tip. There may be an involucre of one or two very
short, narrow bracts. The flowers are white or yellow.
There are up to thirty nearly equal rays.
May to July: from North Dakota to Nebraska
and adjacent Wyoming and Colorado.
M. *lineare*, found only near Logan, Utah, is similar, 3–10 inches tall. Bractlets much longer than the
flowers.

PLATE 109

Bupleurum rotundifolium   *Scribner*

Osmorhiza occidentalis   *Frost*

Foeniculum vulgare   *Finne*

Thaspium trifoliatum   *Korling*

Taenidia integerrima   *McDowell*

Bupleurum americanum   *On*

Zizia aptera   *Justice*

Musineon divaricatum   *Oldemeyer*

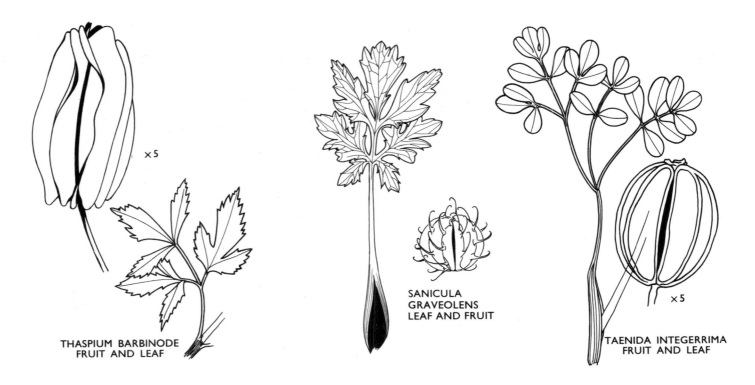

THASPIUM BARBINODE
FRUIT AND LEAF

SANICULA
GRAVEOLENS
LEAF AND FRUIT

TAENIDA INTEGERRIMA
FRUIT AND LEAF

SANICLES (SANICULA)

The involucre of *Sanicula* is a circle of leaflike bracts. The secondary umbels are surrounded by bractlets. The rays of some species are few and unequal. Some flowers lack a pistil; these are stalked. Bisexual-flowers – with both stamens and pistil – have no stalks. The calyx is relatively conspicuous. The leaves of our species are mostly broad, variously divided and cleft, and sharply toothed. The fruits are densely covered with hooked bristles, in our species with swollen bases.

S. GRAVEOLENS (2–20 inches) has basal leaves which
    may originate below-ground. The blades are small for the genus, $\frac{3}{5}$–$1\frac{2}{5}$ inches long, cleft and lobed but scarcely toothed, the segments generally three, pinnately arranged. Upper leaves are smaller, the uppermost without stalks. The flowers are light yellow.
    April to July: on flats and slopes and in open woods from Canada to California and westward to western Montana and to northwestern Wyoming (apparently rare in Idaho).

S. MARILANDICA (16–48 inches) has blades of lower
    leaves 2–6 inches wide, palmately cleft or divided and sharply toothed. The flowers are greenish-white.
    June: in moist ground and on wooded slopes from northeastern Washington to southwestern Montana, thence to Wyoming and Colorado; and eastward.
    The eastern *S. canadensis* is found in Nebraska and Oklahoma. Its leaf-blades are deeply cleft or divided palmately into three, the side lobes less deeply cleft into two or three lobes; all toothed. The flowers are white, with a calyx of narrow bractlets longer than the petals. Each secondary umbel forms three fruits; their bristles with markedly swollen bases. Another eastern species, *S. gregaria*, may be found in eastern Kansas. The leaves are divided palmately into three or five segments. The flowers are greenish-yellow, with a calyx shorter than the petals.

Guide to Genera of Umbelliferae

Continued from page 312

B. General with leafy stems and flowers mostly not yellow (white except as noted). See also *Sanicula* under A.

1. Eighteen genera are represented in our range either west of the Continental Divide (these marked with *) or across our entire range: *Osmorhiza* (leaves

broad, divided palmately, the segments ovate; rays few and unequal; flowers yellow or whitish; fruits narrow, bristly); *Daucus* (leaf-segments numerous, small; bracts of the involucre pinnately divided into very narrow segments; fruit spiny); *Caucalis** (leaf-segments numerous, narrow; fruit narrow, prickly on the ribs); *Eryngium* (flowers in dense blue heads; leaves undivided, spiny-toothed); *Hydrocotyle* (leaves small, round, undivided; flowers minute; plants on wet ground or in water); *Apium* (leaves pinnately divided into few, broad segments; umbels in the axils, short-stalked or without stalks); *Berula* (leaves once pinnately divided; stem-leaves commonly with threadlike segments; fruit with threadlike ribs); *Conium* (leaves much divided pinnately, the segments small; stem spotted with purple; bracts with whitish margins and green center; fruit roundish, with prominent ribs at first wavy); *Cicuta* (leaf-segments lanceolate or ovate, well separated; many rays; fruit ovate, with prominent corky ribs); *Heracleum* (lower leaves very large, the three segments stalked; uppermost leaves with large dilated stalks and small blades; fruit flattish, with dark oil-tubes visible on the faces); *Oxypolis** (lower leaves divided pinnately into mostly seven or nine ovate or lanceolate, toothed segments; stem-leaves with sheathing stalks and fewer segments; rays very unequal; fruit oval, flat, broadly winged on the edges); *Sium* (leaves divided once pinnately into narrow segments, mostly toothed, well separated; bracts leaflike, unequal; fruits small, roundish, prominently ribbed); *Carum* (leaf-segments ovate, cleft into narrow lobes; flowers white or rose; fruit oblong, with prominent narrow ribs); *Perideridia* (leaves much divided; flowers white or pink; calyx teeth evident; fruit oblong or round with threadlike ribs); *Conioselinum** (leaf-segments many, ovate, cleft, lobed, and toothed; stem-

leaves with broad sheaths; fruit flattish, winged at the edges and with three ribs close together on each face); *Angelica** (leaf-segments relatively few, broad, toothed or lobed, well separated; from six to forty-five rays; fruit flattish with broad wings on the edges, three ribs on each face); *Ligusticum** (leaf-segments many; flowers white or pink; fruit oblong, prominently ribbed); *Sphenosciadium** (foliage rough; leaf-stalks dilated; inflorescence woolly; flowers white or reddish; fruit winged on the ribs).

2.   The remaining ten genera are limited, in our range, to the plains east of the Continental Divide (largely to Kansas and Oklahoma): *Spermolepis* (leaf-segments hairlike; fruit warty); *Ammoselinum* (leaf-segments very narrow, less than $\frac{1}{2}$ inch long; rays few, short, unequal; fruit oblong, rough with prominent ribs bearing corky appendages); *Torilis* (leaf-segments narrow, sharply toothed; from five to ten nearly equal rays; fruit ovate, flattish, with hooked bristles); *Scandix* (leaf-segments narrow, short; rays one or several; fruit rodlike); *Cryptotaenia* (leaves divided palmately into three toothed segments. Fruit narrow, flattish, with threadlike ribs); *Cynosciadium* (basal leaves lanceolate; stem-leaves palmately divided into three or five narrow segments; rays few, unequal; fruit ovate, beaked, prominently ribbed, the ribs at the sides corky-winged); *Limnosciadium* (basal leaves lanceolate, or pinnately divided, the end segment long; rays mostly few; fruit small, oblong, ribbed); *Falcaria* (leaf-segments narrow, mostly curved, finely toothed; fruit narrow, oblong, flattish, ribbed); *Ptilimnium* (leaf-segments hairlike; fruit flattish, ovate, with threadlike ribs); *Chaerophyllum* (umbels without stalks, the secondary umbels stalked; fruit narrow).

DAUCUS

One species of *Daucus* is widespread throughout North America; another is found in the southeastern corner of our area.

WILD CARROT or QUEEN-ANNE'S-LACE, D. CAROTA (1–4 feet), is a wild relative of our edible carrots. The leaves are divided pinnately into numerous small, narrow final segments up to $\frac{1}{2}$ inch long. The involucre is composed of bracts divided pinnately into narrow sharp segments. The numerous rays are unequal. The bractlets are narrow, undivided, mostly as long as or longer than the flowers. The flowers are white, dusty-

pink, or less commonly yellowish. The fruit is elliptic, the ribs bearing sharp, curved spines.

May to October: a pernicious (but not unattractive) weed of roadsides and waste ground. *Plate 110*. A curious feature is the frequent occurrence of a single dark red flower in the center of the umbel, even in the common white-flowered forms.

D. pusillus, a species mainly of the southeastern states, is found in Kansas and Oklahoma. It is up to 2 feet tall, the umbel is 1–2$\frac{1}{2}$ inches across, the leaves are more finely divided, the segments of the bracts are pinnately cleft. On prairies and dry hills. *Plate 110*.

SWEET-CICELY (OSMORHIZA)

The girl's name of these plants is really seseli, an old Greek name for some sweet-scented plant, still

used for another genus of *Umbelliferae*. Sweet-cicely in England is a different species of this family.

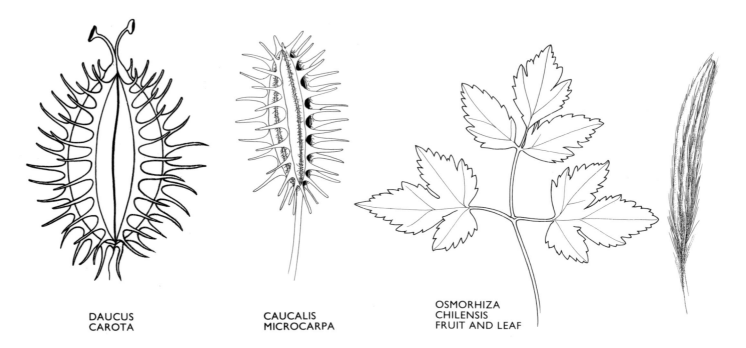

DAUCUS
CAROTA

CAUCALIS
MICROCARPA

OSMORHIZA
CHILENSIS
FRUIT AND LEAF

Osmorhiza owes its names, English and Greek, to the sweet, licorice-like odor of stems and roots when they are broken or crushed.

The leaves are divided into three and then variously again divided, the final segments being mostly ovate, toothed and various cleft or lobed. The plants are generally hairy or bristly. The umbels consist of a few unequal rays; involucre and bractlets are generally lacking or almost so. The fruits are narrow, often tapering at both ends, ribbed and mostly bristly.

Our species grow in woods, except as noted.

O. OCCIDENTALIS (16–48 inches) is aromatic. The leaf-segments are lanceolate or ovate, mostly 1–4 inches long, coarsely toothed. There are from five to twelve rays. The flowers are yellow. The fruit is smooth.

April to July: in thickets and on open slopes at low and moderate altitudes from northern Washington to California and eastward to Montana and Colorado. *Plate 109.*

O. CHILENSIS (12–40 inches) has ovate leaf-segments up to 2½ inches long. There are from three to eight rays. The flowers are greenish-white.

April to June: in woodlands from near sea level to moderate altitudes from Canada to California and eastward to western South Dakota and Colorado; in the Northeast; and in Chile and Argentina. *Plate 110.*

O. *depauperata* (6–24 inches) is similar in most respects. The leaf-segments are ½–2 inches long. There may be a single leaflike bract beneath the umbel. There are from two to five rays. The flowers are greenish-white. The tip of the fruit is rounder, not beaklike. May to July: in woodlands from Alaska to northeastern California and southern Nevada and eastward to western South Dakota; and in New England and South America. This is the commoner species in the southern parts of our range; O. *chilensis* is more abundant northward.

O. *purpurea* (1–2 feet) is also similar to O. *chilensis*, differing chiefly in its pink or reddish (not "purple" in the modern sense) flowers; they may be greenish-white. There are from two to six rays. June and July: in meadows, by streams, and on moist open slopes up to high altitudes in northern Washington, Idaho, and northwestern Montana.

O. LONGISTYLIS (2–4 feet) has ovate or lanceolate leaf-segments 1–4 inches long, coarsely toothed and cleft or lobed. The involucre is of one or more lanceolate bracts, fringed with hairs. There are from three to six rays. The several bractlets are like the bracts, a little shorter, and turned down. The flowers are white; the long styles project beyond the petals.

May and June: in woods and thickets from North Dakota to Oklahoma, and eastward. *Plate 110.*

O. *claytoni* is similar, with much shorter styles, and with stipules which may be fringed but not woolly. In eastern Kansas and eastward.

CAUCALIS

One species of *Caucalis* is found in our range.

C. MICROCARPA (4–16 inches) is slender and delicate. The leaves are divided into three, the segments pinnately divided, the final segments very narrow and short and tipped with a minute spine. The involucre is of several leaves. There are from one to nine longish rays. The bractlets may be pinnately cleft; they have

PLATE 110

Eryngium integrifolium   *Johnson*

Eryngium prostratum   *Johnson*

Daucus pusillus   *Kirtley-Perkins*

Eryngium articulatum   *Spellenberg*

Apium graveolens   *Myrick*

Daucus carota   *Rickett*

Osmorhiza longistylis   *Gottscho*

Osmorhiza chilensis   *Spurr*

whitish margins. The fruit is narrow, only $\frac{1}{8}-\frac{1}{3}$ inch long. Four rows of hooked prickles on each side alternate with five bristly threadlike ribs.

April to June: along streams and on moist slopes along the Cascade Mountains in Washington and Oregon and eastward to Idaho; from Europe.

ERYNGOES (ERYNGIUM)

The flowers of *Eryngium* are in dense heads which do not suggest the *Umbelliferae*. Underneath the head is a ring of bracts, the involucre; and, within this, bractlets may generally be seen. In most species, including most in our range, the leaves and bracts are spiny-toothed. The fruit is roundish, lacking ribs, generally scaly.

E. ARTICULATUM (1–3 feet) has basal leaves which

may have lanceolate or ovate, spiny-toothed or jagged blades, or no blades at all. The uppermost leaves are in pairs. The heads are blue, $\frac{2}{5}-\frac{4}{5}$ inch long. The bracts are narrow, turned down; the bractlets are similar.

May to September: along streams and on wet banks of lakes from eastern Washington and Idaho to California. *Plate 110*.

E. alismaefolium (2–12 inches) has numerous branching stems. The basal leaf-blades may be cleft pinnately, with coarse spiny teeth. The heads are less than $\frac{1}{6}$ inch across; the few spiny bracts are longer than the heads. The fruit is scaly. July and August: in moist places at moderate altitudes in south-central Oregon, northeastern California, and northern Nevada.

The remaining species of our range are eastern, found in Oklahoma and Kansas. *E. yuccifolium* (to 6

feet or more) has stiff, narrow leaves, the lowest up to 3 feet long, with widely spaced spiny teeth. The heads are an inch across, with up to ten spreading bracts. July and August: on prairies and in woodlands. *E. aquaticum* (1–4 feet) may have basal leaves without teeth or with a few teeth. The upper leaves may be spiny-toothed or even pinnately cleft. The heads are not more than $\frac{3}{5}$ inch long, with up to ten bracts turned down. The fruit is scaly. In our southeastern corner. *E. integrifolium* (1–3 feet) has basal leaves with plain or scalloped edges; only the uppermost very narrow and spiny-toothed. The heads are blue, $\frac{1}{5}-\frac{3}{5}$ inch across, with from six to ten narrow bracts which may be toothed or not. Fruit scaly on the angles. In Oklahoma. *Plate 110*. *E. prostratum* has stems prostrate or bending upward, up to 30 inches long. The leaves have ovate or lanceolate blades up to 2 inches long, some palmately lobed, on long stalks. The stem-leaves are smaller, the upper without stalks. The heads are numerous and small, on threadlike stalks, commonly blue, $\frac{1}{6}-\frac{1}{3}$ inch long. In wet meadows, etc. in Oklahoma. *Plate 110*. *E. diffusum*, also in Oklahoma, is low, widely branching, some stems perhaps prostrate, up to 16 inches tall. The basal leaves have hardly any stalk, the blades 1–2 inches long, palmately cleft, the lobes spiny-toothed or lobed. The heads are many, short-stalked, small, bluish, up to $\frac{1}{2}$ inch long.

HYDROCOTYLE

The leaves of *Hydrocotyle* are small, round. The tiny flowers are in simple umbels: that is, each ray bears a flower, not a secondary umbel; the ray is a flower-stalk; it is very short or even lacking in our species. The flowers are white or greenish. The fruit is round or elliptic, and flat. The aspect of the plant does not suggest the *Umbelliferae*; but individual flowers are characteristic of the family. The plants grow in wet places, even in water.

H. VERTICILLATA has a unique type of inflorescence.

The umbels, if one can call them that, are disposed along a more or less erect stem up to 7 inches long, on stalks up to $\frac{2}{5}$ inch, or without stalks. There

may be an involucre of a few small bracts. The leaves are attached to their stalks in the middle of the round blade, which may reach 2 inches in diameter.

April to September: in swamps and on shores and low ground along our southern borders from Oklahoma to California; and in South America and the West Indies. (Reported also from Oregon, probably erroneously.) *Plate 111*. In one variety the inflorescence is forked, on some plants several times.

H. ranunculoides, a species mainly of the southern states, may enter Oklahoma. It has lobed leaves attached to the stalk at a deep cleft. The leaf-stalks, and the flower-stalks in their axils, rise from a prostrate stem. In shallow water or on shores. *Plate 111*.

APIUM

Celery, *A. graveolens*, grows wild in wet places throughout the United States. It is up to 5 feet tall,

with leaves divided pinnately into a few pairs of broad segments up to 2 inches long. The umbels, in the

PLATE 111

Hydrocotyle ranunculoides   *Johnson*

Hydrocotyle verticillata   *Johnson*

Sium suave   *Korling*

Oxypolis fendleri   *Wilson*

Perideridia gairdneri   *Lomax*

Conium maculatum   *McIntyre*

Cicuta maculata   *LeBaron*

Cicuta douglasii   *Korling*

Heracleum lanatum   *Johnson*

axils, have a short stalk or none, no involucre, from seven to sixteen rays up to an inch long, bearing secondary umbels of short-stalked white flowers. Bractlets are lacking. The fruit is flattish, with prominent threadlike ribs. *Plate 110*.

A. leptophyllum (up to 2 feet), in the southeastern states and tropical America, may be found in Oklahoma. The leaves are divided several times pinnately, the final segments threadlike. The umbels have from three to five rays less than an inch long.

BERULA

The only species of *Berula* is found practically throughout our range.

WATER-PARSNIP, B. ERECTA (8–32 inches), is slender, with leaves pinnately divided into segments $\frac{3}{5}$–$1\frac{3}{5}$ inches long, with or without teeth or lobes. The involucre is of up to eight narrow or lanceolate unequal bracts $\frac{1}{5}$–$\frac{3}{5}$ inch long; they may be toothed. The bractlets are similar but shorter and not toothed. From

The culinary herb coriander, *Coriandrum sativum*, occasionally spreads from gardens. It is a smooth plant 1–2 feet tall. The lower leaves are divided into segments about $\frac{1}{2}$ inch long, variously

six to fifteen nearly equal rays, bearing small flowers. The fruit is oval or round, $\frac{1}{12}$ inch long, with threadlike ribs.

June to October: in wet ground and shallow water.

In volume 1 of this series this species was named *B. pusilla*; it has recently been shown that our plants are a variety of the European *B. erecta*; and that the name *B. pusilla* violates the rules of botanical nomenclature.

toothed or lobed. There is no involucre. The few rays are up to an inch long. A few small bractlets surround the white or rose flowers. The fruit is roundish with slender ribs.

CONIUM

The one species of *Conium* that has migrated from the Old World to the New is another good argument for knowing and not nibbling the plants of this family; it is deadly poisonous.

POISON-HEMLOCK, C. MACULATUM, is supposedly the plant used for the execution of criminals in ancient Greece, much as some American states use poisonous gas. The philosopher Socrates was thus executed. It is a plant which may reach 10 feet in height. The leaves are pinnately divided and the segments again pinnately divided, the ultimate segments being ovate or oblong and pinnately cleft or lobed.

The stem is spotted with purple. The small flowers are in umbels about 2 inches across. The bracts have a green center and whitish edges. Bractlets are present. The fruit is round and marked by prominent thick ribs which at first are distinctly wavy, apparently becoming straight later. All parts are dangerous; children have been poisoned by blowing into whistles made from the hollow stems. (That I escaped such a fate was due not to teaching but to providence!)

April to August: common on roadsides, in moist disturbed soil, and on waste ground especially in cities, throughout our area and most of the United States; and in Mexico, Africa, and Asia. *Plate 111*.

CICUTA

Our three species of *Cicuta* are deadly poisonous. All parts of the plants are dangerous, the tuberous roots and the thick base of the stem especially so. Dr. Cronquist writes of *C. douglasii*, "the basal parts of one plant are enough to kill a cow"; and this species has indeed caused many deaths of livestock in the West. There are records of the death of children in the eastern states from chewing leaves of *C. maculata*.

The leaves are twice or thrice pinnate into lanceolate or ovate, well-spaced, toothed segments. There may be an involucre of one or several narrow bracts, or none. Rays are numerous. Bractlets are generally present. The flowers are white or greenish. The fruit is ovate, with prominent corky ribs.

WATER-HEMLOCK, C. DOUGLASII (2–7 feet), has lanceolate or narrow bractlets shorter or longer than the flowers. On the fruit the side ribs are about as thick as those on the faces. June to August: in marshes and ditches and wet places in general practically throughout our range from the Cascades and Sierra Nevada as far as the Rocky Mountains. *Plate 111*.

C. maculata (2–6 feet) has narrow bractlets shorter than the flowers. On the fruit the side ribs are thicker than those on the face. June to September: in meadows and ditches and on prairies through the eastern states and from North Dakota to Oklahoma. *Plate 111*.

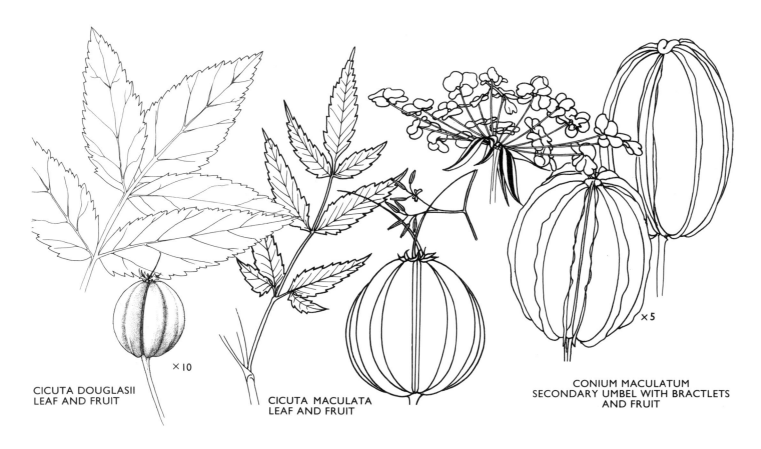

CICUTA DOUGLASII
LEAF AND FRUIT
×10

CICUTA MACULATA
LEAF AND FRUIT

CONIUM MACULATUM
SECONDARY UMBEL WITH BRACTLETS
AND FRUIT
×5

C. BULBIFERA (1–4 feet) is named for the clusters of little bulbs in the upper axils. The leaf-segments are narrow. Rays are short, also the flower-stalks (up to $\frac{1}{5}$ inch). Mature fruit is rarely seen. It is round, only $\frac{1}{12}$ inch across, all the ribs broad.

August and September: in marshes, bogs, wet meadows, and shallow water from southern Oregon to Nebraska. Not common.

HERACLEUM

One species of *Heracleum* grows throughout our range.

COW-PARSNIP or MASTERWORT, H. LANATUM (3–10 feet), has enormous leaves, up to 3 feet long, divided into three stalked segments up to 16 inches long, variously lobed and coarsely toothed. The leaf-stalk may be a very broad sheath; the uppermost leaves are mostly this, with a diminutive blade. The principal umbel is 4–8 inches across. There is an involucre of lanceolate bracts, which may fall; bractlets are present. The outer petals of the outermost flowers are lobed or forked. The fruit is slightly heart-shaped, flattish, with narrow wings on the edges and thread-like ribs on the faces; conspicuous oil-tubes appear as dark lines alternating with the ribs and extending part-way down from the tip.

April to August: in moist ground. *Plate 111.*

OXYPOLIS

We have one species of *Oxypolis.*

O. FENDLERI (2–4 feet) is a slender plant with leaves divided pinnately into mostly seven or nine ovate or lanceolate, toothed segments up to 2 inches long. The stem-leaves have broad sheaths and fewer segments. There is no involucre; from five to fourteen very unequal rays, the longest over 2 inches; no bractlets. The white (or red?) flowers have a relatively conspicuous calyx. The fruit is oval, flat, with broad wings on the edges and threadlike ribs on the faces.

June to August: on stream-banks high in the mountains from Wyoming to southeastern Utah and Colorado. *Plate 111.*

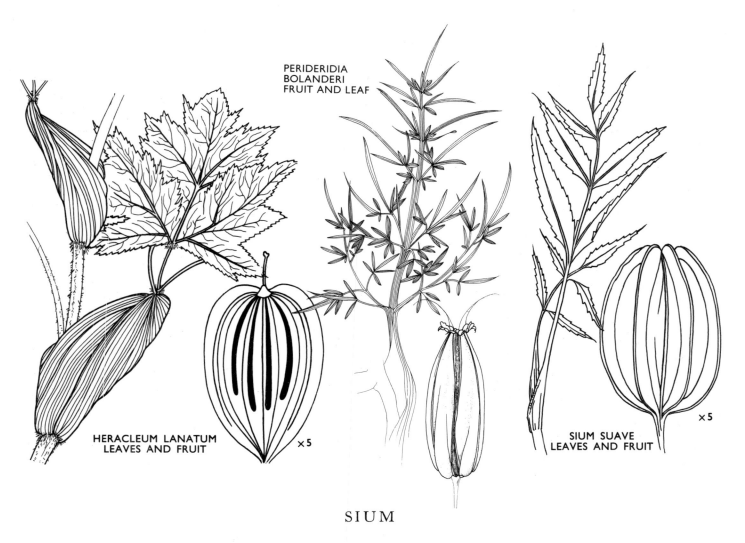

PERIDERIDIA
BOLANDERI
FRUIT AND LEAF

HERACLEUM LANATUM
LEAVES AND FRUIT   ×5

SIUM SUAVE
LEAVES AND FRUIT   ×5

SIUM

One species of *Sium* is widespread in our range.

WATER-PARSNIP, S. SUAVE (2–4 feet), has once-
pinnately divided leaves (the segments not themselves divided). The segments are lanceolate or narrower, 1–6 inches long, generally toothed, and well
separated. The leaf-stalks are commonly hollow. The
involucre consists of unequal, lanceolate, leaflike
bracts; they may be sharply toothed. There are from
six to fifteen nearly equal rays, with bractlets up to
$\frac{1}{5}$ inch long. The small roundish fruits are flattish with
prominent ribs.

July and August: in marshes and other wet places
throughout our range. *Plate 111.*

CARUM

One species of *Carum* is established in North
America.

C. CARVI (1–4 feet) is slender, with leaves pinnately
divided into ovate segments about an inch long,
cleft into narrow lobes. The stem leaves have dilated
stalks. The involucre, if any, is of a few threadlike
bracts. The rays are from seven to fourteen, unequal.
The bractlets are like the bracts but shorter; or lacking. The flowers are commonly white, rarely rose. The
fruit is oblong, flattish, with prominent narrow ribs.

June and July: in meadows and on roadsides in
Washington and eastward across the country to North
Dakota. From Europe.

PERIDERIDIA

Our species of *Perideridia* have oblong or round,
slightly flattish fruits with threadlike ribs. The flowers
are white or pink, with relatively conspicuous calyx-
teeth. Involucre and bractlets are usually present.

PLATE 112

Conioselinum scopulorum   *Ure*

Ligusticum filicinum   *Korling*

Ligusticum porteri   *Uttal*

Chaerophyllum tainturieri   *Johnson*

Sphenosciadium capitellatum   *Johnson*

Angelica lineariloba   *Buckalew*

Angelica pinnata   *Korling*

Angelica arguta   *Spellenberg*

P. GAIRDNERI (1–4 feet) has leaf-blades commonly
    once pinnately divided into long narrow seg-
ments (more rarely twice divided or divided in threes).
The involucre is of one or two bristles, or lacking.
There are from eight to twenty rays. The fruit is
roundish.

    July and August: in woodlands and on meadows
from Canada to California and eastward to South
Dakota. *Plate 111*.

P. BOLANDERI (10–32 inches) has leaves several times
    divided into oblong or threadlike segments; the
stalks and midrib somewhat distended. There are
from ten to twenty rays. The fruit is oblong.

    May to July: in dry open places from western
Idaho and northeastern Oregon to Nevada, north-
eastern Utah, and western Wyoming, and in the
Sierra Nevada.

    Wild-caraway, *P. parishii* (8–32 inches) lacks an
involucre (or there may be one bract). It has from
eight to fifteen rays. The small bracts are papery or
colored. The fruit is oblong or ovate. July and August:
in moist soil in pine woods and dry meadows from
California to Nevada.

    P. americana (2–4 feet) is an eastern species
which reaches Kansas. The leaf-segments are narrow,
to 2 inches long. From six to fourteen rays. Fruit
ovate.

CONIOSELINUM

One species of *Conioselinum* is in our range.

C. SCOPULORUM (1–4 feet) is slender, with few
    branches, the leaves divided into many ovate
segments 1–2½ inches long, much cleft, lobed, and
toothed. The stem-leaves have broad sheaths for stalks.
The involucre may consist of one or more threadlike
bracts, or there may be none. There are from ten to

twenty nearly equal rays. Bractlets are present, a little
shorter than the flowers. The flowers are white. The
fruit is rather like that of *Angelica*, oval, with three low
ribs close together on each face and corky wings at
the sides.

    August and September: in the Rocky Mountains
(*scopulorum*, "of cliffs") in Wyoming and Colorado.
Plate 112.

ANGELICA

The leaves of *Angelica* are divided into broad,
distinct, toothed or lobed segments. The plants are
generally tall, some up to 8 feet, most not less than
1 foot. The rays range from six to forty-five. An involucre is lacking in most of our species, and bractlets
also. The fruit is flattish with wings on the edges and
ribs, which may bear narrow wings, on the faces.

A. ARGUTA (2–7 feet) has ovate or lanceolate leaf-
    segments 2–6 inches long, spiny-toothed. There
may be a few threadlike bractlets. Up to forty-five
nearly equal rays. Flowers white or pink. Fruit about
⅓ inch long.

    June to August: from Montana and Wyoming
to Utah and northern California. *Plate 112. A. ampla*
(5–8 feet) is similar, with white flowers, and narrower
wings on the fruit: in Wyoming and Colorado.

    A. dawsonii (1–3 feet) has a single umbel, with
an involucre of bracts up to an inch long and bractlets
nearly as long as the rays; up to twenty rays. June to
August: in northern Idaho and northern Montana.
A. grayi (1–2 feet) is an alpine species in Wyoming
and Colorado, with reddish-brown flowers, many rays,
an involucre of one leaflike bract or none, and a number of lanceolate bractlets. *A. hendersoni* (1–5 feet) has
up to forty-five rays; white flowers; toothed leaves
woolly underneath.

A. ROSEANA (1–3 feet) has leaves divided into three,

and again into three or pinnately; the final segments
ovate, spiny-toothed. There may be an involucre of a
few threadlike or even leaflike bracts, and there are a
few narrow bractlets. There are up to thirty-five unequal rays. Flowers are white or pink.

    July and August: in rocky places from eastern
Idaho and western Montana to Utah and Colorado.

A. PINNATA (1–3 feet) has pinnately divided leaves,
    with generally toothed segments. The rays are
relatively few (from six to twenty-five) and unequal.
The flowers are white or pink. Involucre and bractlets
lacking. The fruit is almost circular.

    July and August: in wet meadows and other
moist places from Idaho and Montana to northwestern
Wyoming, Colorado, and Utah. *Plate 112*.

    A. canbyi (2–4 feet) is roughish. Leaves divided
into three, then pinnately; segments toothed, cut
jaggedly, or lobed. From fifteen to twenty-five rays.
Flowers white. July to September: moist places, central Washington and adjacent Oregon. *A. kingii* (1–3
feet): Similar but leaf-segments with few or no teeth,
and fewer rays (from seven to fourteen). June to
August: Eastern California, Nevada, Idaho. *A. wheel-
eri* (20–40 inches): Smooth. Leaf-segments variously
toothed. Many rays (from thirty to forty). Utah.

    A. lineariloba (2–5 feet) is a species of the Sierra
Nevada, in our range in western Nevada. Leaf-segments narrow, 1–4 inches long, not toothed. From

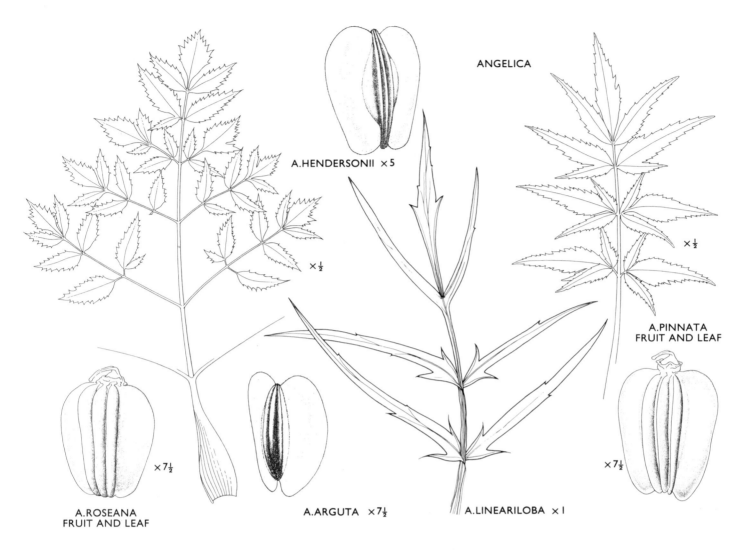

A.HENDERSONII × 5

ANGELICA

× ½

A.PINNATA
FRUIT AND LEAF

× 7½

A.ROSEANA
FRUIT AND LEAF

A.ARGUTA × 7½

A.LINEARILOBA × 1

twenty to forty rays. Flowers white or pink. *Plate 112.* *A. breweri* (3–4 feet), in the Sierra Nevada, may be

hairy. Leaf-segments 2–5 inches, with or without teeth. Several narrow, hairy bractlets. Flowers white.

LIGUSTICUM

The leaves of *Ligusticum* are divided into many segments. An involucre is lacking or of a few narrow bracts; bractlets the same. The flowers are white or pink. The fruit is oblong, hardly flattish, with prominent ribs which in some species bear narrow wings.

Lovage, a potherb used especially in Scotland, is a species of *Ligusticum*.

L. FILICINUM (20–40 inches) has leaves divided into narrow, sharp segments. There are from ten to twenty nearly equal rays.

July and August: on open and wooded slopes and ridges from eastern Idaho to northern Utah, western Wyoming, and western Montana. *Plate 112.*

CHUCHUPATE, L. PORTERI (20–40 inches), has leaves up to 2 feet long, much divided into ovate segments which are cleft, lobed, or toothed. There is no involucre. The rays, from eleven to twenty-four,

bear bractlets and white or pink flowers. The calyx-teeth are evident.

June to August: in mountains from Nevada and Wyoming southward. A useful forage plant. *Plate 112.*

L. VERTICILLATUM (3–6 feet) has leaves not so finely divided, the segments 1–3 inches long, toothed or lobed. There are up to thirty unequal rays. There are several narrow bractlets. The flowers are white. The fruit is slightly winged.

May to August: in thickets and on wooded slopes, by streams, in swamps, etc. in northern Idaho and western Montana.

L. GRAYI (8–24 inches) has scarcely any leaves on the stem. The basal leaves have toothed leaflets about an inch long. There are from seven to fourteen rays.

July to September: on open and wooded slopes

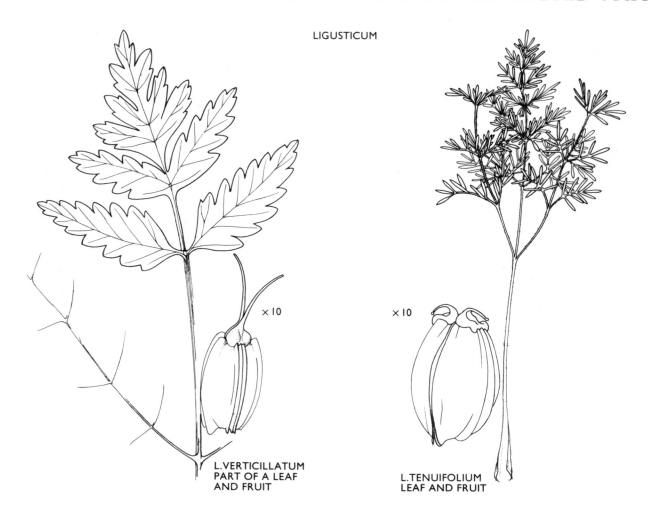

LIGUSTICUM

×10

L.VERTICILLATUM
PART OF A LEAF
AND FRUIT

×10

L.TENUIFOLIUM
LEAF AND FRUIT

and meadows from the Cascades and the Sierra Nevada to Idaho and Nevada. *Plate 113.*

L. canbyi is similar. There may be forty rays in the principal umbel. The stem-leaves are well developed. In moist places from Washington and northeastern Oregon to western Montana.

SPHENOSCIADIUM

One species of *Sphenosciadium* is found in the West.

S. CAPITELLATUM (2–6 feet) has rough foliage and a woolly inflorescence. The leaves are once or twice divided, the final segments ½–5 inches long, toothed and cleft. The leaf-stalks are "dilated" and sheathing; the upper stem-leaves consist of these sheaths only. The secondary umbels are spherical, on long rays. The flowers are white or reddish. The fruit is flat, woolly, with ribs bearing wings.

July and August: in the mountains from eastern Oregon to central Idaho, the Sierra Nevada, and western Nevada. *Plate 112.*

SPERMOLEPIS

The fruit of *Spermolepis* is distinctive: roundish and covered with warts or spines. There is no involucre. The flowers are few and inconspicuous, white. The bractlets are few, shorter than the flowers. The leaves are divided into hairlike segments. *S. divaricata* is found in Kansas and Oklahoma. It is 4–28 inches tall, with from three to seven nearly equal rays. *S. inermis* differs in having from five to eleven unequal rays. *S. echinata* has been reported in Oklahoma. Its fruit is covered with hooked spines.

AMMOSELINUM

The Texan *A. popei* reaches Oklahoma and Kansas. It is up to 14 inches tall. The leaves are divided into three primary segments, these divided pinnately, the final segments very narrow, $\frac{1}{12}$–$\frac{2}{5}$ inch long. An involucre is lacking, or there may be a single leaflike bract. From three to ten very short, unequal rays.

There are a few narrow bractlets longer than the flower-stalks (up to $\frac{1}{2}$ inch). The fruit is oblong or ovate, flattish, more or less rough with callous teeth, and with prominent ribs, the lateral with corky appendages. March to June: in sandy (*ammo-*) soil.

TORILIS

One Old-World species of *Torilis* is established in the eastern states and found in Kansas and Oklahoma. Hedge-parsley, *T. japonica* (1–3 feet) is much branched, with leaves mostly pinnately divided into narrow, sharply-toothed lanceolate segments $\frac{1}{5}$–2

inches long. The involucre is of as many small bracts as there are rays, from five to ten; the rays are nearly equal. The bractlets are awl-like. The fruit is ovate, flattish, covered with short hooked bristles. June to August: in fields, wasteland, and open woods.

SCANDIX

One species of *Scandix* has become naturalized in the United States.

Venus'-comb, *S. pecten-veneris* (6–12 inches), is rather bristly. The leaves are pinnately divided, the final segments narrow, up to $\frac{1}{8}$ inch long. There is no involucre; only one or two rays; one or two bractlets.

The fruit is rodlike, about $1\frac{1}{2}$ inches long (only the lower one-fourth with seeds). The cluster of these straight, bristly bodies forms the "comb of Venus"; each also called, in England, shepherd's-needle. May to July: a weed in South Dakota. From the lands of the Mediterranean.

CRYPTOTAENIA

One species of *Cryptotaenia* crosses our eastern boundaries. Honeywort or wild-chervil, *C. canadensis* (1–4 feet), has leaves divided palmately into three lanceolate or ovate segments 1–6 inches long, doubly serrate* (or on some plants lobed). The umbels have

no involucre, or one small bract. There are a few unequal rays. Bractlets are lacking or minute. The small flowers are white. The fruit is narrow, flattish, smooth, with threadlike ribs. June to September: in woods from Nebraska to Oklahoma and eastward.

CYNOSCIADIUM

One species of *Cynosciadium* enters Oklahoma from the east. *C. digitatum* (up to 6 inches) has narrowly lanceolate leaves at the base, 2–5 inches long. The stem-leaves are palmately divided into three or five long narrow segments. The umbel may have a

few narrow bracts or none; the secondary umbels likewise. There are from two to ten unequal rays, bearing white flowers. The fruit is ovate, beaked, ribbed, the ribs at the sides bearing corky wings. May and June: in low wet areas. *Cynosciadium* means "dog's parasol."

LIMNOSCIADIUM

One species of *Limnosciadium* is in our southeastern area. *L. pinnatum* (4–32 inches) may have undivided, narrowly lanceolate basal leaves 2–8 inches

long; or they may be pinnately divided, with a long end segment. The stem-leaves are mostly pinnately divided into up to nine narrowly lanceolate segments 1–4 inches long. The involucre consists of several narrow bracts up to $\frac{1}{4}$ inch long, bent down along the

*That is, with primary teeth themselves bearing smaller teeth.

stem. There are from three to twelve rays. Several small bractlets surround the secondary umbel. The flowers are white. The fruit is oblong, to $\frac{1}{6}$ inch long, ribbed. May and June: in ditches and on low ground in Kansas and Oklahoma. *Limnosciadium* means "marsh parasol."

FALCARIA

One species of *Falcaria* is established in the eastern states. Sickleweed, *F. sioides* (1–3 feet), has leaves variously divided into narrow segments 2–10 inches long, commonly curved (*falca*, "sickle"), finely toothed. The involucre is of up to twelve narrow, unequal bracts. There are up to twenty rays. Bractlets are like the bracts but shorter. The flowers are white. The fruit is narrowly oblong; flattish, ribbed. August and September: in fields in Nebraska and Kansas. Also named *F. vulgaris*.

PTILIMNIUM

The leaves of *Ptilimnium* are divided into hairlike segments. The involucre consists of pinnately cleft or undivided bracts shorter than the rays. Bractlets are present. The fruit is flattish, ovate, with threadlike ribs on the faces. The flowers are white.

MOCK BISHOP'S-WEED, P. CAPILLACEUM (4–36 inches), has leaves in circles, pinnately divided into hairlike segments $\frac{1}{5}$–$1\frac{1}{5}$ inches long. From four to twenty nearly equal rays. The stamens are red-tipped. The fruit has conspicuous thick ribs at the sides; those on the face are narrower.

June to October: in marshes and swamps in Kansas and Oklahoma. *Plate 113*.

P. nuttallii (1–2 feet) also in Kansas and Oklahoma, has leaf-segments up to $2\frac{2}{5}$ inches long. There are up to thirty nearly equal rays. The stamens are reddish-tipped. The side-ribs of the fruit are not thick.

CHAEROPHYLLUM

The leaves of *Chaerophyllum* are delicate, feathery. The umbels have commonly (in our species) no stalks, so that the rays appear as individual simple umbels (bearing flowers directly, not as secondary umbels). An involucre is generally lacking; bractlets are present around the flowers. The flowers are white. The fruit is narrow, without wings.

WILD-CHERVIL, C. TAINTURIERI (6 inches–3 feet), has bristly stems. Bractlets are ovate, fringed with hairs. There are from one to five rays.

April to June: in open woods in Kansas and Oklahoma. *Plate 112*. C. *procumbens* (6–30 inches) has bractlets edged with soft hairs. Only two or three rays. The spaces between ribs on the fruit are wider than the ribs. In Kansas. C. *texanum* (10–30 inches) has conspicuous, ovate bractlets, turned back around the fruit. From two to four rays.

GROUP VIII

SEPALS generally two, four, or five. Petals four or five, separate, radially symmetric. Stamens mostly as many as the petals or twice as many. Generally one style. Fruit a legume or capsule or breaking into nuts. Leaves lobed, cleft, or divided, or without division or lobing; borne singly or in pairs.
Exceptions: in the loosestrife family there may be six or seven petals; in the evening-primrose family petals may be lacking; in the mimosa family they may be partly joined; in the portulaca family there may be only two or three petals, and few or many stamens; in the cassia and evening-primrose families petals may be slightly bilateral in symmetry; the mimosa family may have many stamens; some species of the evening-primrose family have all flower parts in two's or three's.

I. *Genera with pinnately divided leaves; fruit a legume.*

 A. Genera with numerous flowers in heads or spikes; petals pink or white; stamens ten or more: mimosa family.

 B. Genera whose flowers are not in heads or spikes; petals yellow; stamens five or ten: cassia family.

II. *Genera with leaves not divided (deeply cleft in some); fruit a capsule or nut.*

 A. Plants with two sepals; leaves without lobes or division: portulaca family. (One genus of the evening-primrose family.)

 B. Plants with four or more sepals.

 1. Genera with ten stamens; leaves lobed or cleft; pistil and fruit with a conspicuous beak: geranium family.
 2. Genera with from four to seven stamens or twice as many; ovary surrounded by (not joined with) a floral tube: loosestrife family.
 3. Genera with four or five, or eight or ten stamens; ovary inferior: evening-primrose family.
 4. Genera with ten stamens; leaves evergreen, or the plant without any green color: shinleaf family.

III. *Genera with pinnately divided leaves; fruit not a legume: caltrop family.*

Besides the above families, Group VIII includes several represented in our range by a single (or possibly two) species. These families may be identified by the illustration or text: in *Malpighiaceae, Janusia gracilis*; in *Rutaceae, Thamnosma montana* (and perhaps *T. texana*); in *Sterculiaceae, Ayenia pusilla*; in *Limnanthaceae, Floerkea proserpinaca*; in *Frankeniaceae, Frankenia jamesii*. Most of these are southern species just crossing our southern limits.

THE MIMOSA FAMILY (MIMOSACEAE)

The *Mimosaceae* (with the following family) really form part of the great bean family (in the broad sense the *Leguminosae*); when all species of the world are considered, it is impossible to separate them. But the flowers of our species are quite different, and in the artificial arrangement here adopted to facilitate identification, it is convenient to keep the three families distinct (the bean family then being the *Fabaceae*). The flowers of *Mimosaceae* have five sepals and five radially symmetric petals which may be partly joined, and five, ten, or many stamens. They are generally in heads or spikes. The fruit is a legume, like a bean pod (in some species much curved or coiled). The leaves are twice pinnately divided – the primary segments themselves divided; the segments many and small.

The family is represented in our area only in our easternmost states. Most species are southern.

SENSITIVE-BRIERS (SCHRANKIA)

The stems of *Schrankia* mostly trail, forming tangles; they are beset with curved prickles, as are the seed-pods. The leaves are twice pinnate, the final segments very many and very small. The small pink flowers are in round heads at the tips of branches growing from the axils. The calyx is minute; the petals are joined into a five-lobed funnel. There are generally ten stamens; some flowers may have a few more. The stamens are pink like the corolla, and much more conspicuous; the heads seem to be a mass of stamens only. The leaf-segments are sensitive, folding together when disturbed. Some species are called shame-vines.

CAT'S-CLAW, S. UNCINATA,* has elliptic leaf-segments up to $\frac{1}{3}$ inch long, the veins prominent on the under side. Seed-pods may be 5 inches long.

May to September: in dry, especially sandy ground from South Dakota to Oklahoma and southeastern Colorado. *Plate 113.*

S. microphylla is similar; leaf-segments not more than $\frac{1}{4}$ inch, not prominently veined; flower-heads not more than an inch through. Probably in Kansas and Oklahoma.

S. roemeriana has smooth or nearly smooth stems; leaf-segments about $\frac{1}{5}$ inch; pods about 2 inches. April and May: on prairies and rocky slopes in Oklahoma. *Plate 113. S. occidentalis*, also in Oklahoma, is similar except for a fine down on the stem, and pods up to 4 inches long.

PRAIRIE-MIMOSAS (DESMANTHUS)

The prairie-mimosas are mostly bushy, erect, not prickly; some are shrubby. The greenish-white flowers are in heads at the tips of branches growing from the axils. The calyx is five-toothed; corolla of five separate petals; five or ten stamens.

For the use of the name mimosa, see under the genus *Acacia*.

D. ILLINOENSIS (1–8 feet, generally 3–4 feet) has from thirty to fifty flowers in a head. There are five stamens. The pods are strongly curved, those of one head forming a ball.

May and June, and perhaps later: on roadsides and prairies, by railroads, in ditches from North Dakota to Colorado and Oklahoma. *Plate 113.*

D. leptolobus, found in Kansas, differs in having straight or nearly straight pods up to 2 inches long.

D. COOLEYI has from eight to fifteen pairs of leaf-segments on each primary segment. The stems, to 20 inches long, may be bushy-branched or may trail. The flowers and pods are comparatively few. There are five stamens.

June to August: from Nebraska to Oklahoma.

ACACIA

Most species of the vast genus *Acacia* are trees and shrubs, native in Australia, Africa, and Mexico. Many are cultivated, some being known to horticulture as mimosa, a name properly that of another genus. Some species yield products of economic value, such as gum-arabic. One herbaceous species is found in southeastern Kansas and Oklahoma. *A. angustissima* (up to 5 feet) is handsome and varied. The foliage is feathery, with from eight to fourteen pairs of final segments. The stems lack prickles but may be hairy. The cream or salmon flowers are in small round heads in a branching inflorescence. May to September: in rocky soil. *Plate 113.* Several varieties have been named.

* In volume 1 the name *S. nuttallii* was mistakenly used for this species.

PLATE 113

Acacia angustissima *Hesselberg*

Desmanthus illinoensis *Scribner*

Hoffmanseggia densiflora *Roberts*

Schrankia roemeriana *Henze*

Schrankia uncinata *Rickett*

Ligusticum grayi *Korling*

Stockert

Hoffmanseggia drepanocarpa

Kirtley-Perkins

Ptilimnium capillaceum

NEPTUNIA

One species of the southern genus *Neptunia* is within our southeastern limits. *N. lutea* generally spreads over the ground, the stems up to 6 feet long. It has up to eighteen pairs of final segments not more than ¼ inch long. The flowers are in heads on branches rising from the axils; they are yellow, the petals to ⅛ inch long and fragrant. The pistil is stalked above the level of the perianth; the flat pod may be raised on this stalk ½ inch above the calyx. May and June: generally in disturbed soil in Oklahoma.

THE CASSIA FAMILY (CAESALPINIACEAE)

For the relation of this family to the *Fabaceae*, see the description of the *Mimosaceae*. The three families share the same type of fruit: the legume. The leaves of *Caesalpiniaceae* are pinnately divided. The flowers are nearly but generally not quite radially symmetric. There are typically five sepals, five petals, and five or ten stamens; but there is considerable variation. The petals are yellow or orange.

In our range this family, except one species of *Cassia*, is found only on the plains east of the continental divide.

HOFFMANSEGGIA

The leaves of *Hoffmanseggia* are twice pinnately divided, the final segments small, paired, generally numerous. The plants of some species are shrubs; others are herbaceous. The flowers are in racemes, the small petals yellow or orange; they have ten stamens. The flat seed-pod may be curved.

HOG-POTATO, H. DENSIFLORA (to 16 inches), has from five to eleven primary leaf-segments, each divided again into from six to ten pairs of crowded small final segments. The orange petals are less than ½ inch long; the pod about an inch.

April to September: in alkaline soil in deserts and by the sides of roads and railroads in Kansas and Oklahoma. *Plate 113.*

H. drepanocarpa (to 8 inches) is named for its curved pod (*drepano-*, "sickle"). The primary leaf-segments number from seven to eleven, each with from four to ten pairs of downy final segments. May to September: from Colorado southward. *Plate 113.*

H. JAMESII (8–16 inches) is slightly woody. It may be distinguished by the conspicuous black glands on the under side of the leaf-segments. There are five or seven primary segments, each with from four to ten segments about ⅛ inch long, clothed in a whitish down. The seed-pod is crescent-shaped, widest between middle and tip, beset with black glands and minute tufts of whitish hairs, and containing two or three seeds.

May to August: on dry plains and mesas in western Kansas and eastern Colorado at moderate altitudes. *Plate 114.*

H. repens (4–5 inches) is hoary, with short curled hairs. It forms loose mats. The leaves have seven or nine primary segments each with from two to seven pairs of segments, which may have a few glands or none. The pod is roundish or oblong, hoary, about ½–1 inch long, with usually two seeds. In sandy soil in washes and deserts, generally with sagebrush, in Utah, flowering in May.

THE SENNAS (CASSIA)

The great genus *Cassia* is mostly tropical. Many species are woody. We have seven herbaceous or slightly shrubby species. All are characterized by leaves divided pinnately into an even number of segments themselves undivided. The flowers are borne apparently singly or in racemes on branches growing from the axils of leaves and in some species also in branching inflorescences at the summit of the stem. The five petals are yellow and handsome, in many species slightly unequal in length. There are mostly five or ten stamens, some of which may form no pollen. Technically the species are classified by characteristics of the seed-pods and by the presence or absence of glands on the leaf-stalks or midrib.

The drug called senna is obtained from several Old-World species.

PARTRIDGE-PEA or BEE-FLOWER, C. FASCICULATA (to 3 feet), is common and widespread. There are from ten to fifteen or even more pairs of segments, up to $\frac{4}{5}$ inch long and $\frac{1}{8}$ inch wide. The petals are up to $\frac{3}{5}$ inch long; they may have a purple spot at the base. The ten stamens are tipped with yellow or reddish.

July to September: in sandy open ground and on dry roadsides from South Dakota to Oklahoma, and eastward. *Plate 114.*

SENSITIVE-PLANT, C. NICTITANS (to 16 inches), has narrow, downy leaf-segments up to $\frac{1}{2}$ inch long; there may be twenty-five pairs or even more. The flowers are small, the lowest petal much longer than the others. There are five stamens.

March to September: in sandy soil in Kansas and Oklahoma. *Plate 114.*

C. marilandica (up to 4 feet), also in Kansas and Oklahoma, has from ten to sixteen segments. The flowers are clustered in the axils. The joints or sections of the pod are shorter than they are wide. July to October: in moist woods and along streams. *Plate 114.* Coffee-senna, *C. occidentalis*, is a southern species which reaches eastern Kansas. It has only from four to six pairs of segments; they are ovate, sharp-pointed, up to 3 inches long. The pod is slightly curved, 3–5 inches long, about a tenth as wide. August and September: in low open ground. *Plate 114.*

Sickle-pod, *C. obtusifolia* (up to 3 feet), is a malodorous tropical species which reaches eastern Kansas. Leaf-segments number commonly three pairs, the end ones up to 3 inches long, broadest between middle and tip. The narrow pod is strongly curved. July to September: in moist woods and waste ground. *Plate 114.* Also known as *C. tora. C. roemeriana* (up to 2 feet) has leaves divided into only one pair of segments. These are downy (as is the stem), narrowly lanceolate, 1–2$\frac{1}{2}$ inches long. The long racemes have from two to five flowers, with petals about $\frac{1}{2}$ inch long. April to May or later: in rocky places in Oklahoma. *Plate 114.*

C. armata is shrubby, to 5 feet tall, the leaves divided into from one to four pairs of segments; commonly two or three pairs. These are ovate or almost round, less than $\frac{1}{2}$ inch long. Leaves may be lacking during dry seasons. The flowers are in a branched inflorescence, the petals small and veiny. A species of the southwestern deserts, in our range in southern Nevada.

THE PORTULACA FAMILY (PORTULACACEAE)

The portulacas and their relatives mostly have narrow, succulent leaves. The flowers have two sepals, generally five petals (but fewer in some species), and from one to many stamens. The petals are mostly small, but bright-colored, usually in some shade of pink or lavender. The style may be branched or not. Differences between genera are precise but rather small.

I. *Genera whose fruit (seed-pod) splits lengthwise when mature.*

A. Genera whose sepals remain attached around the fruit: *Claytonia* (five petals; five stamens; two leaves on the stem; flowers in a false raceme); *Montia* (from two to five petals and stamens; several leaves, usually in pairs, on the stem; flowers in a false raceme); *Calandrinia* (petals variable, averaging five; stamens seldom of the same number; flowers in a leafy inflorescence); *Calyptridium* (three or four petals; from one to three stamens; style unbranched; flowers in a false raceme or spike, coiled when young; leaves basal, widest near the end).

B. Genus whose sepals soon fall: *Talinum.*

II. *Genera whose fruit opens by the separation of a circular upper part.*

The number of petals and stamens varies greatly: *Portulaca* (stems leafy; sepals partly joined to each other and to the ovary; from seven to many stamens; style with three branches); *Lewisia* (leaves basal; five or more stamens; style with from three to eight branches).

CLAYTONIA

The flowers of *Claytonia* are in a false raceme, in two rows on one side of the stem, with a small bract often present opposite the lowest flower (not beneath it). There are two sepals, and five stamens; the style has three branches. There are two leaves on the stem, and generally several basal leaves growing from the underground corm or cluster of thick roots. The leaves are rather thick.

C. LANCEOLATA may have several stems about 6

inches long; they grow from a corm deep in the soil, so that part of the length is underground. There are generally one or two stalked basal leaves; the leaves on the stem lack stalks and are lanceolate or ovate, up to 3 inches long. The petals are pink, or in some varieties yellowish, up to ½ inch long.

April to July: in moist woods, along streams, and high on alpine slopes from the Cascade Mountains to Wyoming and Colorado. *Plate 114.*

C. umbellata is similar, with stems largely underground. The stem-leaves are stalked, the blades ½–1 inch long. The flowers have white or rose petals about ¼ inch long. In moderate and high altitudes in eastern Oregon and western Nevada, from June to August.

C. virginica is found in woods along our eastward limits. It has narrow leaves, from five to twenty flowers on a stem. *Plate 114.*

C. MEGARHIZA has many leaves which form a dense tuft. The flowers, white, pink, or rose, appear from under the leaves, especially the outer leaves.

June to August: in gravelly soil, rock crevices from the Wenatchee Mountains of central Washington to northeastern Oregon and eastward to Montana, southward to northern Nevada, Utah and Colorado. *Plate 115.*

C. nevadensis, of the Sierra Nevada, may just be in our range. The flowers are white with a pink center.

MONTIA

The difference between *Montia* and *Claytonia* is slight. *Montia* has a variable number of petals and stamens, from two to five, white or pink. The style has three branches, as in *Claytonia*; but the capsule contains not more than three seeds. The flowers are mostly in false racemes; the bracts, when present, being on the side of the stem away from the flower, not beneath it; and the flowers in two rows on one side of the stem. In some species of *Montia* there are more than two leaves on the stem, generally in pairs; other species have only two. These are small plants growing in both wet and dry places, widespread through our area.

I.   *Species with leaves on the stem in pairs.*

    A. Plants with one pair of leaves on the stem, generally quite different from the basal.

MINER'S-LETTUCE or INDIAN LETTUCE, M. PER-FOLIATA (4–12 inches), is easily recognized by the flat disks formed by the two opposite leaves joined around the stem. There are also long-stalked, broad-bladed leaves (narrow-bladed in some varieties), at the base of the stem.

February to July: common and varying, in many situations, mostly shady and moist but also high and dry, from eastern Wyoming to Utah and North and South Dakota. *Plate 115.* This species – if it is a species – has had at least sixteen different botanical names, as botanists noticed differences in color, stature, shape of leaves, size of petals, and so forth. As for the English names, the plants did provide a salad for Indians, prospectors, and early settlers.

M. SIBIRICA (6–18 inches) has long-stalked basal leaves with lanceolate or ovate blades, and leaves on the stem without stalks; these are mostly sharp-pointed, 1–3 inches long. Many bracts are present in the inflorescence. The petals are white with pink lines, ⅓–½ inch long.

March to September: in moist shady places from Washington to California and eastward to Montana and Utah. *Plate 115.* Including a number of varieties.

M. arenicola, from central Washington to northwestern Oregon and adjacent Idaho, has leaves less than ¼ inch wide. Flowers may be pink, or white with pink lines. March to June: on moist rocks and hillsides and in pine woods.

M. CORDIFOLIA (4–12 inches) generally grows in clumps. The basal leaves have blades 1–2 inches broad, commonly not so long, generally heart-shaped ("*cordi-*"), on very long stalks. The leaves on the stem have similar blades but no stalks. The inflorescence lacks bracts above the lowest flower. The white petals are ⅓–½ inch long.

May to September: in wet soil, commonly along streams, through the Cascade Mountains to northern California and eastward to western Montana and northern Utah. *Plate 115.*

M. spathulata (1–2½ inches) inhabits the mountains of Oregon and California at the western limits of our range, and westward. It forms dense tufts of narrow, thick leaves about as long as the stems. The stem-leaves are small, lanceolate; on some plants joined on one side. The petals are white or pink, about ⅛ inch long. There is only one bract in the inflorescence, opposite the lowest flower. February to July: on dry open slopes. *Plate 115.*

    B. Plants with more than one pair of leaves on the stem, much like the basal leaves.

M. CHAMISSOI (2–8 inches) has nearly leafless runners which form bulblike offsets and erect flowering stems. The leaves are up to 2 inches long, gradually narrower towards the base. The inflorescence

PLATE 114

Claytonia lanceolata   *Korling*

Claytonia virginica   *Elbert*

Cassia obtusifolia   *Kirtley-Perkins*

Cassia occidentalis   *Horst*

Cassia nictitans   *Evans*

Hoffmanseggia jamesii   *Henze*

Cassia roemeriana   *Whitaker*

Cassia marilandica   *Foote*

Cassia fasciculata   *Johnson*

arise in the axils and at the tip, with a bract commonly opposite the lowest flower-stalk. The petals are white or pink, $\frac{1}{4}$–$\frac{1}{3}$ inch long.

May to August: in wet and boggy places from Alaska to California and eastward in Washington and Oregon and to Colorado. *Plate 115.*

M. fontana has delicate stems spreading horizontally, the tips growing upwards. The leaves are $\frac{1}{6}$–$\frac{3}{5}$ inch long, with or without short stalks. The tiny ($\frac{1}{20}$ inch) flowers have petals about $\frac{1}{20}$ inch long. In wet places, sometimes floating, from Washington and Oregon to Idaho and from California to Nevada.

II.   *Species with leaves borne singly on the stem.*

M. PARVIFOLIA spreads by horizontal stems which form bunches of leaves with narrow or roundish blades commonly about an inch long, on stalks as long. Among these rise leafy runners, and one or more flowering stems up to 2 foot tall. The leaves on these stems are much smaller than those at the base. The inflorescence has numerous tiny bracts. The five petals are pink or white with pink or lavender veins, $\frac{1}{3}$–$\frac{3}{5}$ inch long.

May to August: in moist places, especially among rocks, from Alaska to California, Idaho, and Montana. *Plate 115.*

M. LINEARIS (2–8 inches) has branching stems bearing leaves up to $1\frac{1}{2}$ inches long. There is no basal tuft or rosette. The small flowers are white, the petals about $\frac{1}{5}$ inch long.

April to July: in moist soil, on banks and in meadows from British Columbia to California and eastward to Montana and Utah. *Plate 116.*

M. dichotoma (generally less than 3 inches) is similar but smaller. Leaves $\frac{1}{4}$–$\frac{3}{4}$ inch. Petals scarcely longer than the sepals, about $\frac{1}{10}$ inch. In moist lowlands from Washington to California and eastward to Idaho and western Montana.

CALANDRINIA

One species of *Calandrinia* is found in our range.

RED-MAIDS, C. CILIATA, has very narrow leaves up to 3 inches long, some at the base of the plant, some singly on the stems. The stems, 4–12 inches long, spread horizontally, the tips bending up and each bearing a single flower. The petals are commonly deep rose-red or purple, less than $\frac{1}{2}$ inch long.

February to May: common in grassy places and cultivated land. *Plate 116.*

CALYPTRIDIUM

Our species of *Calyptridium* have most leaves at ground level, in rosettes; they are widest between middle and tip. The flowers are in false racemes, spikes, or heads, generally coiled when young, the flowers on the upper side. They have three or four petals and from one to three stamens. Except in the first species, the petals do not fall but form a cap — *calyptra* — over the seed-pod.

PUSSY-PAWS, C. UMBELLATUM, has stems up to 10 inches long, spreading over the ground or standing erect. The flowers are in heads. There are four pink or white petals; the sepals are similar. The style is long, threadlike.

May to August: in sandy and gravelly places from Montana southward to Wyoming, Utah, and California. *Plate 116.*

C. ROSEUM has leaves widest near their tip, $\frac{1}{5}$–$1\frac{1}{2}$ inches long. There are only two petals, white, less than $\frac{1}{10}$ inch long.

May and June: in sagebrush desert and dry forest from central Oregon to eastern California, Nevada, and Utah; and southern Idaho. *C. pygmaeum* is only an inch tall, the leaves less than $\frac{1}{2}$ inch. The flowers have four petals up to $\frac{1}{8}$ inch long. Rare in sandy and gravelly places at high altitudes in the Sierra Nevada, barely in our range.

C. monandrum is in Mono County, California and adjacent Nevada. The stems are generally prostrate. The sepals are minute, with white margins. There are generally three tiny petals. *C. parryi* is similar. The flowers have no stalks. The sepals are longer than $\frac{1}{10}$ inch. From southern California to western Nevada.

FAMEFLOWERS (TALINUM)

The flowers of *Talinum* are small but colorful. They are borne in clusters at the summit of the stem or singly in the axils of leaves. They have two sepals which soon fall, five petals, and from four to many stamens. The style has three branches. These are plants of rocky or sandy places.

PLATE 115

Montia parvifolia *Wilson*

Montia sibirica *Hull*

Montia cordifolia *Lomax*

Montia spathulata *Johnson*

Montia chamissoi *Baum*

Montia perfoliata *Reineking*

Claytonia megarhiza *Randall*

T. BREVIFOLIUM, not more than 4 inches tall, has
crowded, thick leaves up to ½ inch long. The
flowers are lavender or rose. They are borne singly or
in few-flowered inflorescences (cymes) which are in
the axils.

May to September: in southern Utah.

T. PARVIFLORUM has a leafless stem up to 10 inches
tall, rising from a cluster of narrow, thick leaves
up to 2 inches long. The flowers are lavender or rose,
the petals ⅙–⅓ inch long. There are from four to ten
stamens.

May to September: in bare soil from North
Dakota to Colorado and Oklahoma. *Plate 116.*

T. okanoganense is a cushion less than 2 inches
across, the leaves very narrow, not more than ½ inch

long. The inflorescences rise to 1½ inches, generally
with from three to nine flowers. The flowers are white,
pink, or yellowish. May to July: on exposed slopes
and ledges in north-central Washington.

T. CALYCINUM has one or more short stems bearing
very narrow leaves 1–2 inches long. The petals,
from eight to ten, are bright rose, about ½ inch long.
There are thirty or more stamens.

June to August: on cliffs, sand, and dry barrens
from Nebraska to Oklahoma, and eastward. *Plate 116.*

T. spinescens, known only among rocky outcrops
in central Washington, forms a cushion, with leaves
up to an inch long. The stem is covered with spine-
like lower parts of old leaves. The flowers are in cymes,
the petals from pale rose to crimson-magenta.

PURSLANES AND MOSS-ROSES (PORTULACA)

The plants known as purslane or pussley are unattractive and troublesome weeds; the moss-roses are
handsome garden plants. In general, our species of
Portulaca have succulent leaves and attractive flowers,
which generally open only in sunshine. They have
two partly joined sepals, five petals — or many in cultivated species — from seven to numerous stamens, and
a style with three or more branches. A technical
characteristic which distinguishes the genus is the
union of the calyx with the lower half of the ovary. The
top of the round seed-pod comes off at maturity, dis-
charging the seeds through the opening.

MOSS-ROSE, P. GRANDIFLORA, is a colorful garden
flower, a native of South America. The leaves are
rodlike, borne singly except those just beneath the
flowers, which form a circle or involucre. There are
long hairs in the axils. The flowers are often nearly 2
inches across, with many petals of various brilliant
shades. This escapes from cultivation in the southeastern states of our area. *Plate 117. P. parvula* has
yellow or coppery petals about 1/10 inch long. In
Oklahoma.

P. RETUSA may be prostrate. The leaves are thick but
flat and broad. The flowers are yellow, the petals
about ⅕ inch long.

August to October: in sandy soil from southern
Kansas and Oklahoma to Utah. *Plate 116.*

P. mundula has very small red-purple flowers. In
Kansas, and Oklahoma. *Plate 117.*

PURSLANE, P. OLERACEA, known as pussley by the
country-folk, is a plant that lies on the ground,
often in our gardens. The leaves, borne paired or
singly, are succulent. The flowers are small, in the
axils of leaves, with yellow petals. This common weed
needs no introduction to gardeners. It is almost impossible to kill by ordinary cultivation, pieces of its
succulent stems withstanding the sun on the surface
of the soil and quickly rooting. Its redeeming feature
is that it may be cooked for "greens."

June to November: a native of Europe or Asia,
now abundant throughout this country. *Plate 116.*

P. neglecta has horizontal stems with branches
tending upwards; leaves up to 2 inches long; from
twelve to eighteen stamens. In Kansas and Oklahoma.

LEWISIA

The leaves of *Lewisia* are thick and succulent,
mostly in a basal rosette. The stems generally lack
leaves other than some small bracts. The flowers are
showy, with from five to eighteen petals and from five
to fifty stamens. There may be more than two sepals.
The style is tipped with three narrow stigmas.

The genus is named for Captain Meriwether
Lewis, one of the leaders of the famous Lewis and
Clark Expedition. (For *Clarkia* see the evening-

primrose family.) With two exceptions, our species
have single flowers or compact clusters at the tip of
each flowering stem.

I.   *Species whose flowering stems are generally less than
4 inches tall.*

As usual among plants, occasional individuals
of group I may be more than 4 inches; and of
group II, less than 4 inches.

PLATE 116

Montia linearis   *Wilson*

Portulaca oleracea   *Horne*

Scribner

Talinum calycinum   *Johnson*

Portulaca retusa   *Hesselberg*

Talinum parviflorum

Calyptridium umbellatum   *Johnson*

Calandrinia ciliata   *Reineking*

BITTER-ROOT, L. REDIVIVA ($\frac{1}{2}$–$1\frac{1}{4}$ inches), has one
flower on each stem, with a circle of narrow
bracts at some distance below. The flower has from
four to nine sepals and from six to nine whitish or rose
petals $\frac{3}{4}$–$1\frac{1}{2}$ inches long. There are from thirty to
fifty stamens; the style has from four to eight branches.

March to July: on gravelly slopes and among
rocks, with sagebrush and in the lower mountains,
from Canada east of the Cascade Mountains to California, eastward to Montana and Colorado. *Plate 117*.

L. nevadensis occurs in the mountains along our
western boundaries, at moderate and high altitudes.
It has two bracts on the stem, lanceolate and translucent. There is one or rarely two flowers on the stem,
with from six to ten white petals about $\frac{1}{2}$ inch long.
This has been treated as a variety of *L. pygmaea*.
L. sierrae is a plant of high altitudes in the southern
Sierra Nevada. It forms stems no more than an inch
tall. Each stem bears a pair of bracts and from one to
three flowers, the pink petals $\frac{1}{4}$ inch long. Near our
southern limits in Nevada *L. maguirei* is found. It has
stems up to $\frac{4}{5}$ inch tall, bearing three or four flowers
with from seven to nine white or pink petals about
$\frac{1}{2}$ inch long. The leaves are narrow.

L. PYGMAEA ($\frac{1}{2}$–3 inches) is distinguished by the
glandular margins of its sepals. There are two
narrow bracts on a stem and one flower with generally
seven petals $\frac{1}{4}$–$\frac{3}{4}$ inch long, ranging from white to
deep pink and lavender.

May to September: in damp, open, gravelly
places at high altitudes from Washington southward
through the Cascades and Sierra Nevada, eastward to
Montana, and southward through the Rockies.
Plates 117, 118.

In *L. kelloggii* ($\frac{1}{2}$–2 inches), also with gland-
edged sepals, there are several bracts immediately below the sepals and resembling them. The flower is
cream, the petals about eight, $\frac{1}{3}$–$\frac{1}{2}$ inch long. The
leaves may overtop the flowers. In the northern Sierra
Nevada and in central Idaho. *Plate 117*. *L. brachycalyx* (1–2 inches), near our southern limits in California and Utah, has a single white flower on each
stem, at least $\frac{1}{2}$ inch long. The sepals are not glandular.
Plate 117.

L. TRIPHYLLA (1–4 inches) usually lacks the basal
leaves at flowering time; there may be two or
three (rarely up to five) narrow leaves on the stem just
above the ground, mostly all at the same level. The
flowers are in a somewhat raceme-like cluster, with
small bracts; there may be up to twenty-five. Each
has from five to nine white or pink petals $\frac{1}{4}$ inch long.

May to August: from eastern Washington
southward through the Sierra Nevada and eastward
to Montana and Colorado.

II.　*Species whose flowering stems generally exceed 4
inches in height.*
See the note on group I.

L. TWEEDYI (4–8 inches) has ovate or lanceolate
basal leaves, as long as the flowering stems or
nearly so, tapering to a broad stalk. Each stem has
several flowers (not always more than one open at a
time), with from seven to nine salmon, pale peach-
colored, or almost white petals 1–$1\frac{1}{2}$ inches long.

May to July: on rocky slopes and in crevices,
generally with pines, in the Wenatchee Mountains of
central Washington. *Plate 118*.

L. columbiana (4–12 inches) grows mostly west
of our range, but one variety is found in northeastern
Oregon and adjacent Idaho. The basal leaves are
numerous and narrow, up to 4 inches long. The
flowers are borne in branched inflorescences with
small toothed bracts. The petals are white with pink
veins, or rose-magenta, $\frac{1}{4}$–$\frac{1}{2}$ inch long. May to
August: on gravelly soil and rocky slopes. *Plate 117*.

THE GERANIUM FAMILY (GERANIACEAE)

The geranium family is characterized by
numerical precision: five sepals, five petals, ten
stamens in two circles (in *Erodium* one circle
forms no pollen), and a pistil composed of five
parts. This pistil forms a curious fruit: at maturity
the five parts of the ovary, each containing a
seed, separate; each is attached to a slender part
of the style, which either curls upward or coils
spirally. The style, before this happens, forms a
long beak something like the bill of a heron or
crane or stork; *Geranium* is derived from the
Greek word for "crane." The leaves of *Geraniaceae* are palmately (in *Geranium*) or pinnately
(in *Erodium*) divided, cleft, or lobed.

The plants generally known as geraniums
and grown in gardens and in houses are species
of *Geraniaceae* but not of *Geranium*; they belong
in the African genus *Pelargonium*. Plants are
occasionally found growing wild but probably
do not become established.

PLATE 117

Portulaca grandiflora *Horst*

Lewisia pygmaea *Korling*

Geranium fremontii *Ure*

Lewisia rediviva *Roberts*

Lewisia columbiana *Johnson*

Lewisia kelloggii *Koerber*

Lewisia brachycalyx *Messinger*

Portulaca mundula *Amerson*

THE WILD GERANIUMS OR CRANE'S-BILLS (GERANIUM)

The leaves of *Geranium* have palmately lobed, cleft, or divided blades (the lobes or segments may be pinnately lobed or cleft). The flowers of some species are in an ample or compact inflorescence; in others they terminate the stems, often in pairs. The five parts of the ovary separate and are lifted up by the curving of the segments of the style which remain attached at their tips to a central shaft.

The sepals are tipped with a bristle in the following species except as noted.

I. *Species whose petals are less than ½ inch long.* Most of these have petals no more than ⅖ inch long.

G. CAROLINIANUM (up to 16 inches) is densely clothed with short hairs. The leaves are deeply cleft into five or seven narrow lobes which are themselves lobed or cleft pinnately. The inflorescence is compact. The petals are pink or almost white, about as long as the sepals.

April to July: in grassy places, waste ground, and woods throughout our range. *Plate 118.* Plants with crowded flowers, rose petals about ½ inch long, have been named *G. sphaerospermum.* They grow from Washington to California and eastward to Montana and South Dakota.

G. rotundifolium has some gland-tipped hairs on the stems. The petals are crimson or violet. A weed in Kansas, from Europe.

G. columbinum lacks glands on the calyx, the lobes of which are bristle-tipped. The plant is covered with hairs lying flat. The leaves have stalks longer than the blade, which are divided and cleft into narrow lobes. A weed from Europe (in England known as dove's-foot; *columba* is a dove). In North and South Dakota. *Plate 118. G. bicknellii* is similar, with densely glandular flower-stalks and hairy flowering branches. It occurs in wooded areas in North Dakota. *Plate 118.*

DOVE'S-FOOT, G. MOLLE, is softly downy (*molle*, "soft"). The five or seven rather broad lobes of the leaves are scalloped or bluntly lobed at their end. The flowers are generally in pairs on rather long stalks. The petals are rose-purple, notched or two-lobed.

April to August: in grassy and brushy places and waste ground throughout our range. *Plate 118.* From Europe.

G. pusillum, from North Dakota to Kansas, has petals and sepals about $\frac{1}{10}$–⅙ inch long; the sepals lack bristle-tips. The flowers are mostly two on each stalk from the axils. From Europe. *Plate 118.*

II. *Species whose petals are ½ inch long or longer.*

G. RICHARDSONII (up to 3 feet) has few stems, smooth or nearly so. The leaf-blades are up to 6 inches across, five- or seven-lobed, the lobes sharp-toothed and lobed. The generally long flower-stalks are beset with gland-tipped hairs. The flowers, generally in pairs, have white or pale pink petals.

July to September: in moist woods and mountain meadows throughout our range from the Rocky Mountains westward. *Plate 119.* Plants with light lavender flowers may represent crossing with *G. fremontii.*

G. FREMONTII has spreading stems up to 20 inches long, nearly smooth. The leaves have three or five lobes which are toothed or lobed. The flowers, with rose-purple petals up to an inch long, are in an ample inflorescence.

June to September: in forests in Wyoming and Colorado. *Plate 117.*

G. VISCOSISSIMUM (1–3 feet) has hairs spreading or lying flat on the lower part of the stem, which may have gland-tipped hairs in the inflorescence. The leaf-blades may be 5 inches broad, deeply cleft into three toothed lobes. The petals are up to ⅘ inch long, pink-lavender or purplish, rarely white.

May to August: from British Columbia to northern California and eastward to South Dakota and Colorado. *Plate 118.* Southern plants with smooth stems have been named *G. nervosum.*

G. maculatum is a common eastern species, in our range from North Dakota (?) to Oklahoma. It lacks evident glands. The petals are ½–1 inch long, much longer than the sepals. The flowers are in an inflorescence at the end of the stem. April to June, in woods and meadows. *Plate 119.*

G. CAESPITOSUM has erect and horizontal stems up to 3 feet long; downy but not glandular. The flowers are rose-purple.

May to September: common in pine forests in Colorado and Utah. *Plate 119.* In Utah *G. marginale* is found, 4–16 inches tall, very finely downy, with leaf-blades about an inch wide, cleft into three or five lobes, each lobe with three teeth. The petals are light pink or rose.

G. PARRYI (4–18 inches) forms tufts of erect, glandular stems. The leaves are up to 3 inches wide, with three or five cleft and lobed lobes. The flowers are generally in pairs, occasionally in threes. The petals are rose or deep rose-purple, ½–¾ inches long.

June to August: in cañons or on rocky ground in foothills and mountains from Wyoming and western Colorado to Utah. *Plate 119.*

PLATE 118

Geranium bicknellii *Williamson*

Geranium molle *Wilson*

Geranium pusillum *McDowell*

Lewisia pygmaea *Dilley*

Geranium viscosissimum *Bowen*

Geranium columbinum *McDowell*

Geranium carolinianum *Allen*

Lewisia tweedyi *Johnson*

STORK'S-BILL (ERODIUM)

We have one widespread species of *Erodium* and another along our southern limits.

ALFILARIA or FILAREE, E. CICUTARIUM, has
stems spreading horizontally up to 20 inches long, more or less downy, with leaves up to 4 inches long. The blades are pinnately divided into segments which are variously toothed and cleft. The sepals bear white bristles. The rose-lavender petals are a little longer than the sepals, up to $\frac{1}{3}$ inch.

February to May: common in open places throughout the United States. *Plate 119*. From the Mediterranean countries.

E. texanum has horizontal stems up to 16 inches long; the leaves are an inch long or longer, three-lobed. The purple petals may be nearly an inch long, longer than the sepals. The style may be $\frac{1}{4}$ inch long. March to May: in open ground in southern Utah.

THE LOOSESTRIFE FAMILY (LYTHRACEAE)

The *Lythraceae* can with difficulty be characterized by the numbers of parts of their flowers, for these vary greatly. Most of our species have from four to six petals. These are reddish or purplish, and are borne at the end of a floral tube which surrounds the ovary but is not joined with it (the ovary is not inferior). There may be as many stamens as petals, or up to twice as many. The flowers are generally in the axils or on short branches which grow from the axils. The leaves are mostly in pairs, and are undivided and without lobes. The plants are generally in wet places.

LYTHRUM

Species of *Lythrum* are generally called the purple-loosestrifes, to distinguish them from the "true" loosestrifes in the primrose family. I have not emphasized this common name, since their flowers are not modern purple but crimson (classical purple was derived from a Mediterranean shellfish). The flowers of *Lythrum* generally have six small petals on a ribbed floral tube up to $\frac{1}{4}$ inch long. There are from four to twelve stamens.

Most of our species are found in the plains east of the Rocky Mountains.

L. ALATUM (up to 4 feet) is slender, with flowers
borne singly in the axils of the lanceolate or ovate leaves. The upper leaves are generally borne singly. There are two types of flowers: one with short stamens and a long style, the other with long stamens (attached farther up) and a short style. This arrangement facilitates cross-pollination.

June to September: in swamps and meadows from North Dakota to Oklahoma, and eastward. *Plate 119*.

L. californicum is within our southern limits. It is up to 6 feet tall, with narrow leaves, an inch long or longer, borne singly. The petals are up to $\frac{1}{4}$ inch long. *Plate 119*.

L. lanceolatum has narrowly lanceolate or elliptic leaves, mostly borne singly. It grows in swamps and moist sandy places; in Oklahoma and eastward. *Plate 120*.

Purple-loosestrife, *L. salicaria*, is listed as having been found in INT (I have no more exact record). It is an European species, well established in the eastern states, where it forms wide colonies of tall (up to 6 feet), magenta ("purple") flower-spires growing in shallow water, swamps, etc. The lanceolate leaves may be in circles of three. There are three types of flowers, with ten stamens at two levels: all stamens low, long style; all stamens high, short style; and high and low stamens with style of intermediate length. I have never found all these types in any one colony.

CUPHEA

The large tropical American genus *Cuphea* is represented in our range only by *C. petiolata*, clammy or blue waxweed. It is found in our range in southeastern Kansas and Oklahoma. It is generally less than 2 feet tall; covered with clammy or sticky hairs. The flowers are single or in pairs in the axils. The base of the flower is a rather long tube, expanded into a sack on the upper side so that the stalk seems to be attached on the lower side. The sepals form six triangular teeth, and there are six unequal red-purple petals; all on the rim of the tube. In open woodlands. *Plate 119*.

PLATE 119

Erodium cicutarium *P. R. Ferguson*

Lythrum californicum *Koch*

Lythrum alatum *Johnson*

Geranium caespitosum *Wilson*

Geranium parryi *Uttal*

Geranium richardsonii *Hesselberg*

Geranium maculatum *Gottscho*

Cuphea petiolata *Rhein*

Rotala ramosior *Johnson*

In addition to the above, four not very attractive or conspicuous species of three genera of *Lythraceae* are found within our limits.

The most widespread is *Ammania coccinea*. It may be known by very narrow leaves, up to 2 inches long, with small groups of almost stalkless flowers in the axils. The calyx is not more than $\frac{1}{5}$ inch long, the blade of the petals only about $\frac{1}{25}$ inch. Four stamens. In wet places through most of the United States, from Washington to Montana and from North Dakota to Oklahoma; and in INT. *Plate 120. A. auriculata*, differing in having mostly stalked flowers or flower-clusters, and petals from white to violet, is found in Kansas and Oklahoma.

Tooth-cup, *Rotala ramosior*, generally not more than 8 inches tall, has narrowly lanceolate, mostly stalked leaves, with the flowers mostly single in the axils; these have four minute, white or pink petals and four stamens. In wet places in eastern Kansas and Oklahoma, and probably also in western Nevada and Washington. *Plate 119.*

Peplis diandra has no petals; four stamens (in spite of the name). It grows by or in shallow water; the leaves when under water are long and broad-based, when above the surface shorter and tapering at the base. In Kansas and Utah.

THE EVENING-PRIMROSE FAMILY (ONAGRACEAE)

The flowers of *Onagraceae*, except in one small genus, have four sepals, four petals, and four or eight stamens. The ovary is inferior. In some of the largest genera there is a floral tube above the position of the enclosed ovary, bearing the perianth on its rim. This may be mistaken for a flower-stalk; but there is generally a swelling at its base, where the ovary is.

The family is abundant in the West, the largest genera being *Oenothera* and *Epilobium*. In all, we have over one hundred species.

Many species adorn our homes. *Oenothera* and *Clarkia* contribute ornamental species; *Fuchsia* belongs to the same family.

Guide to Genera of Onagraceae

I. *Genera with a prominent floral tube above the ovary.*

A. Plants with a seed-pod that splits lengthwise into four parts when mature: *Oenothera* (petals white, yellow, or rose; flowers mostly in axils of leaves or leaflike bracts); *Zauschneria* (petals intense red; floral tube funnel-shaped); *Clarkia* (petals showy, not yellow; sepals bent down at one side, sticking together; leaves undivided and unlobed); *Boisduvalia* (petals mostly pink or rose, less than $\frac{1}{2}$ inch long, notched or deeply cleft).

B. Plants with a nut-like pod which does not open: *Gaura* (petals white, pink, or red, in two pairs, stalked); *Stenosiphon* (petals white, less than $\frac{1}{4}$ inch long; floral tube whitish, threadlike).

II. *Genera with no prominent floral-tube (one may be present but short).*

A. Plants with four or five sepals, four or five petals or none: *Ludwigia* (petals four or five, yellow, or none; stamens four, eight, or ten; sepals present on the seed-pod; plants of wet places); *Epilobium* (petals four, white, pink, or rose, in some species notched; pod rodlike; seeds with a tuft of hairs); *Gayophytum* (petals four, white, mostly $\frac{1}{10}$ inch long, in one species up to $\frac{1}{5}$ inch; stems very slender; leaves mostly very narrow).

B. Plants with two sepals, two petals cleft to seem four, two stamens: *Circaea* (pod bristly).

THE EVENING-PRIMROSES (OENOTHERA)

The evening-primroses are, of course, not primroses (*Primula*). The "evening" refers to a number of species that open their flowers at that time of day; they remain open through the night (being pollinated by night-flying insects) and close in the morning.

The flowers have four sepals which are bent down at flowering, four petals, and four or, generally, eight stamens. The ovary is inferior, embedded in the flower-base; and from it rises a slender floral tube, cylindric or funnel-shaped, which bears the perianth on its rim. The floral-tube is sometimes mistaken for the flower-stalk, all the more readily that the flowers generally have no stalk. The fruit is a narrow capsule, straight, curved, or coiled.

PLATE 120

Oenothera speciosa   *Henze*

Oenothera caespitosa   *Stockert*

Oenothera deltoides   *Reineking*

Oenothera triloba   *Morris*

Ammania coccinea   *Johnson*

Lythrum lanceolatum   *Johnson*

Oenothera pallida   *Korling*

It is natural that such a large and varied genus has in the past been divided into a number of genera, and still is by some botanists. The last word on this problem has not yet been said. It may be noted that several of the fairly easily distinguished groups outlined in what follows correspond to the genera that some botanists have recognized.

We have fifty-six species.

I.   *Species whose stigma is four threadlike branches at the tip of the style.*
Most of these bloom in the evening.

A. Plants whose flowers are not yellow.
See also *O. laciniata* under B.

1.   In the first four of these the seed-pods (capsules) are prominently angled or ribbed (or both) lengthwise. Except the first, these are species east of the continental divide.

O. CAESPITOSA (4–12 inches) usually has all leaves at ground level. They may be smooth, or in various subspecies downy or hairy. The blades are 1–5 inches long, widest near the end, generally toothed or pinnately cleft, their stalks flat-margined.

April to September: mostly on dry slopes almost throughout our area. The fruit is cylindric in Washington, Idaho, and Colorado. In other subspecies it is ovate and may be curved. There are differences also in hairiness and leaf-lobing and toothing. *Plate 120.* O. *triloba*: Similar. Nearly smooth, or glandular. Leaves in a dense tuft, pinnately cleft, up to 8 inches long. Petals 4–8 inches long. Capsule four-winged. In places wet at times, Kansas and Oklahoma. *Plate 120.* O. *canescens* (4–8 inches): Bushy. Hoary. Leaves narrowly lanceolate, commonly toothed. Petals white or pink. June and July: in dried ponds from Wyoming and Nebraska southward.

O. SPECIOSA has several horizontal leafy stems 4–20 inches long. The leaves are mostly smooth, those at the base wide near the tip, those on the stem short-stalked, pinnately cleft. The flowers are single in the upper axils, opening in the morning, the buds drooping. The petals are white, turning pink. The capsule is eight-ribbed.

May to July: in grassland and open woodland in Kansas and Oklahoma. *Plate 120.*

2.   In the remaining species of group A the pods are not prominently ribbed or angled.

O. DELTOIDES may have erect stems 2–10 inches tall with spreading branches up to a foot long, variously downy or smooth. The leaves are somewhat diamond-shaped, with or without small teeth, or some pinnately cleft, up to 3 inches long, tapering to stalks.

The stem-leaves are commonly more toothed or cleft and without stalks. The flowers are single in the axils, opening in the evening, their buds drooping, the sepals bent down, the petals white (aging pink). We have three subspecies, differing in type of hairiness, length of petals (up to 1½ inches in the southwestern deserts), toothing or lobing of leaves, etc.

March to May: from eastern Oregon to eastern California and through Nevada to southwestern Utah. *Plate 120.* O. *pallida* (4–20 inches): Mainly erect, whitish ("pallid"), nearly smooth or hoary. Leaf-blades ovate, lanceolate, or narrower, with or without teeth, with short stalks or none. Buds drooping. Sepals joined. May to September: in dry sandy places from eastern Idaho to southwestern Wyoming and western Colorado, and from North Dakota to Oklahoma and Colorado. The "pallid" plants are mostly in Idaho. The toothless leaves are commoner in our eastern states. In the central regions the stems are reddish, the sepal-tips not spreading apart in the buds. *Plate 120.*

O. *linifolia* (4–12 inches): Smooth. Basal leaf-blades ovate, stalked, less than an inch. Stem-leaves threadlike, up to 1 inch. Flowers few, in short spikes. Sepals bent down. April and May: in sandy and stony places in Kansas and Oklahoma.

O. ALBICAULIS (to 4 feet) tends to be ashy-gray and hairy. The leaves in the rosette have blades widest towards their tips, up to 2 inches long, mostly without teeth, short-stalked; the stem-leaves are lanceolate, generally deeply pinnately cleft. The flowers are single in the axils, their buds drooping. The petals are white turning pink. The pod is ribbed but not prominently.

March to July: largely in disturbed soil from Montana and South Dakota to Oklahoma, Colorado, and southern Utah. *Plate 121.*

O. *coronopifolia* (2–10 inches): Usually hoary. Leaves crowded, with bunches in the axils. Stem-leaves pinnately cleft into narrow lobes. Flowers few, in the upper axils; buds drooping; sepals bent down; petals white aging pink, ½ inch long. Open grasslands and coniferous forest from Idaho to South Dakota and southward to Utah and Oklahoma. *Plate 121.* O. *avita* (4–32 inches): Some plants with long shaggy hairs. Basal leaves from toothed to deeply cleft. Deserts, from northeastern California to Nevada and southern Utah.

O. NUTTALLII (16–40 inches) is quite smooth, with a white skin which peels off. The leaf-blades are pale green, narrowly oblong, mostly without teeth, 1–2 inches long, with or without stalks. The flowers have a disagreeable odor. The sepals cohere. Petals white, fading pink, up to an inch long.

July and August: especially in sandy places in grasslands and pine woods from Montana and North Dakota to Colorado. *Plate 121.*

PLATE 121

Oenothera albicaulis   *Hesselberg*

Oenothera xylocarpa   *Weisser*

Oenothera fendleri   *Uttal*

Oenothera brachycarpa   *Roberts*

Oenothera flava   *Stockert*

Oenothera primiveris   *Reineking*

Oenothera coronopifolia   *Wilson*

Oenothera biennis   *Gottscho*

Oenothera nuttallii   *Uttal*

B. Species with threadlike stigma-lobes and yellow petals.

1. The first seven of these have seed pods ribbed or winged lengthwise.

O. FLAVA has no stem above ground, or a very short one. The leaves, up to 8 inches long, form a tuft, with pinnately cleft blades on short stalks. The flowers are surrounded by the leaves. The petals are pale yellow, $\frac{2}{5}$–$\frac{4}{5}$ inch long. The capsule is ovate, with four wings.
May to July: in meadows through the Rocky Mountains and eastward to northeastern California. *Plate 121.*
O. xylocarpa has leaves all at the ground, pinnately cleft, commonly red-spotted, densely downy; the end lobe the largest. The petals, an inch long or longer, may turn red in age. The capsule is rather woody (*xylo-*), tapering to a slender tip, with wings on the angles.
July and August: on dry ledges among pines in the southern Sierra Nevada and adjacent Nevada. *Plate 121.*

O. BRACHYCARPA has a very short stem, rarely about 4 inches tall. The leaves, up to 6 inches long, are in a tuft, the blades variously toothed or cleft, the stalks about as long as the blades. The broad petals are up to 2 inches long. The pods are narrowly winged, mostly near the tip; they are ovate or nearly cylindric.
May to July: in dry places, especially among rocks, from southwestern Idaho to Colorado, Utah, extreme western Kansas, and Oklahoma. *Plate 121.*

FLUTTER-MILLS, O. MISSOURIENSIS, may have almost no stem above ground, or may be 20 inches tall. It may be quite smooth, or somewhat hoary. The leaf-blades range from narrowly lanceolate to ovate, commonly very finely toothed, tapering into broad stalks. The flower-buds droop; they are generally mottled with red. The petals are 1–2 inches long and wide. The pods, up to $2\frac{1}{2}$ inches long, have wings from $\frac{1}{3}$ to nearly 1 inch wide.
May to September: on prairies, rocky hillsides, and roadsides from Nebraska to Oklahoma. *Plate 122.* Several varieties differ in type of hairiness; the southernmost plants are silvery. The species is cultivated, especially in "rock gardens." Other names are Missouri-primrose and Ozark-sundrops; the first misleading, since it was named for the river, not the state; and it is not a primrose.
O. fremontii forms tufts with scarcely any leafy stem. The leaves are narrow, up to $2\frac{1}{2}$ inches long, with a few small teeth or none. The flowers are few, in the axils, the petals nearly an inch long. On stony hills in Nebraska and Kansas. The square pod is narrowly winged on the angles; up to an inch long.

O. spachiana (4–12 inches) is erect. The leaf-blades are mostly lanceolate, rarely toothed, on short stalks. The petals, up to $\frac{3}{5}$ inch long, are pale yellow. The pod is generally less than $\frac{1}{2}$ inch long, club-shaped, with broad wings. On prairies in Oklahoma.

SUNDROPS, O. FRUTICOSA, is very varied, with seven recognized varieties which have acquired some twenty-five names; it may be a group of species instead of just one. In general it is, in the West, 1–3 feet tall, downy or hairy, the leaf-blades from narrowly lanceolate (on the stem) to ovate (at the ground), with or without small teeth. The sepals are generally bent back; in bud their tips may not be joined. The petals are $\frac{1}{2}$–1 inch long. The pod tends to be club-shaped, with a narrow base, and four sharp angles.
May to August: in woods and fields in Oklahoma. Commonly cultivated.

2. The remaining species of group B, with yellow petals and threadlike stigmas, have seed-pods not ribbed or sharply angled.
With three exceptions, these are restricted in our range to the plains east of the Rocky Mountains.

O. PRIMIVERIS (one subspecies) has almost no stem above ground. The plant is hairy. The leaves have blades up to 5 inches long, mostly deeply cleft and toothed, tapering into flat stalks. The petals are 1–$1\frac{1}{2}$ inches long, notched at the outer edge; they turn reddish in age. The pod is angular and ribbed, tapering to a narrow tip.
March to May: on dry plains and hillsides from Nevada to Colorado. *Plate 121.*
O. laciniata may have an erect stem up to 4 inches tall, or horizontal branches up to a foot long. Leaves pinnately cleft, toothed, or wavy-edged, about 2 inches long. Flowers small, in the axils, the pale yellow or white petals $\frac{1}{5}$–$\frac{3}{5}$ inch. Disturbed soil, South Dakota. *O. grandis:* Manner of growth similar. Petals 1–$1\frac{1}{2}$ inches, deep golden-yellow. Sandy soil. Kansas and Oklahoma. *O. biennis* (1–7 feet): Leaves lanceolate. Flowers in a tall terminal inflorescence, commonly with short side-branches; gland-tipped hairs present. Petals $\frac{1}{2}$–1 inch long. Pods narrow, tapering. Mostly dry open soil, North Dakota to Oklahoma. *Plate 121. O. strigosa:* Similar; densely grayish with hairs lying flat or standing out. Gland-tipped hairs rare in inflorescence. Kansas and Oklahoma. *O. rhombipetala* (1–3 feet): Stem commonly silky. Leaves ovate or oblong, the basal perhaps toothed. Flowers many in a spike; petals about $\frac{1}{2}$ inch. Pod generally curved. In sandy places, from North Dakota to Oklahoma. *Plate 122.*

O. HOOKERI (1–5 feet) is a handsome and varied assemblage of plants, with petals, in a many-flowered inflorescence, 1–2 inches long, commonly

PLATE 122

Oenothera lavandulaefolia

Korling

Oenothera rhombipetala

Horne

Oenothera greggii

Koch

Oenothera serrulata

Johnson

Oenothera missouriensis

Henze

Oenothera brevipes

P. R. Ferguson

Oenothera hookeri

Rickett

notched, becoming orange or red in age. The plants are generally branched, with spreading branches turning upwards. The leaf-blades have generally lanceolate blades, commonly finely toothed, the basal long-stalked. The pod is angled and tapering.

June to September: mostly in moist soil in the mountains from Washington to Idaho and Colorado, and southward to eastern California, Nevada, and Utah, and in Kansas and Oklahoma. *Plate 122.* Some varieties are said to form spreading and matted stems.

O. longissima (4–10 feet) has reddish stems with a fine grayish down; leaves gray-green, narrow, wavy-edged, finely toothed, the blades up to 8 inches long, tapering to stalks. Petals pale yellow becoming orange or reddish, about $1\frac{1}{2}$ inches long and wide. Pod four-faced. In wet places from southeastern California to Utah and Colorado. *O. jamesii*, in Oklahoma, is similar. About 5 feet. Stem finely white-downy; leaves with hairs lying flat; those on the stem finely toothed.

II. *Species whose stigma is a slightly lobed or four-sided disk.*

O. LAVANDULAEFOLIA (2–8 inches) is somewhat shrubby. Stems and leaves are grayish with fine hairs lying flat. The leaves are narrow, less than an inch long. The petals are rather diamond-shaped, turning reddish as they age, $\frac{1}{2}$–1 inch long.

May to July: on dry soil from Wyoming to Utah and Colorado and from Nebraska to Oklahoma. *Plate 122.* Some botanists have suggested that this is a variety of the more southern *O. hartwegii*, a taller plant with narrow leaves and not grayish, minutely glandular. It is found in Oklahoma.

O. GREGGII (4–12 inches) is somewhat shrubby, and rather hairy. The leaves are very narrow, or lanceolate, up to an inch long, with or without small teeth. The petals are diamond-shaped, up to an inch long.

April to June: on dry stony or grassy slopes in Kansas, Colorado, and Oklahoma. *Plate 122. O. fendleri*: Similar but not hairy, bright green. Leaves lanceolate, $\frac{2}{5}$–$1\frac{1}{5}$ inches. Petals $\frac{3}{5}$–1 inch. Kansas and Oklahoma. *Plate 121. O. serrulata* (less than 8 inches): Hoary. Floral tube funnel-shaped. Petals not more than $\frac{1}{4}$ inch. Pod cylindric, four-angled, narrow. North Dakota to Oklahoma. *Plate 122.*

III. *Species whose stigma is a round disk, not lobed.* Most of these are morning-bloomers.

A. Species with yellow petals. See also *O. clavaeformis* and *O. minor* in B. These are all species west of the continental divide.

1. The first four of these have petals $\frac{1}{3}$ inch long or longer. See also *O. walkeri* under 2.

O. BREVIPES (1–30 inches) has leaves up to 6 inches long, most of them forming a rosette at the base of the stem. The flowers are in a raceme which may be bent down when the flowers are in bud, or (in the subspecies illustrated, south of our area) the buds individually drooping.

March to May: on dry slopes in southern Nevada and southwestern Utah. *Plate 122.* A variable species growing mostly south of our range. In one variety the petals are less than $\frac{1}{4}$ inch long. The leaves are variously toothed and hairy, and on some plants the veins are red on the under side.

SUN-CUP, O. HETERANTHA, forms tufts of leaves 2–8 inches long, variously shaped, and wavy-edged, toothed or not; many lobed or cleft near the base. The flowers have practically no stalks, but the threadlike floral tube is 1–4 inches long. The pod is $\frac{1}{2}$–$\frac{3}{4}$ inch long, four-angled, slender-pointed. The whole plant is smooth.

April to July: on meadows and by streams from plains to mountains from eastern Washington to the Sierra Nevada and eastward to Montana and Colorado. *Plate 123.*

O. graciliflora is similar in manner of growth, forming tufts; or it may have horizontal branches an inch long or longer. The leaves are very narrow, with or without small teeth. Petals $\frac{1}{3}$–$\frac{1}{2}$ inch, notched. Pod ovate, leathery, $\frac{1}{3}$–$\frac{1}{2}$ inch, four-winged in the upper half. Southeastern Oregon.

O. TANACETIFOLIA has no leafy stem above ground, the rather hairy, deeply pinnately cleft leaves all at ground level, up to 8 inches long. The petals are $\frac{2}{5}$–$\frac{2}{3}$ inch long; they may turn purplish in age. The four-sided capsule is slightly winged.

June to August: in moist meadows, on river-banks in sagebrush plains, in pine forests from Washington to the Sierra Nevada and eastward to Montana. *Plate 123.*

The more western species *O. dentata* has one variety that may be found in western Montana. Plant bushy, 2–8 inches, leaves narrow, petals $\frac{2}{5}$–$\frac{2}{5}$ inch, pod narrow.

2. The remaining yellow-flowered species have petals not more than $\frac{1}{3}$ inch long.

O. BREVIFLORA forms tufts, lacking a leafy stem above ground, the leaves deeply pinnately cleft into many unequal sharp lobes, with or without teeth. The petals are $\frac{1}{4}$–$\frac{1}{3}$ inch long. The capsule is rather four-sided, tapering to the tip.

May to July: in dry meadows and on stream-

PLATE 123

Oenothera heterantha   *Spurr*

Clarkia rhomboidea   *Myrick*

Oenothera scapoidea   *Nichols*

Clarkia pulchella   *Dye*

Oenothera andina   *Myrick*

Oenothera clavaeformis   *Roberts*

Oenothera multijuga   *Roberts*

Clarkia purpurea   *Reineking*

Oenothera tanacetifolia   *Hull*

banks from eastern Oregon to northeastern California and eastward to Montana and Wyoming, at moderate altitudes.

O. palmeri grows in a rather similar way, with horizontal branches which form tufts at their ends. The leaves have narrow blades which taper to a stalk which expands suddenly where it meets the stem. Petals are $\frac{1}{8}$–$\frac{1}{5}$ inch long. Pod four-angled, winged in the upper half. Southeastern Oregon to California and Nevada.

O. CONTORTA (2–10 inches) has slender, leafy stems.

The leaves are very narrow, short-stalked, finely toothed, up to an inch long. The petals are about $\frac{1}{10}$–$\frac{1}{8}$ inch long.

May and June: in sandy soil from Washington to California and eastward to Montana, Wyoming, and Utah.

O. andina (1–6 inches) is found over much the same range. Leaves are few or none on the lower parts of stems and branches. They are narrow, up to an inch long or a little longer, lacking teeth. The flowers form a rather close inflorescence; the petals not more than about $\frac{1}{10}$ inch. May to July: in dry soil (especially sandy). *Plate 123*. *O. hilgardii* is very similar to the preceding, by some treated as a variety of it. The petals may reach $\frac{1}{6}$ inch.

O. SCAPOIDEA (1–18 inches) has leaves mostly in a basal rosette, up to 8 inches long, with side segments in some subspecies. Stem-leaves are much smaller. The petals are $\frac{1}{10}$–$\frac{1}{4}$ inch long. The pods (up to $1\frac{1}{2}$ inches long) are commonly curved.

May and June: on clay and gravel from Oregon to Idaho and Wyoming and southward to Nevada, Utah, and western Colorado.

O. multijuga (to 5 feet) has ovate leaves, mostly pinnately cleft, up to a foot long, at and near the ground. The petals are $\frac{1}{6}$–$\frac{1}{3}$ inch long. The seed-pod is narrow, $\frac{2}{5}$–$1\frac{2}{5}$ inches long. In deserts and cañons from western Colorado to eastern California. *Plate 123*.

O. parryi is similar and is considered by some a variety of *O. scapoidea*. It is taller, hairy, with ovate leaves. *O. walkeri*: Stem slender, hairy, to 2 feet. Leaves at the base and on the stem, those at the base double-toothed. Petals in Colorado $\frac{1}{20}$–$\frac{1}{8}$ inch; in eastern California $\frac{1}{8}$–$\frac{1}{4}$ inch. In rocky places. *O. eastwoodae* (1–12 inches): Succulent. Leaves mostly basal, with or without a few teeth; the blades from heart-shaped to lanceolate with the broader part out, to 3 inches long. Inflorescence drooping. Petals $\frac{1}{4}$–$\frac{1}{3}$ inch, red-dotted at the base. Clay and sand, west-central Colorado, eastern Utah.

B. Species with round, unlobed stigma, and petals not yellow.

The ten species under this head may be arranged in three groups by the shape of the seed-pod: whether club-shaped (i.e. broader in the upper or outer half); cylindric (of approximately uniform diameter throughout); or tapering to the tip. Of course, if seed-pods are not available, one must search all three groups.

1. Species with club-shaped capsules.

O. CLAVAEFORMIS (1–30 inches) branches mostly at the base. The principal leaves are in a basal rosette, pinnately divided on some plants, up to 8 inches long; the upper smaller. The inflorescence is bent down. The petals are yellow or white, bent down, $\frac{1}{20}$–$\frac{1}{3}$ inch long. The stigma is greenish. The pod is up to $1\frac{1}{2}$ inches long, straight or curved.

May to July: on sandy flats and washes from southern Oregon to California and eastward to southwestern Idaho and Nevada. *Plate 123*. Very variable in our area in the number of leaf-segments (none in one subspecies) and in the presence or absence of hairs and glands. Petals yellow in eastern California and from southeastern Oregon to southwestern Idaho.

O. pterosperma: Stems slender, 2–6 inches, hairy in the lower parts, glandular above. Leaves up to $1\frac{1}{2}$ inches. Petals up to $\frac{1}{10}$ inch, white with yellow base, turning rose. Well-drained slopes, from southeastern Oregon to western Utah and southeastern California.

O. heterochroma (4–36 inches): Glandular-downy or smooth in the upper parts. Leaf-blades undivided, unlobed, wavy-edged, up to 3 inches on stalks 2 inches long. Petals 1–2 inches, lavender, commonly with a yellow base. Pod glandular, $\frac{1}{8}$–$\frac{1}{2}$ inch. Eastern California, western Nevada. *O. megalantha* (1–30 inches): Similar. Leaf-blades triangular, toothed, to 2 inches. Petals about $\frac{2}{3}$ inch, lavender, darker-dotted near the base. Southern Nevada.

2. Species with cylindric pods.

O. BOOTHII (6–16 inches) varies greatly in type of hairiness, from glandular-downy or glandular-hairy to smooth. The leaves are near the base or well distributed on the stem, the blades ovate or lanceolate, mostly without teeth, the lower stalked. The inflorescence is spikelike, the flowers drooping in bud. The petals range from white to red, $\frac{1}{8}$–$\frac{3}{8}$ inch long. The capsule is thicker at the base; it may be twisted or merely curved.

June and July: from eastern Washington to eastern California and eastward to Idaho, Nevada, and Utah. *O. nevadensis* (1–2 inches): Tufts, or prostrate stems to 6 inches long, forming tufts at their tips. Leaves narrowly lanceolate, without teeth, to $1\frac{1}{2}$ inches long. Inflorescence spikelike, with flowers mostly on one side. Petals white, to $\frac{1}{5}$ inch. Dry places, western Nevada.

3. Species with pods tapering to the tip.

O. MINOR (2–12 inches) is finely hoary, with basal leaves almost without teeth, the blades to $1\frac{1}{2}$ inches long, on slender stalks; the stem-leaves smaller and narrower. The flowers are borne singly in the axils. The petals are pale yellow or white, $\frac{1}{10}$ inch long. The pods are generally twisted.

June and July: on dry flats and slopes from eastern Washington and Oregon to northeastern California, southern Wyoming, western Colorado, and Nevada.

O. pygmaea (1–12 inches): Similar. Flowers in a one-sided spike. Pod almost straight. Eastern Washington and Oregon. O. chamaenerioides (4–20 inches): Stems commonly reddish, somewhat glandular and sticky. Basal leaf-blades 2–4 inches, ovate or lanceolate, on slender stalks. Flowers in a raceme; petals white, about $\frac{1}{8}$ inch. Pod very narrow. Deserts, eastern California, southern Nevada, southwestern Utah. O. refracta (6–16 inches): Similar. Petals $\frac{1}{6}$–$\frac{1}{3}$ inch, nearly round, white. Pod very narrow, straight or curved. Deserts, eastern California, southern Nevada.

ZAUSCHNERIA

One species of *Zauschneria* is in our range.

Z. GARRETTII (6–12 inches) has leathery leaves, hairy or almost smooth, veiny and sharp-toothed, $\frac{2}{5}$–$1\frac{1}{5}$ inches long. The flowers, in a spike, horizontally spreading, are bright red, petals, sepals, floral tube (an inch long) all the same color. The four petals are cleft into two. Eight stamens. The seed-pod is four-angled.

June and July: in rocky places from western Wyoming through Utah and Nevada to southern California.

CLARKIA

The flowers of *Clarkia* are in a leafy raceme atop the stem. They have four sepals, generally bent back and joined in pairs or all joined at one side; four petals, in our species from pink to red, rose, crimson, and lavender; eight stamens (four of which may bear no pollen); the color of their tips may be useful in identification; and a four-lobed stigma. The leaves are undivided and unlobed.

A number of handsome species are grown in gardens; some under the name *Godetia*. The species in our group II might be placed in *Godetia*; but botanically it is impossible to make a clear separation into two genera. Some late-spring-flowering species are known as farewell-to-spring.

I. *Species whose petals have a narrow stalk-like base. A "claw" in botanical jargon.*

C. RHOMBOIDEA (1–4 feet) has broadly lanceolate leaves, 1–3 inches long, their width generally less than one-third of their length. The petals are not more than $\frac{1}{2}$ inch long, pinkish-lavender with or without darker flecks, generally red at the base, commonly very slightly three-lobed, with a pair of teeth on the "claw." Eight stamens, the tips lavender or crimson.

May to July: on dry slopes from eastern Washington to the Great Basin. *Plate 123*.

C. PULCHELLA (to 20 inches) has narrowly lanceolate leaves, or some broadest at the tip, with or without small teeth, to $2\frac{3}{4}$ inches long. The flowers are few, the buds drooping; the petals lavender or rose, three-lobed, the middle lobe the widest; the "claw" with a pair of short teeth. Four stamens with pollen, tipped with white or lavender.

May and June: in open ground from Washington east of the Cascade Mountains to southeastern Oregon and eastward to western Montana. *Plate 123*.

II. *Species whose petals have no narrow, stalk-like base.*

C. PURPUREA (4–24 inches) has leaves 1–3 inches long, very narrow. The flower-buds are erect. The fan-shaped or elliptic petals range from red to crimson, lavender, and purple, the paler ones commonly with a wedge- or shield-shaped crimson spot; they may be pointed or notched at the tip, and commonly finely toothed. The tips of the stamens range from cream to crimson. The pollen may be deposited directly upon the stigma by the curving of the stalks of the stamens.

April to June: in open ground from Washington to California. *Plate 123*. Because of the great variation in color and marking of petals, many subspecies have been named, and by some have been treated as species. The plants are common, and have many names.

C. GRACILIS (6–24 inches) has narrowly lanceolate leaves (their length about ten times their width). The whole inflorescence droops in bud, becoming gradually erect as the flowers open. The petals are nearly an inch long, pink or lavender, with or without a red spot, more or less fan-shaped. The stamens are tipped with cream or yellow, their stalks lavender.

June and July: in open places from central and southeastern Washington to southern Oregon and northeastern California.

C. lassenensis is similar. The capsules have eight grooves and are largest at the middle. From southeastern Oregon to northeastern California.

BOISDUVALIA

The leaves of *Boisduvalia* are undivided and unlobed, without stalks; the upper borne singly, the lower commonly paired. The small flowers are in the axils of leaves or form a leafy spike. The four petals are two-lobed, from white or pink to red or crimson. There are eight stamens. The stigma has four short lobes. The floral tube tends to be funnel-shaped.

B. DENSIFLORA (1–4 feet) is commonly hairy. The leaves are lanceolate, about 2 inches long, with or without small teeth. The flowers range from white to pink and crimson, the four small petals (less than $\frac{1}{2}$ inch long) cleft nearly half-way. The tube is short.

May to August: in moist places from Washington to California and eastward to Idaho and Nevada. *Plate 124.*

B. STRICTA (4–20 inches) is grayish with soft hairs. The leaves are narrow, up to 2 inches long, with or without a few teeth. The petals are rose, violet, or pale pink with darker veins, $\frac{1}{20}-\frac{1}{8}$ inch long.

May to July: in moist places from Washington and Idaho to southeastern California and Nevada.

B. GLABELLA (4–12 inches) has slender, spreading branches which curve up. The leaves are lanceolate or ovate, up to $\frac{3}{4}$ inch long, finely toothed, almost smooth. The flowers are crowded, with leafy bracts. The pink or purplish-red petals are $\frac{1}{10}-\frac{1}{6}$ inch long.

May to August: on drying mud, by pools dry in summer, and in other such places from eastern Washington to North and South Dakota and southward to southern California, Nevada, and Utah.

GAURA

Only two species of the largely southern genus *Gaura* are widespread in our range; one is eastern, reaching the high plains; the rest come from Texas into Oklahoma and Kansas. They are mostly slender plants ranging from a few inches to 4 or even 6 or 10 feet tall, with leaves borne singly on the stem and flowers in a terminal inflorescence, generally a spike. The flowers open in the evening. The four pink petals stand at one side (being thus bilateral in symmetry). There are normally eight stamens. A curious feature is a small cup-like ring around the style just beneath the stigma. The stigma is four-lobed. The fruit is nutlike and does not open.

The genus is easily recognized, but to distinguish species the petals and other parts must be measured.

I.   *Species with white, pink, or red petals, mostly not more than $\frac{1}{4}$ inch long.*
     Our two wide-ranging species are in this group; the other two are not found west of the Rockies.
     The distinction between this and group II is not always clear. The white or whitish petals generally turn red as they age.

G. PARVIFLORA (8–80 inches) is named for its small (*parvi-*) petals, about $\frac{1}{12}$ inch long, no longer than the sepals. The stamens have rose stalks and reddish tips. The plants are softly hairy. The seed-pod is $\frac{1}{4}-\frac{2}{5}$ inch long.

April to October: by streams and in waste ground and disturbed soil from eastern Washington to the Rocky Mountains and adjacent plains and southward to California, Nevada, and Utah. *Plate 124.*

G. COCCINEA (4–20 inches) varies from smooth to roughly hairy. The leaves of some varieties may have crisped or wavy-toothed edges. The petals are $\frac{1}{8}-\frac{1}{4}$ inch long. The tips of the stamens are yellow or red, on white or yellowish stalks. The seed-pod is angular, in our varieties $\frac{1}{5}-\frac{1}{4}$ inch long.

April to September: in grassy and stony places and deserts practically throughout our range. *Plate 124.*

G. BIENNIS (1–10 feet) is softly hairy or downy (the leaves may be almost smooth), much branched, with a basal rosette of leaves up to a foot long and widest between middle and tip, and lanceolate stem-leaves up to 4 inches long, all with short, flattish stalks. The sepals are generally red, bent back in pairs. The petals are white, turning pink in age, about $\frac{1}{5}$ inch long, stalked. The stamens have whitish stalks and

PLATE 124

Ludwigia palustris   *D. Richards*

Ludwigia alternifolia   *Johnson*

Gaura biennis   *McDowell*

Stenosiphon linifolius   *Scribner*

Gaura coccinea   *Koch*

Gaura villosa   *Scribner*

Boisduvalia densiflora   *Mackintosh*

Ludwigia peploides   *Johnson*

Gaura parviflora   *Koch*

white or pink tips. The seed-pod is angular and ribbed $\frac{1}{6}$–$\frac{1}{3}$ inch long.

June to October: on prairies and meadows from Nebraska to Oklahoma. *Plate 124.*

G. hexandra (stems 1–2 feet long) is characterized by three sepals, three petals, and six stamens. The petals are $\frac{1}{8}$–$\frac{1}{6}$ inch long, turning red in age. These curious plants may not be a real species, but forms of other species. This needs further investigation. In our range only in Oklahoma.

II. *Species with white or pink petals, mostly $\frac{1}{3}$ inch long or longer.*

These are found in our range only east of the Rockies.

G. VILLOSA (2–4 feet) is somewhat shrubby, with several stems, which, with their branches, are all rather hairy or hoary. The leaves commonly have small teeth on the crisped, wavy edges. The petals are white, turning red, about $\frac{1}{3}$ inch long. The stamens have red tips. The seed pod is wing-angled, about $\frac{1}{3}$ inch long.

July and August: in sandy places in Kansas and Oklahoma. *Plate 124.*

G. neomexicana (2–3 feet) is, as its name indicates, a New-Mexican species. It extends north into Colorado. It is not very branched. The stems may be softly hairy. The pink petals are $\frac{1}{3}$–$\frac{2}{5}$ inch long.

G. sinuata (1–3 feet) is smooth, and branched. The leaves on the stem are crowded; they vary from very narrow to lanceolate. The white petals, $\frac{1}{3}$–$\frac{2}{5}$ inch long, turn red in age. The stamens have reddish tips. In Oklahoma. *G. suffulta* (8–30 inches) may be found in southern Oklahoma. The stems are softly hairy. The basal leaves are pinnately cleft, those on the stem perhaps wavy-edged. The petals are white turning pink, about $\frac{2}{5}$ inch long. The stamen-tips are red.

STENOSIPHON

The genus *Stenosiphon* comprises a single species.

S. LINIFOLIUS (2–10 feet) bears crowded lanceolate leaves mostly 1–2 inches long. The flowers are in dense narrow spikes, the stem, and the flowers themselves, beset with glands. The flowers are crowded, with four white petals $\frac{1}{5}$ inch long. The genus is named for the very narrow (*steno-*) floral tube (*siphon*); this is threadlike, whitish. The fruit is nut-like, not opening at maturity, and containing a single seed.

May to July (and later): on limestone outcrops and in sand and clay from south-central Nebraska to Oklahoma. *Plate 124.*

PRIMROSE-WILLOWS AND FALSE LOOSESTRIFES (LUDWIGIA)

Most plants of *Ludwigia* grow in wet places, some floating on water. The leaves of most species are borne singly; they are mostly undivided and unlobed. The flowers are generally yellow (but a few species lack petals). They are borne in the axils in our species, generally singly and without stalks. There are four or five petals, the same number of stamens or twice as many, and a generally unlobed stigma.

Plants with eight or ten stamens have long been treated as a separate genus, *Jussiaea*; but modern opinion unites them with *Ludwigia*. The chief difference is the number of stamens.

This is an eastern genus, only one species found in our range west of the Rocky Mountains.

I. *Species with four or five stamens.*

These are the "false loosestrifes"; the "true" loosestrifes are *Lysimachia*; other loosestrifes are *Lythrum*.

L. PALUSTRIS has a creeping or floating stem (4–20 inches long) bearing paired, stalked leaves with lanceolate or elliptic blades up to an inch long (cf. *L. peploides*). The minute flowers have no petals; the sepals are not more than $\frac{1}{20}$ inch long. The seed-pod is nearly cylindric (slightly four sided), up to $\frac{1}{5}$ inch long and nearly as thick, with four green stripes.

June to September: in shallow water and mud throughout our range (and most of the United States). *Plate 124.*

L. repens, in our range only in southeastern Kansas, is similar, with diamond-shaped leaf-blades up to almost 2 inches long, and four minute yellow or reddish petals which soon fall. Seed-pod $\frac{1}{8}$–$\frac{1}{4}$ inch long.

L. alternifolia (1–4 feet) is erect, smooth, with short-stalked, lanceolate leaves borne singly. Sepals and petals are about $\frac{2}{5}$ inch long. The seed-pod is almost a cube, with four sharp angles, about $\frac{1}{4}$ inch long, crowned with the four sepals. In Kansas and Oklahoma, and eastward, *Plate 124.* *L. glandulosa* (1–3 feet) is bushy, the stems at first prostrate then erect, densely leafy, the leaves borne singly. Petals are lacking, but four glands are present in their place. The capsule is almost cylindric, to $\frac{1}{3}$ inch long. In Kansas and Oklahoma, and the southeastern states. *L. polycarpa* (to 3 feet), only in Kansas in our range, has lanceolate leaves borne singly. There may be minute greenish petals or none.

PLATE 125

Epilobium paniculatum   *Korling*

Epilobium obcordatum   *Johnson*

Epilobium coloratum   *Gottscho*

Epilobium adenocaulon   *Scribner*

Epilobium minutum   *Spellenberg*

Epilobium latifolium   *Mary Ferguson*

Epilobium palustre   *Gottscho*

Epilobium angustifolium   *Fulling*

II.   *Species with eight or ten stamens.*
    These are the plants formerly named *Jussiaea*. They are in our range only in our southeastern states.

PRIMROSE-WILLOW, L. PEPLOIDES, of course no
    relative of primroses or willows, floats or creeps on shallow water or mud, bearing leaves singly, their blades up to 4 inches long. There are five sepals and five yellow petals $\frac{1}{3}$–1 inch long. The stigma is shallowly lobed. The seed-pod is cylindric, slightly five-angled, up to nearly 2 inches long.

June to October: in and by pools, ditches, swamps, and other wet places in Kansas and Oklahoma, and eastward; and far southward, to South America. *Plate 124.*
    L. decurrens (16–100 inches), in our range only in southeastern Kansas, is also known as primrose-willow. The leaf-bases are continuous with sharp angles running down the stem below them; this is the meaning of "decurrent." There are four yellow petals about $\frac{1}{5}$ inch long. The pistil becomes a four-angled seed-pod $\frac{1}{2}$–$\frac{3}{4}$ inch long. In wet places, in the southern states and South America.

EPILOBIUM

The best-known species of *Epilobium* are tall plants with showy rose-magenta or lavender flowers. There are also a larger number of small plants with very small flowers. The leaves mostly have small teeth or none, and are not lobed or divided. There are four sepals, four petals which in most species are notched or cleft, and eight stamens. The floral tube is short. But the seed-pods are slender, rodlike (well shown in some of the illustrations on plate 125); they are sometimes mistaken for flower-stalks that have lost the floral parts.

I.   *The large-flowered species (petals more than $\frac{1}{2}$ inch long).*

FIREWEED, E. ANGUSTIFOLIUM (4 inches–6 feet,
    or taller), is familiar throughout most of the United States. The flowers are in tall spires. The unopened buds at the tip point down but rise as they open. The petals range from $\frac{2}{5}$ to $\frac{4}{5}$ inch; they are not notched or lobed; the color varies from rose-magenta to lilac, purple, or even white. The style bends downward. The stigma has four lobes. The numerous lanceolate leaves are borne singly.
    July to September: in disturbed soil, especially after fires (whence the name), throughout our range; also in Eurasia. *Plate 125.* With such a range it is not surprising that a number of varieties have been found. In England known as willow-herb.

E. OBCORDATUM is low, matted, the stems up to 6
    inches long, the leaves elliptic or ovate, $\frac{1}{4}$–1 inch long, in pairs. The flowers are borne singly in the axils. The rose-magenta petals are two-lobed.
    July to September: mostly at high altitudes from northeastern and central Oregon to central Idaho and eastern California and Nevada. *Plate 125.*

E. LATIFOLIUM forms dense mats with horizontal or
    arching stems 4–20 inches long. The leaves are lanceolate or ovate, in pairs or nearly so, rather thick,

1–3$\frac{1}{2}$ inches long. The flowers are in short racemes with leafy bracts. The petals range from white to magenta, mostly $\frac{1}{2}$–1 inch long, not notched or lobed.
    July and August: in wet rocky places generally at high altitudes from Alaska to the Sierra Nevada and eastward to Idaho, Montana, and northeastern Oregon. *Plate 125.*
    E. luteum, readily distinguished by its yellow petals, may possibly cross our western boundary in the Cascade Mountains. The leaves are in pairs, with flowers in their axils.

II.   *The small-flowered species (petals mostly less than $\frac{2}{5}$ inch long).*
    These are confusing species, differing only in minor details, and variously merged by different botanists.
    The leaves are in pairs except in the first.

E. PANICULATUM (1–7 feet) is distinguished by
    having at least most of its leaves borne singly (the lowermost generally in pairs). They are narrow, finely toothed, short-stalked, up to 2 inches long, with short stalks, and bunches of smaller leaves in the axils. The flowers are in a widely branching inflorescence (a "panicle"). The petals range from white to pink and rose; they are deeply cleft, $\frac{1}{12}$–$\frac{1}{2}$ inch long.
    June to September: in dry open places from Washington to North and South Dakota and southward to California and Colorado. *Plate 125.*
    E. suffruticosum (4–12 inches) is somewhat shrubby, with many branching stems extending horizontally and slanting upwards. The leaves are lanceolate or elliptic, not toothed, $\frac{1}{2}$–1 inch long. The few flowers are in the upper axils; the petals pale yellow, $\frac{1}{5}$–$\frac{2}{5}$ inch long, one larger than the others. On gravelly stream-banks and in moist rocky places from central Idaho to Montana and Wyoming.

E. GLABERRIMUM (4–24 inches) has several unbranched stems, bending up from a horizontal

PLATE 126

Epilobium hornemannii *Jarrett*

Epilobium alpinum *Scribner*

Pyrola picta *Scribner*

Pyrola asarifolia *Korling*

Circaea alpina *Hesselberg*

Scribner

Epilobium glaberrimum *Johnson*

Epilobium glandulosum

Epilobium leptocarpum *Korling*

base. It is smooth, with a bloom. The leaves are lanceolate or ovate, up to 2 inches long. The flowers are in the axils of the somewhat smaller upper leaves. The petals are almost white or crimson, $\frac{1}{6}$–$\frac{1}{3}$ inch long, notched.

July and August: on stream-banks and generally in moist spots from Canada to California and eastward to western Montana, Idaho, and Utah. *Plate 126*.

E. minutum (2–12 inches) has rather succulent, narrowly lanceolate leaves less than an inch long. The flowers are in the upper axils, the petals white or lavender, deeply cleft petals $\frac{1}{12}$–$\frac{1}{6}$ inch long. In dry soil from Washington to Montana and southward to California. *Plate 125*.

E. PALUSTRE (4–16 inches) has curved hairs on the stem. The leaves are lanceolate, $\frac{1}{2}$–2 inches long. There may only be one flower, at the tip; or there may be several. The tip of the stem droops before the flowers open. The petals are white, pink, or lilac, about $\frac{1}{5}$ inch long, notched.

June to August: in bogs and marshes from the Cascades in Washington eastward to North and South Dakota and southward to Oregon and Colorado. *Plate 125*. *E. leptophyllum* differs in height (8–40 inches), narrower leaves, tip of the stem not drooping, petals white or pink, $\frac{1}{6}$–$\frac{1}{4}$ inch long. Recently this has been included in *E. palustre*. *E. coloratum* (20–40 inches) is bushy, and downy. The leaves are narrowly lanceolate, 2–6 inches long, toothed, short-stalked. Inflorescence much branched, with many flowers which may droop. Petals pink, about $\frac{1}{8}$ inch long, notched. In wet ground from North Dakota to Kansas. The hairs on the seeds are cinnamon. *Plate 125*.

E. ADENOCAULON (1–4 feet) has ovate or lanceolate, toothed leaf-blades 1–3 inches long, on very short flat stalks; they may be downy. The numerous flowers are in the axils or at the ends of many short leafy branches; these are glandular. The petals are white, pink, or crimson, deeply notched, about $\frac{1}{8}$ inch long. The hairs on the seeds are white.

July to September: in moist ground practically throughout the country. *Plate 125*. By one authority this is merged (as a variety) with the following species, *E. glandulosum*. By another it is included in the (otherwise) western coastal species *E. watsonii*** Certainly the differences among all these species are slight. *E. watsonii* lacks glands and has longer petals (to $\frac{2}{5}$ inch). *E. glandulosum* (1–3 feet) lacks leaf-stalks and overwinters by certain bulb-like branches of the rhizomes. Petals crimson, 2–4 inches, notched. In Washington

---

* If either course is followed, it must take the earlier name, *E. glandulosum* or *E. watsonii*.

and Oregon, and through the Rockies to Colorado. *Plate 126*. *E. ciliatum* is another member of this complex group. It lacks glands, is less branched, and has pale green, elliptic or oval leaves which taper to slender stalks; they may be borne singly. Petals $\frac{1}{8}$–$\frac{1}{4}$ inch long, white or pink. In damp ground, scattered through our area. *E. leptocarpum* (2–8 inches) is marked by a fine down extending down the stem in lines from the leaf-base (it is otherwise smooth). Leaves broadly lanceolate or oval, blunt, $\frac{1}{2}$–1$\frac{1}{2}$ inches long, with a few teeth, short-stalked. Flowers few, crowded near the tips of leafy branches; petals pale pink, not more than $\frac{1}{8}$ inch. Hairs on seeds cinnamon. In Oregon and Washington. This, with a number of other supposed species (which may be perfectly valid), is also now included in *E. glandulosum*. *Plate 126*. *E. boreale* (1–2 feet) has stems with few or no branches. Leaves ovate, tapering to a sharp point, manytoothed, some with short stalks, the blades 1–2$\frac{1}{2}$ inches long. Petals rose, about $\frac{1}{5}$ inch. In cold damp ground, in Montana, Colorado, Washington, and Oregon. One botanist has distinguished our plants from those of the Old World, making them a variety of *E. glandulosum*.

E. ALPINUM (2–12 inches), like the preceding species, is a complex of closely related plants which have by many botanists been treated as distinct species. (Just which is the correct disposition of any of these is perhaps more a matter of taste than of science.) They are low, commonly matted, with stems erect or bending up, generally unbranched, rather smooth. The leaves range from ovate to very narrow, with or without short stalks, up to 2 inches long, with or without small teeth. The flowers are few, with petals from white to pink or lilac, $\frac{1}{8}$–$\frac{1}{2}$ inch long, notched.

June to September: on moist banks, rock slopes, mountain meadows throughout western North America. *Plate 126*. The above description includes (among various supposed species): *E. anagallidifolium*, which forms dense tufts up to 6 inches tall, with spreading shoots; the leaves elliptic, blunt, less than 1 inch long, not toothed; petals about $\frac{1}{5}$ inch. In damp moss or on wet rock throughout our area. *E. hornemannii*, in tufts or mats, up to 10 inches tall, with stem-leaves up to 2 inches long, tapering both ways, with few teeth; petals $\frac{1}{4}$–$\frac{2}{5}$ inch. On wet rocks, etc. throughout our range. *Plate 126*. *E. lactiflorum* (4–16 inches), with short prostrate branches bearing small leaves, and many erect stems mostly unbranched and smooth. Leaves few, thin, pale, almost toothless, 1–2 inches, the upper commonly borne singly. Flowers few, single, in the upper axils; petals white or pink, $\frac{1}{8}$–$\frac{1}{6}$ inch. On stream-banks and other moist places, mostly alpine, throughout our range.

GAYOPHYTUM

The leaves of *Gayophytum* are so narrow, the plants so weedy, the flowers generally so minute that the amateur naturalist will scarcely notice the genus. The flowers are in the axils, commonly in small groups at and near the ends of hairlike branches.

Because of the necessity for microscopic technique in distinguishing species, it is not surprising that even professional botanists have jumbled the names and misidentified the plants. Some species seem to have crossed, yielding plants of intermediate character. Maximum size would be useful — if all plants attained it. The following notes cannot pretend to be a definitive treatment, but may perhaps enable a sufficiently painstaking reader to put a tentative name on a plant.

I. *Plants that branch near the base, the branches themselves not again branched.*
    The petals are not more than $\frac{1}{25}$ inch long.

The flowers are borne along the branches. The seed-pods are not lumpy. *G. humile* does not exceed 6 inches in height. *G. racemosum* may reach 16 inches.

II. *Plants whose branches are themselves forked or bear branches.*
    The flowers are not near the base of the plant. Seed-pods are commonly lumpy (constricted between seeds). *G. heterozygum*: Perhaps 30 inches tall; petals $\frac{1}{8}$–$\frac{1}{6}$ inch long; seed-pod conspicuously lumpy. *G. decipiens*: Not more than 1 foot tall; petals about $\frac{1}{15}$ inch; pod slightly constricted. *G. ramosissimum*: Up to 20 inches tall; profusely branched; petals less than $\frac{1}{15}$ inch; pod scarcely constricted. *G. diffusum*. Two subspecies, one with petals up to $\frac{1}{8}$ inch, the other with petals $\frac{1}{8}$–$\frac{1}{3}$ inch; up to 2 feet tall; branched near the base. *Plate 127.*

CIRCAEA

Two species of *Circaea* are in our range. They are small plants, their leaves stalked, with ovate or lanceolate blades. The flowers are in a slender raceme. They are unique among our *Onagraceae* in having two sepals, two petals (cleft or notched), two stamens. The ovary with surrounding flower-base forms a small nut-like fruit covered with hooked bristles. As it matures, the stalk turns down.

C. ALPINA (4–20 inches) has ovate leaf-blades, commonly sharply toothed, scarcely 3 inches long. The petals are not more than $\frac{1}{10}$ inch long, cleft

deeply enough so that they seem to be four.

June to September: in moist woods mostly in mountains throughout our range except Kansas and Oklahoma. *Plate 126.* Variable in leaf-toothing and other details.

Enchanter's-nightshade, *C. lutetiana* (8–36 inches), is commoner eastward; in our range from North Dakota to Oklahoma. The leaves, lanceolate or ovate, are up to 6 inches long, wavy-edged but not toothed, the blades $\frac{1}{10}$–$\frac{1}{7}$ inch long. In woods. *Lutetiana* means "of Paris"; our plants are a variety of the magical herb of medieval Parisian botanists.

THE SHINLEAF FAMILY (PYROLACEAE)

The shinleaf family is a group of rather small plants, some evergreen, some without green color at any time, all generally woodland plants. The leaves are undivided. There are usually five sepals, five petals, ten stamens, and one pistil with five chambers in the ovary. One distinctive feature is that the pollen-bearing heads of the stamens discharge the pollen through tubes in the end. Many of these characteristics are shared

by the heath family; the two families are often merged.

I. *Plants with green leaves.*
    Pyrola: leaves at and near the base, flowers along the end part of the stem (in a raceme).
    Moneses: leaves only at or near the base, and a single flower at the summit.
    Chimaphila: leaves on the stem, flowers hanging at the ends of stalks at or near the tip.

II. *Plants lacking green color.*

Monotropa: white, red, or tawny, with one or several flowers on the bent-over tip of the stem.

Pterospora: purplish-brown, clammy, with many small white or red flowers in a raceme.

Sarcodes: thick-stemmed, flowers numerous, crowded in a red leafy raceme.

Allotropa: stem red- and white-striped lengthwise; flowers in a tall raceme.

SHINLEAF (PYROLA)

The evergreen leaves of *Pyrola* are at and near the base of the stem. The flowers are in slender racemes, with small bracts. There are five petals and ten stamens. The style projects visibly. As the flowers generally face downwards, the stamens are pendent and the style also is directed down.

The English name is said to be derived from an early use of the leaves in making plasters for injured shins! The leaves, generally rather dark green, and lasting through winter, are all at or near the base of the stem.

Leafless or almost leafless plants have been named *P. aphylla. Plate 128*. Most of these are actually *P. picta*; a few are *P. dentata, P. asarifolia,* or *P. virens*, which may nearly lack leaves.

I. *Species whose style is sharply bent.*

P. PICTA (4–40 inches) has mottled and veined leaves (*picta*, "painted"); they may be lacking. The petals are greenish-white or cream; one form, which generally lacks leaves, has red-purple sepals and pink petals with white margins.

June to August: in coniferous forest through the Cascade Mountains and the Sierra Nevada and eastward to the Rocky Mountains and the Black Hills in South Dakota. *Plate 126*.

A subspecies with leaves not mottled and tapering to a narrow base has been treated by some botanists as a distinct species, *P. dentata*; over much the same country.

P. ASARIFOLIA (8–16 inches) has broadly elliptic or ovate leaves up to 3 inches long, finely toothed or scalloped. The flowers are pink, red, or purplish.

June to September: in moist ground from Washington to northern California and eastward to North and South Dakota and Colorado. *Plate 126*.

P. ELLIPTICA (5–12 inches) has dull green, broadly elliptic, rather thin leaf-blades on stalks as long. The petals are white or cream. This is the commonest shinleaf of the northeastern states; in our range in Idaho and North and South Dakota. *Plate 127. P. virens* is similar, occurring in North and South Dakota. Its leaf-blades are shorter, on longer stalks. The petals are greenish (*virens*). The plants are known as *P. chlorantha*.

II. *Species whose style is straight.*

P. SECUNDA (2–6 inches) has shining leaf-blades 1–2 inches long, commonly finely toothed or scalloped, on short stalks. The flowering stem is generally arched, with all the flowers on one side (this is the botanical meaning of "secund"). The petals are greenish.

July to September: in deep woods practically throughout our area (except the southeast). *Plate 127. P. minor*, with much the same range, has roundish leaf-blades scarcely an inch long on stalks about as long. The raceme is not one-sided. The petals are white or pink. *Plate 127*.

MONESES

There is only one species of *Moneses.*

ONE-FLOWERED-WINTERGREEN, M. UNIFLORA (1–5 inches), has a cluster of small leaves at ground level, roundish, veiny, and toothed. The stem bears a single flower, on the bent-over tip. This is white or rose, fragrant, with five sepals, petals, and stamens, and a pistil tipped with a five-lobed stigma.

June to August: in mossy woods across Canada and southward to Colorado, Utah, and Oregon. *Plate 127*. While it is correct to call any plant wintergreen that is green all winter, that name is generally reserved for a species of the heath family, *Gaultheria procumbens*, which yields the familiar flavoring.

PIPSISSEWA OR WINTERGREEN (CHIMAPHILA)

The flowers of *Chimaphila* hang from the tips of bent stalks which arise at and near the tip of the stem.

They have five sepals, five concave, round petals, ten stamens, and a pistil with scarcely any visible style,

PLATE 127

Gayophytum diffusum   *Myrick*

Monotropa uniflora   *D. Richards*

Pyrola minor   *Uttal*

Chimaphila umbellata   *Ryker*

Chimaphila menziesii   *Johnson*

Pyrola elliptica   *Elbert*

Pyrola secunda   *Jarrett*

Monotropa hypopithys   *Johnson*

Moneses uniflora   *Horne*

the stigma large, disk-like with a scalloped edge. Leaves are borne both at ground level and on the lower half of the stem. Our plants flower from June to August.

For the name wintergreen, see under *Moneses*. *Chimaphila* means winter-loving.

PRINCE'S-PINE, C. UMBELLATA (4–12 inches), has broad, sharp-toothed leaves 1–3 inches long. The flower stalks tend to form a small raceme (rather than an umbel). The petals are generally pink.

Mostly in forests from Alaska to California and eastward to North Dakota and Colorado. *Plate 127.*

C. MENZIESII (2–6 inches) has ovate, toothed leaf-blades up to 1½ inches long; some may be mottled with pale areas. The flowers are few; only one on some plants. The petals are white.

In woods from Canada to California and eastward to Montana. *Plate 127.*

MONOTROPA

The leaves of *Monotropa* are merely small scales; there is no green color (chlorophyll) in the plant. The flowers are borne singly or in a short raceme at the tip of the stem. The stalk of the single flower or the entire raceme is bent over during the flowering period, straightening as fruit develops. The numbers of petals and stamens vary: commonly five and ten respectively. The stigma is a broad disk on a short style.

Because of the lack of chlorophyll these plants cannot make food from inorganic substances. Instead, they absorb the organic materials from the plant remains in which they grow, like mushrooms and toadstools. Such plants are known as saprophytes (compare *Pterospora*).

INDIAN-PIPE, M. UNIFLORA (2–12 inches), is commonly white, turning black as the fruit ripens. There is, as the botanical name indicates, a single flower. A pink form is also known, developing a little later than the common type.

June to September: in woods among dead and decayed leaves throughout our range. *Plate 127.*

PINESAP, M. HYPOPITHYS (4–12 inches), is tawny or bright red, with a raceme of several flowers at the tip. The sepals and petals are generally four or five, with twice as many stamens.

June to August: in deep forests, largely coniferous, practically throughout our area. *Plate 127.*

PTEROSPORA

The genus *Pterospora* has a single species.

PINE-DROPS, P. ANDROMEDEA (1–3 feet), is a reddish-brown, clammy plant quite lacking in proper leaves (which are represented by lanceolate scales), and with no green color. The small drooping flowers are in a long raceme. Petals white or red.

June to August: in coniferous forests in the Cascade Mountains and the Sierra Nevada and eastward to the Rocky Mountains. *Plate 128.* Because of the lack of chlorophyll, these plants cannot make their food from inorganic substances. Instead, they are attached to the roots of other plants and take food directly from them: they are parasites.

SARCODES

There is only one species of *Sarcodes*.

SNOW-PLANT, S. SANGUINEA (6–12 inches), scarcely needs detailed description. The thick stem with the vivid red color resembles some sort of flesh, which is what the name of the genus means. The red flowers are in a raceme, accompanied by large red bracts.

May to July: in forests from Oregon to California in the mountains and eastward to Nevada. *Plate 128.*

ALLOTROPA

The only species of *Allotropa*, candy-stick or sugar-stick, *A. virgata* (4–20 inches), may cross our western boundaries in the Cascade Mountains and the Sierra Nevada. It can scarcely be mistaken for any other plant, because of the red and white striping. The leaves are whitish scales. The flowers are in a tall spike, with bracts longer than they are. They have five whitish sepals, no petals, ten stamens.

PLATE 128

Tribulus terrestris   *Stockert*

Fagonia californica   *Johnson*

Peganum harmala   *Todsen*

Thamnosma montana   *Spellenberg*

Vicia americana   *Johnson*

Janusia gracilis   *Hesselberg*

Pterospora andromedea   *Korling*

Pyrola "aphylla"   *Brandow*

Sarcodes sanguinea   *Johnson*

THE RUE FAMILY (RUTACEAE)

The rue family is certainly represented in our area only by one species. Turpentine-broom, *Thamnosma montana*, has flowers in a raceme, with four sepals, four purplish-blue petals, and eight stamens. The pistil has a two-lobed ovary with a single style. The plant is somewhat shrubby at the base, with rather succulent, narrow leaves, borne singly, less than an inch long. March to May: on desert slopes and mesas in southern Nevada and Utah. *Plate 128*. The name refers to the strong disagreeable smell, resembling that of turpentine (which it does not yield). It is said to have been used medicinally by the Indians; perhaps they shared a common theory that what tastes very bad must be good for you!

T. texana, with threadlike leaves and greenish or yellowish flowers, may possibly be within our southern limits in Utah or Nevada.

THE MALPIGHIA FAMILY (MALPIGHIACEAE)

The *Malpighiaceae* are represented in our area only by one species. *Janusia gracilis* has slender, twining stems up to 10 feet long, bearing narrowly lanceolate, paired leaves, with several small glands near the base. The flowers are in the axils. There are five sepals, some or all with a conspicuous gland on the under side; five yellow petals with wavy edges and a stalk-like base; and a fruit with two or three wings. March to October: on rocky slopes along our southern limits. *Plate 128*.

One rather inconspicuous species of the meadow-foam family (*Limnanthaceae*) is found through much of the United States, growing in wet places. False mermaid, *Floerkea proserpinacoides*, has leaves pinnately divided into segments less than an inch long. The flowers are minute, in the axils, with three sepals not more than ⅛ inch long and three white petals half as long. There are three stamens, and three pistils, joined at the base, which become achenes. "True mermaid," or mermaid-weed, is a member of the frogbit family (*Haloragidaceae*), growing in shallow water or on wet shores.

Another family, the generally southern chocolate family (*Sterculiaceae*) contributes one scarcely noteworthy species to our range. *Ayenia pusilla* crosses our southern boundaries, growing in dry rocky places. The leaves are ovate or lanceolate, minutely toothed. The small brownish or crimson flowers are in clusters in the axils. Five stamens with pollen alternate with five with none. The ovary forms a spherical, warty fruit.

THE CALTROP FAMILY (ZYGOPHYLLACEAE)

The herbs and shrubs of the *Zygophyllaceae* have four or five petals, which may be blue, white, yellow, or orange in our species. Leaves are borne singly or in pairs; they are variously divided. The flowers are in the axils of the leaves. The stamens are usually twice as many as the petals; and the pistil has the same number of parts as there are petals or twice as many.

The common creosote-bush, *Larrea divaricata*, is in this family.

TRIBULUS

We have one species of *Tribulus*.

CALTROP or PUNCTURE-WEED, T.TERRESTRIS, has trailing stems which may be 3 feet long or longer. The leaves are pinnately divided into many small segments. The flowers are borne singly in the axils, with five yellow petals and ten stamens. The objectionable feature of the species, responsible for both English and Latin names, is the fruit, which separates into five small nuts each bearing two strong, sharp spines up to ¼ inch long.

May to September: along roads and railroads and in fields and waste ground in eastern Washington and Oregon and southward to Utah, and from North Dakota to Oklahoma. *Plate 128*. "One of the worst weeds in much of w. U.S." Other names are bullheads and goatheads. The spiny fruits are injurious to grazing animals, besides causing painful wounds on barefoot children and agricultural workers; not to mention automobile tires.

ZYGOPHYLLUM

The mostly subtropical genus *Zygophyllum* contributes one herbaceous species to our area. Bean-caper, *Z. fabago*, a native of western Asia and the Mediterranean region, has become established in a few places in our range, in Washington, Idaho, Colorado, and possibly Kansas. It is succulent, much branched, with each leaf-blade divided into two segments. The flowers are in the axils, about $\frac{1}{2}$ inch across, with five copper-colored or yellow petals scarcely longer than the sepals, and ten stamens.

FAGONIA

One species of *Fagonia* crosses our southern boundary. *F. californica* is somewhat shrubby, up to 16 inches tall, with leaves palmately divided into three lanceolate segments less than $\frac{1}{2}$ inch long. The stipules are stiff and sharp. The flowers are in ample clusters. They have five purplish-blue petals with stalk-like bases ("claws"). In southern Utah and Nevada. *Plate 128.* The ovary forms five angular, one-seeded nuts.

A cultivated species of *Peganum*, *P. harmala*, may be found growing wild. It has leaves cleft pinnately into narrow lobes. The flowers are borne singly in the axils; they have five white petals. The stalks of the fifteen stamens are flat at the base. *Plate 128.*

KALLSTROEMIA

Two species of *Kallstroemia* are in our area.

K. intermedia is similar to *Tribulus terrestris* except for the lack of spines on the fruit. It has five sepals, five pale yellow petals less than $\frac{1}{2}$ inch long. The fruit separates into about ten small nuts; the central axis, ending in a long beak, remains. The plant is roughly hairy. It is found in Kansas and Oklahoma. *K. californica*, with yellow-orange petals only $\frac{1}{8}$ inch long, stems with a whitish down, and a short beak on the fruit, is found in southern Colorado.

THE FRANKENIA FAMILY (FRANKENIACEAE)

The *Frankeniaceae*, in the southwestern United States, are plants of deserts and salt-marshes. *Frankenia jamesii* may be found in alkaline soil in Colorado. It is woody at the base, much branched, to 10 feet tall, with pairs of very narrow leaves. The small white flowers are borne singly in the forks of the stems and clustered near their tips. They have from four to six sepals not more than $\frac{1}{3}$ inch long, and as many stamens. The fruit is a capsule, enclosed in the calyx.

GROUP IX

Sepals three, four, or five; petals four or five,* in certain families some (not all) of them joined, bilaterally symmetric; stamens four, five, or ten. Leaves divided or undivided, with or without lobes.

I. *Plants with some petals joined.*

    A. Plants whose flowers have the two lower petals joined to form a keel which encloses the pistil and five or (more commonly) ten stamens: bean family.

    B. Plants that have the two petals at each side joined; five stamens; all partly enclosed by a large sac-like, petal-like sepal: touch-me-not-family.

II. *Plants with all petals separate.*

    A. Plants whose petals are equal to or (more commonly) longer than the sepals, which are green: violet family.

    B. Plants whose petals are much shorter than the sepals, which are crimson: rhatany family.

THE BEAN FAMILY (FABACEAE)

The bean family is one of the great families of plants; great in numbers, great in distribution over the earth, great in importance to man. It is also one of the most difficult for the amateur, with such genera as *Lupinus* and *Astragalus*. It is estimated to contain 10,000 species. These grow all over the world from the boreal zones to the tropics. Among them are beans and peas, soybeans and cow-peas, clovers and alfalfa, sweet-peas and lupines, peanuts and chick-peas, laburnum and wisteria and broom, indigo and various insecticides. There are trees, shrubs, vines, and herbs in the list.

This vast group of plants has a remarkably constant flower. There is typically a calyx of four or five lobes joined to form a tube or cup. One petal, the standard (also called the banner), stands behind or above the others, in many flowers erect. Two are at the sides, the so-called wings. And the two lowest, joined along one edge, form the keel. The stamens and pistil are mostly within the keel. There are generally ten stamens, their stalks all joined, or nine joined and one – on top – free; forming a sheath around the pistil. This type of flower is called papilionaceous, "butterfly-like." The pistil typically becomes a legume, a pod containing one row of seeds and splitting along two lines into two halves (a pea-pod is an example). But there are many exceptions. See *Petalostemon* and *Amorpha* for flowers that do not conform to the general pattern. And pods of

*In the touch-me-not family there are apparently three separate petals; those at each side are two-lobed, each formed of two joined petals. In two genera of the bean family there is apparently only one petal.

Lespedeza and other genera contain only one seed, and those of *Petalostemon* and others do not open. The leaves are generally divided. Note that leaves with only three segments are said to be pinnately divided if the end segment has a stalk longer than those at the sides.

Other plants that form legumes but do not have papilionaceous flowers form subfamilies; which in this volume are treated as distinct families. See *Mimosaceae, Caesalpiniaceae*.

In the area of this volume there are 479 species in 39 genera.

Guide to Genera of Fabaceae

I. *Genera whose stems climb or trail.*

(CAUTION: Some of these plants may stand erect when young. Some plants in group II have prostrate stems; see *Lotus, Astragalus*.)

A. Plants with tendrils: *Vicia* (stipules small; wings partly joined to the keel; style hairy at the tip); *Lathyrus* (stipules large; style hairy along the upper side).

B. Plants twining or trailing or scrambling; except the first, with three leaf-segments: *Apios* (petals purplish-brown; keel sickle-shaped; five or seven leaf-segments); *Amphicarpaea* (petals purple; almost triangular leaf-segments); *Phaseolus* (flowers purple or white; keel spirally coiled); *Strophostyles* (petals pink or lavender; keel curved upward); *Galactia* (flower small, reddish; wings and keel partly joined; calyx four-toothed); *Rhynchosia* (flowers yellow; pod flat, generally two-seeded).

II. *Genera whose stems grow without support.*
(The main stem may be prostrate, or bend up only at the tip; flowering branches are generally erect.)

A. Plants with toothed leaf-segments: *Trifolium* (flowers in heads or short dense spikes; leaves mostly divided palmately); *Melilotus* (flowers yellow or white, small, in racemes; leaves divided pinnately); *Medicago* (flowers blue or yellow, in heads or racemes; pods coiled; leaves divided pinnately).

B. Plants whose leaf-segments are not toothed (the leaves are mostly pinnately divided).

1. Plants with gland-tipped hairs or glandular dots, especially on the leaves and calyxes: *Psoralea* (leaves divided pinnately or palmately; flowers mostly purple or white, the petals short-stalked; pods one-seeded); *Petalostemon* (five fertile stamens, five narrow, petal-like, sterile stamens; no wings or keel; inflorescence a dense spike; pod one- or two-seeded); *Dalea* (petals with narrow stalks joined to the stamen-tube; pods as in the preceding); *Amorpha* (shrubby; no wings or keel; pods as in the preceding; spike tapering); *Glycyrrhiza* (leaf-segments narrow, many; flowers yellowish; pod prickly); *Parryella* (shrubs; flowers yellowish; pods one-seeded).

2. Plants lacking gland-tipped hairs and glandular dots. *Arachis* (four leaf-segments); *Crotalaria* (leaves with one segment; seeds loose in the pod); *Stylosanthes* (flower-base a slender tube enclosing the ovary; petals orange-yellow); *Coronilla* (flowers pink, in umbels); *Peteria* (leaf-segments many, small; stipules spine-like; flowers yellow, in a long raceme); *Anthyllis* (flowers red-and-yellow, in a head); *Hedysarum* (flowers large, rose-purple; pods of one-seeded joints); *Lespedeza* (leaves divided pinnately into three segments; flowers in dense heads); *Desmodium* (pods separating into one-seeded, adhesive joints; three leaf-segments); *Thermopsis* (flowers yellow; stamens all separate; three leaf-segments; pods flat, few-seeded); *Baptisia* (flowers blue, yellow, or white; pod stoutly beaked and on a stalk emerging from the calyx); *Sophora* (flowers blue, white, or yellowish; pod constricted between seeds); *Tephrosia* (standard largish, pink, crimson, or white; leaf-segments many; pod flat, with several seeds); *Lotus* (flowers yellow, reddish, or white, single or in small umbels; generally from three to seven leaf-segments); *Indigofera* (flowers pink or white; keel curved; pod one-seeded); *Sesbania* (flowers yellow, in loose racemes; pod very long, thin, curved, many-seeded); *Lupinus* (leaves divided palmately, the segments from three to eleven; calyx two-lipped; pods from two- to twelve-seeded); *Sphaerophysa* (flowers brick-red; pod inflated); *Oxytropis* (like *Astragalus*; leaves mostly basal, with many segments; keel with a beak); *Astragalus* (plants bushy, matted, or prostrate; calyx two-lipped; leaves mostly pinnately divided); *Onobrychis* (flowers pinkish-lavender veined reddish-purple; pod spiny).

THE VETCHES (VICIA)

The vetches are climbing or trailing plants. One or more segments at the ends of the pinnately divided leaves are tendrils. Stipules are small. The flowers are in racemes growing from the axils. Technically, the tuft of hairs (the "beard") at the end of the style distinguishes the genus from *Lathyrus*.

Several Old-World species are now well established in North America. Some are known in England as tares, a New-Testament word. Some have long been cultivated for forage or for the table. *V. faba* is the horse-bean or broad-bean; its old name *Faba* gives a name to the family. Some species are used as "green manure" to restore fertility to worn-out soil (because of their ability, through bacteria in their roots, to turn the nitrogen of the air into nitrates).

Since the following grouping depends on such variable characteristics as number of leaf-segments, a number of plants should always be examined (you may well have the exceptional plant that departs from the usual number).

I. *Species with not more than eight flowers in a raceme.*
    Except the last in this group, the leaves have mostly more than eight segments.

V. AMERICANA has up to eighteen leaf-segments, mostly elliptic, in one variety very narrow, many over an inch long. The closely clustered flowers are bluish-purple, about an inch long. The stipules may be toothed. The raceme is no longer than the adjacent leaves.

April to July: in moist woods and open ground from North Dakota to Oklahoma and westward to Idaho and Nevada. *Plate 128.*

In *V. producta* the racemes have one or two flowers, the stem extending beyond the uppermost flower. The flowers are pale yellowish, tipped with purple. In Colorado.

Plants known to some botanists as *V. ludoviciana*, to others as a variety of the complex species *V. leavenworthii*, may be found in Oklahoma. There are up to sixteen leaf-segments, but some plants may have fewer than eight. The few flowers are about ¼ inch long, the petals from lavender to purple. In our plants the raceme is nearly as long as the leaves, with as many as fourteen flowers.

The European *V. sativa*, widely cultivated for forage, may be found growing wild. It is distinguished by the position of the flowers, one, two, or three in each axil rather than in a raceme; they are ¾ inch long or longer, the wings commonly red, the standard purplish. The leaf-segments generally number from ten to fourteen; they are broader between middle and end. *Plate 129.* Plants known as *V. angustifolia* have very narrow segments and smaller flowers which rarely have red wings. *Plate 129.* This is perhaps more widespread than *V. sativa*. It is also of European origin. There is a gradual transition between the two, so that some botanists have found it convenient to treat the second as a variety of the first.

V. exigua generally has less than eight leaf-segments, up to an inch long.. The racemes are shorter than the leaves and bear only one or two tiny flowers on very short stalks. In grassy, brushy, and wooded places in southern Utah. *Plate 129.* Farther to the south forms are known that may connect this species with *V. leavenworthii*.

II. *Species with more than eight flowers in a raceme.*

COW-VETCH or CANADA-PEA, V. CRACCA, has from eight to twelve pairs of segments (besides the tendrils). The flowers are many, in a tight raceme; not more than ½ inch long; blue or purple, or rarely white.

May to August: on roadsides and in fields and thickets, widely naturalized in North America, and found in our range in the Rocky Mountains and westward. *Plate 129. V. villosa* is in Kansas and Oklahoma and westward to California. It is softly hairy, the leaf-segments up to twenty, the numerous flowers crowded on one side of the stalk; the keel is white, the other petals violet. *Plate 129. V. dasycarpa* is similar, smooth or merely downy, with fewer flowers. Naturalized in various states and reported in Montana and Kansas. *V. caroliniana* is in southeastern Kansas, and Oklahoma. It has from six to twelve pairs of segments. The small flowers, not more than ½ inch long, are mostly white, some with blue on the keel.

THE VETCHLINGS (LATHYRUS)

The vetchlings differ from the vetches chiefly in their generally larger leaf-segments, stipules, and flowers. The racemes are mostly few-flowered. The stipules (two-pronged) may be as long as the leaf-segments. The "beard" of the style (see *Vicia*) is along the upper side rather than at the tip.

Besides the species described here, several Old-World natives may escape from cultivation. The numerous races of sweet-peas were derived from *L. odoratus*, a wild flower of the Mediterranean lands.

On the use of numbers of parts for identification, see under *Vicia*.

PLATE 129

Vicia villosa *Rickett*

Lathyrus polymorphus *Roberts*

Vicia cracca *Rickett*

Lathyrus leucanthus *Korling*

Vicia exigua *Stockert*

Lathyrus pauciflorus *Korling*

Vicia angustifolia *Korling*

Lathyrus ochroleucus *Elbert*

Vicia sativa *Korling*

I. *Species with only two leaf-segments.*

L. LATIFOLIUS (3–7 feet) has broadly winged, climbing stems. The stipules are up to 2 inches long,
the leaf-segments to 6 inches. The racemes have from
five to fifteen pink-red flowers, nearly an inch long.

May to July: a common escape from cultivation.
Sweet-pea, *L. odoratus*, is similar. There are usually from two to five flowers in a raceme. The flowers
are commonly more than an inch long.

L. pusillus has very small (not more than ⅓ inch),
pale violet flowers. There are usually two on a stalk.
The stems are "winged" (with thin edges). In sandy
soil and on prairies in southern Kansas, and Oklahoma.

II. *Species with at least four leaf-segments on some
leaves.*

A. Species in which the midrib of the leaf is continued beyond the segments, as a bristle instead of as a tendril.
See also *L. lanzwertii, leucanthus, nevadensis*
under B; they are variable in this respect.

L. BIJUGATUS (to 16 inches) has two, four, or six narrow leaf-segments 1–6 inches long. The racemes
have two or three pink or bluish flowers not more than
½ inch long.

May to July: on the lower foothills in extreme
eastern Washington and adjacent Idaho (dubiously
reported from Montana).

L. arizonicus: Two or four segments, to 3 inches
long. Flowers white, from two to five in a raceme,
about ½ inch. Utah.

L. POLYMORPHUS has mostly about eight leaf-segments about an inch long, rather narrow. The
racemes have commonly from two to five flowers about
an inch long; the petals from yellowish to magenta
and violet.

May and June: in dry open ground from southwestern South Dakota to Colorado and Oklahoma.
Plate 129.

L. rigidus (to 16 inches) commonly has from six
to ten veiny leaf-segments, up to 1⅕ inches long. There
are from two to five white or pink (or rarely bluish)
flowers, about an inch long, in a raceme. May and
June: in sagebrush and juniper and pine woods from
northeastern Oregon and western Idaho to northeastern California.

B. Species with coiling tendrils, in many,
branched.

1. Species of the eastern plains of our range (the
first also in the West).

L. OCHROLEUCUS has from four to ten blunt segments mostly 1–2 inches long. The stipules are
broad and may be toothed. The flowers are pale yellow
("ochroleucous"), about ½ inch long, from five to ten
in a short-stalked cluster.

May to July: in moist woods and thickets in
North and South Dakota, northeastern Washington,
Idaho, and Montana. *Plate 129.*

L. palustris has stems up to 4 feet long, some
"winged." The leaves have commonly four or six or
up to ten narrow segments to 3 inches long. There are
from two to nine flowers at the end of a long stalk, each
½–1 inch long, reddish-purple. June to September: in
meadows and marshes around the world in the north
and southward along the coasts and to North and
South Dakota. *L. venosus* has a stouter, square stem,
from eight to twelve segments mostly 1–2 inches long.
The flowers are purplish, from five to thirty in a dense
raceme. North Dakota.

2. Species of the Rocky Mountains and westward.
See also *L. ochroleucus* under 1.

L. PAUCIFLORUS has from eight to ten rather thick
leaf-segments. The flowers are ½–1 inch long,
pink, orchid, or crimson. The keel is shorter than the
wings.

April to June: on dry slopes from central Washington to California and eastward to eastern Idaho,
north-central Utah, and southwestern Colorado. *Plate
129.*

L. brachycalyx is finely softly hairy and grayish.
The leaf-segments are up to 1½ inches long, elliptic or
lanceolate, usually from eight to twelve. There are
from two to six flowers in a raceme, about an inch long,
pink or lilac. In piñon-juniper woodland in Nevada
and Utah. *L. zionis* is smooth or hairy. There are commonly from six to ten narrow leaf-segments, to 3 inches long. The racemes have from three to five flowers,
1 inch long, pink or bluish. The standard is deeply
indented. In sagebrush and juniper in southern Utah.
L. eucosmus has rose or purple flowers. The leaf-segments are rather thick, 1–2 inches long. Southern
Utah. *Plate 130.*

L. LANZWERTII (to 32 inches) has usually from four
to ten leaf-segments, rather narrow, up to 4 inches long; they are apt to be leathery and veiny. The
racemes are from two- to eight-flowered, with rather
small flowers (about ½ inch), lavender or pinkish with
red lines, the wings and keel paler than the standard.

May and June: in sagebrush and pine from
Washington to the Sierra Nevada and eastward to
western Idaho and central Utah.

L. nevadensis (to 32 inches) is softly downy, especially on the under sides of leaves. The leaves have
from four to ten segments, varying from very narrow

PLATE 130

Trifolium agrarium *Fisk*

Trifolium dasyphyllum *Scribner*

Trifolium campestre *Thomson*

Apios americana *Johnson*

Trifolium wormskioldii *Mackintosh*

Amphicarpaea bracteata *Rickett*

Galactia regularis *Elbert*

Lathyrus eucosmus *Roberts*

Strophostyles helvola *D. Richards*

to ovate, up to 5 inches long. Tendrils may be only tiny bristles. The flowers are not more than an inch long, from white to blue or purplish. May to July: from central Washington to the Sierra Nevada and northeastern Oregon and adjacent Nevada.

L. leucanthus has up to ten segments 1–2 inches long. The flowers are white or cream or pale pink with reddish veins, $\frac{1}{2}$–1 inch long, from two to five in a raceme. In open woods, on slopes, etc. from south-central Wyoming to northeastern Utah. *Plate 129.*

APIOS

We have one species of *Apios*.

GROUNDNUT, A. AMERICANA, is conspicuous for its
    purplish-brown, fragrant flowers, $\frac{1}{2}$ inch long or longer, in a dense raceme. The keel is sickle-shaped and somewhat coiled. The four upper teeth of the calyx are very short. The leaves are pinnately divided into five or seven segments. The English name refers

to the underground stem (rhizome) which is thickened at intervals to form a series of small tubers. These are edible, and even palatable when properly cooked, and were often gathered for food by the Indians. It is reported that the pilgrims relied on them during their first year in New England.

July to September: in moist woods and thickets in Colorado and eastward. *Plate 130.*

AMPHICARPAEA

One species of *Amphicarpaea* extends from the East into our easternmost areas.

HOG-PEANUT, A. BRACTEATA, is a straggling vine
    with stems up to 3 feet long. The leaves have three pinnately disposed, ovate segments. The raceme has from two to fifteen pale purple flowers about $\frac{1}{2}$ inch long. The calyx has four teeth. These flowers form

flat pods, whose two halves coil as they separate. There are also, on creeping stems, flowers with rudimentary or no petals, which form round one-seeded pods which do not open and are nearly or quite underground. These are the "peanuts" presumably rooted by hogs; they were also eaten by Indians.

August and September: in woods and thickets from North Dakota to Oklahoma. *Plate 130.*

PHASEOLUS

One species of *Phaseolus* is found in Kansas and Oklahoma. Wild bean, *P. polystachios*, is a twining climber. The leaf-segments are ovate, pointed, com-

monly unequal-sided, mostly 1–3 inches long. The flowers range from white to purple. The keel is coiled in a spiral. Cultivated beans are species of *Phaseolus*.

STROPHOSTYLES

Wild-beans of the genus *Strophostyles* trail or twine. The leaves are pinnately divided into three segments. The pink or rose flowers are in close racemes on long stalks; they may turn green in age. The keel is strongly curved upwards (not coiled). The calyx is four-toothed, the lowest tooth the longest. The two halves of the pod coil as they separate. Our species flower from June to October.

S. LEIOSPERMA is gray with long soft hairs. The leaf-

segments are narrow. The flowers are small, the standard not more than $\frac{1}{3}$ inch long. In dry soil from North Dakota to Oklahoma.

S. umbellata, in Kansas and Oklahoma, has rather diamond-shaped leaf-segments, up to an inch long. The flowers have a standard about $\frac{1}{2}$ inch long and wide. In sandy fields and open woodland. *S. helvola*, also in Kansas and Oklahoma, may have three-lobed leaf-segments, but is otherwise like the preceding. In old fields and thickets. *Plate 130.*

GALACTIA

Two species of the eastern genus *Galactia* are found in southeastern Kansas. They are twining or

trailing plants, with leaves divided into three segments. The flowers, pink or red, are in small racemes.

PLATE 131

Trifolium microcephalum *Myrick*

Trifolium plumosum *Scribner*

Trifolium incarnatum *Johnson*

Trifolium longipes *Korling*

Trifolium variegatum *Myrick*

Trifolium thompsonii *Spurr*

Trifolium nanum *Scribner*

Trifolium cyathiferum *Myrick*

The calyx has four teeth. The pod is flat; the two halves generally twist as they separate. *G. volubilis* generally twines. The leaf-segments are $\frac{1}{3}$–$1\frac{1}{2}$ inches

long. The stem is commonly shaggy. *G. regularis* trails, twining perhaps at the tips. The stems are smooth or nearly so. *Plate 130.*

RHYNCHOSIA

One species of *Rhynchosia* enters our area. *R. latifolia* is a trailing plant, with three broad (*lati-*) leaf-segments 2–3 inches long and nearly as wide, downy

on both surfaces, pinnately disposed. The large yellow flowers are in racemes 2–12 inches long. On sandy prairies and in thickets in Oklahoma and eastward.

THE CLOVERS (TRIFOLIUM)

The most familiar species of clover are those used in agriculture. They furnish valuable forage crops, and enrich the soil through the ability of the bacteria in their roots to capture the nitrogen of the air and transform it into nitrates. Many other species (the genus is a large one in our area) are weeds, or woodland or mountain wild flowers.

The leaves are divided into three (*tri-*) segments generally toothed. The flowers are in heads or short, dense spikes. The uppermost petal, the standard, does not usually stand erect like that of a sweet-pea, but is folded lengthwise over the wings and keel. The petals of many species remain attached even as they wither. The pods are short, mostly concealed in the calyx. Some have only one seed; some do not open. The uppermost leaves (or stipules) of some species form an involucre below the head.

I. *Species with yellow flowers.*

HOP-TREFOIL, T. CAMPESTRE,* has pinnately divided leaves. The stem trails. The flower-head contains twenty or more flowers.

April to September: on roadsides and in fields and lawns through most of the United States. *Plate 130.* Trefoil is of course *Trifolium*; hop trefoil because of the heads of withered flowers which have some likeness to hops. *T. dubium:* Similar. End leaf-segment on longer stalk, heads with from three to fifteen flowers. *T. agrarium†:* Generally erect. Leaf-segments practically without stalks. Twenty or more flowers in a head, turning brown in age. *Plate 130.*

T. lemmonii (6–8 inches): Stipules ovate, coarsely toothed. Leaf-segments from four to six. Heads $\frac{3}{5}$–$\frac{4}{5}$ inch thick. On slopes and in valleys in e Calif and w Nev.

II. *Species whose flowers are not yellow.*

A few may have cream or yellowish flowers tipped with reddish.

A. Plants forming a mat or tuft of leaves and flower-stalks.

T. DASYPHYLLUM (to 6 inches) has very narrow or narrowly lanceolate leaf-segments an inch long or longer. The pink or crimson flowers are in heads up to an inch across, carried well above the leaves. The bracts under the head are tiny or up to $\frac{1}{3}$ inch long, narrow, whitish with green veins.

June to August: in high meadows from western Montana to Colorado and eastern Utah. *Plate 130. T. nanum*, in the same range, forms dense mats, with segments up to $\frac{3}{5}$ inch. Heads from one- to four-flowered, the flowers less than an inch, lilac. *Plate 131. T. brandegei* has broader segments up to an inch long, elliptic or oval. Flowers purple, from six to fifteen in a head. Colo. *T. parryi* (to 2 inches): Smooth or brown-downy. Segments broadly elliptic, $\frac{2}{5}$–$1\frac{3}{5}$ inches. Heads with an involucre, from four to thirty reddish flowers. Moist meadows and stream-banks at high altitudes from e Ida and sc Mont to e Utah and Colo. *Plate 133.*

T. ANDERSONII (2–4 inches) is densely silky-hairy. There are three or five leaf-segments $\frac{1}{3}$–$\frac{4}{5}$ inch long. The heads are 1–$1\frac{1}{2}$ inches through, with the translucent remains of an involucre. Flowers crimson.

May and June: on dry slopes and in valleys from southern Oregon to the Sierra Nevada and western Nevada.

T. monoense, named for Mono County in eastern California, is similar but grayish-hairy. Corolla pink, not more than $\frac{2}{5}$ inch. *T. andinum:* Segments lanceolate, broader near the tip, less than $\frac{1}{2}$ inch, silky-hairy. Heads about $\frac{1}{2}$ inch across, with two or three broad bracts. Wyo and Utah.

T. GYMNOCARPON (less than 6 inches) has many stems, with crowded, overlapping leaves. Generally three leaf-segments, $\frac{1}{5}$–$1\frac{1}{5}$ inches long, sharply toothed. Heads usually not above the leaves. Flowers pale yellowish or flesh-colored. Involucres not evident.

May and June: with sagebrush and pine from northeastern Oregon to northeastern California and eastward to Montana and Colorado. *Plate 132.*

*The correct name may be *T. procumbens*. The names of these small yellow-flowered clovers are considerably confused.
†The name *T. aureum* was widely used for this, as in the earlier volumes of this series.

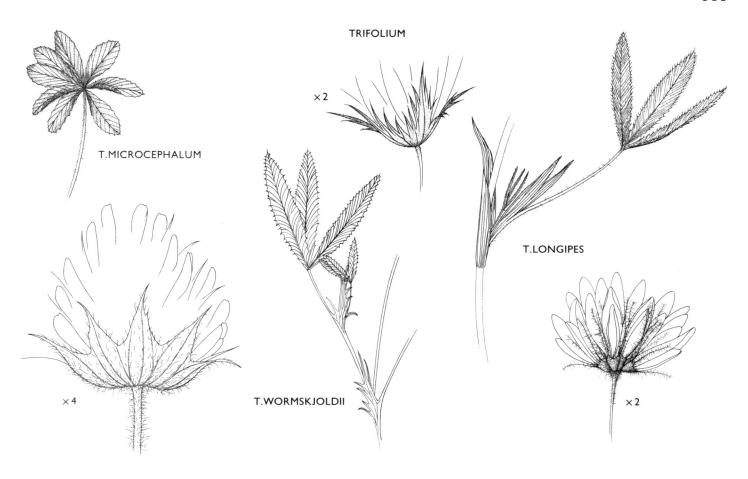

TRIFOLIUM

T.MICROCEPHALUM

×2

T.LONGIPES

×4

T.WORMSKJOLDII

×2

T. leibergii: Hoary with crinkly hairs. Calyx-teeth bristle-tipped. Corolla crimson. Southeastern Oregon. *T. haydeni* (to 2 inches): Smooth. Segments broadly ovate or almost round, finely toothed. Heads above the leaves. Involucre lacking. Flowers from pale yellowish with pink tips to salmon. High slopes and ridges, sc Mont, adjacent Wyo. *T. multipedunculatum* (up to 4 inches): Sparingly downy. Segments lanceolate or broader between middle and tip, rather thick and leathery, $\frac{1}{5}$–$\frac{4}{5}$ inch long, finely spine-toothed. Heads above the leaves. Flowers red or crimson. On high slopes and ridges from c Wash to e Ore.

B. Plants with leafy stems above ground; clovers of familiar aspect.

1. The first group of these is identified by a ring of joined bracts forming an involucre beneath a head.

T. MICROCEPHALUM, in spite of the name, has heads up to $\frac{1}{2}$ inch long. The involucre has lanceolate, papery lobes. Most of the plant is hairy or woolly. The leaf-segments are commonly heart-shaped, about $\frac{1}{2}$ inch long. Flowers white or rose, about $\frac{1}{4}$ inch long.

April to August: in grassy places from Canada to California and eastward to Montana and Nevada. *Plate 131.*

T. cyathiferum: Segments $\frac{1}{5}$–1 inch. Heads 5–30-flowered, $\frac{3}{5}$ inch thick. Involucre shallowly lobed and bristly. Lower calyx-teeth generally cleft. Corolla white, pale yellowish, or pink. In wet meadows and sandy soil, Wash and Ore to Ida. *Plate 131.*

T. variegatum, sometimes found from the Cascades and Sierra Nevada to Montana and Utah, has purple, white-tipped flowers about $\frac{1}{3}$ inch long. Involucre cleft and toothed. *Plate 131.*

T. WORMSKIOLDII has small leaf-segments, scarcely more than an inch long, mostly broadest towards the tip, or narrow and elliptic, toothed. The heads are generally nearly an inch long, or even longer. The involucre is cleft into sharp-pointed and veiny lobes. The flowers range from whitish and flesh-color to purple.

March to October: mostly in moist coniferous forests in Colorado and Utah. *Plate 130. T. fendleri,* by some included in the foregoing, has larger flower-heads and elliptic leaf-segments. Utah, Colo.

T. monanthum ("one-flowered") may have only one or two flowers in a head, or up to six. The small involucre may have from two to four lobes. The flowers are cream with purple-tips. Generally in wet places at high altitudes in the Sierra Nevada and adjacent Nevada.

T. fragiferum, a weed from Europe, has spreading stems 4–12 inches long. The leaf-segments are broadest in the outer half, ½–1 inch long, finely toothed. The heads are many-flowered, the flowers purplish. The calyx becomes much inflated in age.

2. Species with no true involucre. (The uppermost foliage leaves and stipules may be close under the heads and simulate an involucre.)

a. In the first eleven of these, including some common species, the calyx is densely downy or hairy.

T. MACROCEPHALUM (4–12 inches) has from five to nine leaf-segments, rather thick and leathery, to 1 inch long. The heads are up to 2 inches long. The flowers are pink.

April to June: with sagebrush and yellow pine from central Washington to western Idaho and eastern Oregon. *Plate 132*.

T. owhyeense has only three segments, whitish, sparingly toothed. Corolla rose, white towards the base. se Ore. *T. thompsonii* (8–28 inches): Segments from five to eight, narrow or lanceolate. Flowers from reddish-lavender to deep orchid. c Wash. *Plate 131*.

T. plumosum (8–20 inches): Three narrow segments. Heads to 1 inch wide about twice as long. Flowers whitish with pink tips. Calyx softly hairy. se Wash, ne Ore, wc Ida. *Plate 131*. Crimson clover, *T. incarnatum* (8–32 inches), is softly downy. The ovate or cylindric heads are crimson, the flowers about ½ inch long. Naturalized and occasionally found in waste land. *Plate 131*.

T. pratense (1–3 feet), widely naturalized and cultivated, has large heads of pink or red flowers; one or two foliage leaves just under the head may be mistaken for an involucre, and the large veiny stipules for bracts. The plant is downy, the sepals hairy. The leaf-segments are marked by a pale V. *Plate 132*.

T. LONGIPES (2–12 inches) is downy (the calyx may, however, be smooth). The stems may be trailing, bending up. The segments are elliptic, ⅕–2⅕ inches long, with or without fine teeth. The heads are ⅗–1⅖ inches thick, above the leaves. The flowers range from pale yellowish to purplish.

May to August: widespread in the West. *Plate 131*.

T. latifolium (4–16 inches): Moderately downy. Segments ⅕–1⅗ inches, finely toothed. Heads generally shorter than leaves, about an inch thick. Flowers from yellow to purple. In moist meadows and on rocky ridges, ne Ore to w Mont.

T. ERIOCEPHALUM (8–24 inches) is more or less downy-hairy. The leaf-segments range from very narrow to ovate, 1–2¾ inches long. The heads are about an inch thick, with pink or red flowers bent sharply down on very short stalks; the calyx has feathery hairs.

May to July: from south-central Washington to northern California and eastward to western Idaho and south-central Utah. *Plate 132*.

BUFFALO-CLOVER, T. REFLEXUM (4–24 inches) is generally softly hairy. The leaf-segments are elliptic, toothed all round. The flowers are less than ½ inch long, white, pink, or red (the standard generally colored, the other petals commonly white).

May to August: in sandy woods and fields and on prairies from North Dakota to Oklahoma and eastward and southward.

T. carolinianum may be found in southeastern Kansas. Its stems may be prostrate, with long-stalked erect leaves. The petals barely emerge from the calyx; they vary from white to purplish.

b. The remaining species have smooth or nearly smooth calyxes.

See also *T. longipes* under a.

WHITE CLOVER, T. REPENS, is a common naturalized species familiar in lawns, on roadsides, even on mountain meadows, with creeping (*repens*) stems 4–24 inches long, from which erect leaf-stalks and flowering branches arise. The leaf-segments are broadest between middle and tip, less than an inch long, finely toothed. The white flowers, less than ½ inch long, turn pinkish-brown and point downward as they age. *Plate 132*. Alsike, *T. hybridum* (not really a hybrid) has smooth stems up to 3 feet tall. Leaf-segments elliptic or nearly so, ⅗–1⅕ inches long. Flowers, raised above the leaves, pink or pink-and-white, turning brown. Commonly planted and widely naturalized. *Plate 132*. *T. stoloniferum* (called buffalo-clover, like *T. reflexum*) is a native species found from North Dakota to Oklahoma and eastward. Stems partly prostrate, their tips bending up and bearing the leaves and flowers; long runners ("stolons") are also formed. Leaf-segments nearly wedge-shaped, toothed. Flowers about ½ inch long, white tinged with purple. *T. resupinatum* may be found in eastern Kansas. It is named for the upside-down ("resupinate") purplish flowers, the standard outward. From the Old World, now scattered through the eastern and southern states. *Plate 132*.

T. DOUGLASII (16–32 inches) has heads about 1⅕ inches thick, with reddish-purple flowers. The leaf-segments may be very narrow or elliptic, 1⅗–4 inches long, finely spiny-toothed.

June and July: along streams in eastern Washington, eastern Oregon, and adjacent Idaho. *Plate 132*.

T. BECKWITHII (6–20 inches) is smooth. The leaf-segments may be narrowly elliptic or broader

PLATE 132

Trifolium repens   *Scribner*

Trifolium eriocephalum   *Scribner*

Trifolium resupinatum   *Johnson*

Trifolium hybridum   *Gottscho*

Trifolium gymnocarpon   *Frost*

Trifolium douglasii   *Scribner*

Trifolium pratense   *Green*

Trifolium macilentum   *Korling*

Trifolium macrocephalum   *Spurr*

between middle and tip, $\frac{4}{5}$–$2\frac{1}{5}$ inches long, finely toothed. The heads are long-stalked, the flowers $\frac{1}{2}$–$\frac{2}{3}$ inch long, red or pale purple.

May to August: in mountain meadows from southeastern Oregon to west-central Montana and south to the Sierra Nevada.

T. productum (8–20 inches) has segments $\frac{1}{5}$–$\frac{4}{5}$ inch long, more or less lanceolate, spiny-toothed. The stem of the head commonly extends up above the flowers, and may be branched. Flowers $\frac{1}{2}$–$\frac{3}{4}$ inch long, bent down, very short-stalked, whitish with purple

tips. se Ore to the Sierra Nevada.

T. kingii, from southern Oregon to Nevada and Utah, has lanceolate or ovate segments $\frac{1}{2}$–$2\frac{1}{5}$ inches long. The stem of the head may curve. The flowers are all bent down, about $\frac{1}{2}$ inch long, purplish.

T. macilentum (6–16 inches) is smooth, with ovate or lanceolate segments $\frac{4}{5}$–$2\frac{1}{5}$ inches long. The heads, about an inch thick, are commonly on stalks which are bent down. The flowers also are soon bent down, pink or rose, $\frac{3}{5}$–$\frac{4}{5}$ inch long. In meadows in w Colo and s Utah. *Plate 132.*

THE SWEET-CLOVERS (MELILOTUS)

The sweet-clovers can be identified by their fragrance alone. Even the uninjured masses of foliage along roadsides give off, in hot sunlight, the odor of very sweet new-mown hay; this is still more intense when the plants are crushed or dried. The plants are tall and very bushy. The leaves are pinnately divided into three. The small flowers are in numerous spikes which grow from the axils.

WHITE SWEET-CLOVER, M. ALBA, may be 10 feet tall, but the leaf-segments are only an inch long, and the white flowers not more than $\frac{1}{4}$ inch. The leaf-segments are toothed in the outer half.

May to October: on roadsides and in waste lands throughout the United States. *Plate 133.*

YELLOW SWEET-CLOVER, M. OFFICINALIS, is similar to the white, but not so large – 5 feet tall at most. The dimensions of leaf-segments and flowers are about the same as in *M. alba*. The flowers are bright yellow.

May to October: in waste ground and fields throughout the northern states, less common southward. *Plate 133.*

Indian-clover or sour-clover, *M. indica*, is much less widespread in this country; in our range found only scattered in the Intermountain Region; it came from the Mediterranean lands. It has yellow flowers like those of *M. officinalis* but smaller, not more than $\frac{1}{8}$ inch long. The pod is about $\frac{1}{10}$ inch long. The calyx-teeth are blunt.

MEDICAGO

The most important species of *Medicago* is alfalfa or lucerne, grown for forage and frequently found growing wild. The genus also includes a number of small weeds. All are natives of the Old World. The leaves are pinnately divided into three segments. The most striking feature is the spirally coiled pod of most of our species.

ALFALFA or LUCERNE, M. SATIVA (1–4 feet), is our only blue-flowered species. The seed-pod makes two or three spirals.

June to October: chiefly on roadsides and near cultivated fields. *Plate 133.*

Yellow lucerne, *M. falcata*, is rare in our range; established northward in sagebrush in British Columbia. The flowers are pale yellow or, rarely, violet, $\frac{1}{4}$–$\frac{1}{3}$ inch long. The pod is sickle-shaped, not coiled.

BLACK MEDICK or NONESUCH, M. LUPULINA, is a common weed in most of the United States. The stems are prostrate. The leaf-segments are less than an inch long. There are from ten to forty yellow flowers in a headlike raceme, not more than $\frac{1}{8}$ inch long. The pod turns black when mature; it makes a single spiral, the style continuing this into another turn.

April to August: in waste ground and lawns and on roadsides. *Plate 133. M. polymorpha* (or *M. hispida*, the correct name is still controversial) has a prickly pod. The stipules are deeply cleft. The flowers are yellow. Throughout our range. *M. arabica*, spotted medick, also has prickly pods, but may be distinguished by the conspicuous reddish spot in the middle of each leaf-segment. The leaves are almost palmately divided, the stalk of the end segment being very short. Less abundant in our range.

SCURF-PEAS (PSORALEA)

Both English and botanical names of *Psoralea* refer to the small, scalelike glands – "scurf" – which cover the leaves and stem of many species. The leaves

are divided usually into three, five, or seven segments, on some plants more or fewer. Stipules are conspicuous. The flowers, generally purple or white, are in

PLATE 133

Psoralea cuspidata   *Scribner*

Trifolium parryi   *Rickett*

Medicago sativa   *Gottscho*

Medicago lupulina   *Rickett*

Psoralea argophylla   *Johnson*

Psoralea esculenta   *Johnson*

Melilotus officinalis   *McRae*

Melilotus alba   *Scribner*

racemes or spikes. The pod is small, containing only one seed, and does not split open.

P. JUNCEA (to 3 feet) forms a bush. The basal leaves have lanceolate segments about an inch long. The leaves above are merely scales. The flowers are dark blue, in spikes.

July: in sandy places in southeastern Utah.

P. ESCULENTA (4–16 inches) is hairy, with five leaf-segments; the large blue flowers are in a dense raceme.

May to July: on prairies and in dry woods from North Dakota to Oklahoma and eastward. *Plate 133.* This plant has long been known for its starchy tubers, eaten by Indians and European explorers, known as Indian breadroot, wild-potato, and pomme-blanche.

P. CUSPIDATA (4–24 inches) has leaves divided into five segments $\frac{1}{2}$–$1\frac{1}{2}$ inches long. The flowers are blue-violet.

April and May: on prairies from Montana and North Dakota to Oklahoma. *Plate 133.* *P. reverchoni* is less common, on rock outcrops in Oklahoma. It has lavender flowers and roundish bracts.

P. ARGOPHYLLA (to 2 feet) is white with silky hairs. The leaves have three or five segments. The dark blue flowers are in small clusters in the axils of bracts.

June to August: on prairies from North Dakota to Oklahoma. *Plate 133.* *P. digitata* has leaves like those of *P. argophylla*, with three or five segments. The standard is pale lavender, the wings blue-violet. SD to Okla. *P. tenuiflora* (1–2 feet) has mostly three leaf-segments, broadest in the outer half. The flowers are about $\frac{1}{5}$ inch long, blue-violet. ND and Mont to Kan. *Plate 134.* *P. linearifolia* may have some leaves undivided (with only one segment); the rest have three; all very narrow. Flowers blue-violet. Neb to Colo. *Plate 134.*

P. LANCEOLATA (1–2 feet) is markedly glandular. The leaf-segments are three, narrowly elliptic or broader in the outer half, about an inch long. The flowers are dull blue or whitish with a blue-tipped keel.

May to September: in sandy soil from the Cascade Mountains in Washington to Nebraska and southward to California and Nevada. *Plate 134.*

P. aromatica (6–12 inches), in western Colorado, has spreading stems. The flowers are in very short racemes, like heads. The corolla is about $\frac{1}{2}$ inch long, rose-purple or paler.

B. Species with palmately divided leaves whose leafy stem scarcely appears above ground, the leaves all at or near the ground.

P. HYPOGAEA has leaves with from five to seven narrow segments on a stalk mostly more than 2 inches long. The bluish flowers, about $\frac{1}{2}$ inch long, are in short, dense spikes.

April to June: on dry prairies and slopes from Nebraska and Wyoming to Oklahoma and Colorado. *Plate 134.*

P. megalantha, in Colorado and Utah, has from five to seven leaf-segments about an inch long on a stalk 2–3 inches long. The plant is whitish with small hairs lying flat. The flowers, $\frac{1}{2}$–$\frac{3}{4}$ inch long, are bluish, in a dense spike less than an inch long. *P. castorea*, in Utah, has a main stem up to 2 inches and leaf-stalks 2–5 inches long. The bluish flowers, less than $\frac{1}{2}$ inch long, are in dense spikes. s Utah to se Calif. *P. mephitica*, in s Utah, has five leaf-segments, gray-green and copiously downy. The corolla is blue, about $\frac{1}{2}$ inch long. *P. epipsila* is similar. The leaves are bright green, with three or five segments. The stem is 1–3 inches long. The pale violet corolla scarcely emerges from the calyx. s Utah.

II. *Species with pinnately divided leaves.*

SAMPSON'S SNAKE-ROOT, P. PSORALIOIDES (1–3 feet), has leaves divided into segments 2 or 3 inches long, but less than an inch wide. The flower-clusters (spikes) are borne on long stems, well above the leaves. The flowers are bluish-purple. There are at least two varieties, one of which is almost devoid of the scurfy glands.

May to July: on prairies and in open woodland in Kansas and Oklahoma. *Plate 134.* California-tea, *P. physodes* (1–2 feet), mostly west of our range, has been found in Idaho. It may be smooth, or beset with black hairs. The flowers are pale yellowish, the keel purple-tipped.

THE PRAIRIE-CLOVERS (PETALOSTEMON)

The flowers of *Petalostemon* are unlike those characteristic of the family. There is a standard, and four narrow petal-like bodies instead of wings and keel. These four are joined with the tube formed by the stalks of the five stamens that bear pollen. (Whether the petal-like bodies are really themselves stamens is largely a matter of words, since in many families petals may be transformed stamens.) The flowers are in dense spikes at the tips of the stems. The pods contain only one or two seeds. The leaves are pinnately divided.

PLATE 134

Psoralea linearifolia   *Morris*

Oldemeyer

Petalostemon compactus

Psoralea tenuiflora   *Green*

Petalostemon candidus   *Johnson*

Psoralea lanceolata   *Uttal*

Petalostemon purpureus   *Johnson*

Psoralea psoralioides   *Johnson*

Psoralea hypogaea   *Green*

Recently the genus has been merged with *Dalea*, because of the union of petals (if they are petals) with stamens, the stalk ("claw") of the standard, and other details. However, it is useful for our purposes to keep the two separate; our species can be assigned to one or the other with no great difficulty.

The name was originally spelled *Petalostemum*, and this is maintained by many botanists. The altered spelling is among names "conserved" and included in the International Code of Botanical Nomenclature.

I.   *Species whose calyx is smooth, and whose petals are white.*

These are common east of the Rocky Mountains (one occurs also west of the Mountains; one in Utah). The petals may turn yellow in age.

P. CANDIDUS (1–2 feet) has from three to nine (commonly five) leaf-segments mostly ½–1 inch long, lanceolate or very narrow. The leaves are mostly on the lower half of the stem. The blade of the standard is wider than long.

May to September: on low prairies from eastern North Dakota to Kansas and Oklahoma. *Plate 134.* *P. occidentalis* (to 32 inches) bends up from the base; segments from seven to nine. On drier prairies in Montana west of the Rockies; in the badlands of the Dakotas, and Wyoming, Colorado, western Kansas, and western Oklahoma; and in southeastern Utah. This may better be treated as a variety of *P. candidus*. *P. multiflorus*, in Kansas and Oklahoma, is also perhaps a variety of *P. candidus*. It is bushy, to 2 feet tall, with many leaves divided into from three to nine narrow segments. The inflorescence is short, a head rather than a spike.

II.   *Species whose calyx is hairy or velvety.*

"Smooth" in the following descriptions means "except for the calyx."

A. The first group of these species is wholly east of the Rocky Mountains.

P. VILLOSUS (1–2 feet) is bushy, with many crowded leaves divided into up to nineteen densely softly hairy ("villous") segments. The spikes are up to 4 inches long, on relatively short stalks. The petals are rose-purple (rarely white).

July to September: on dunes and prairies from North Dakota to eastern Colorado and Oklahoma. *Plate 135.*

P. MACROSTACHYUS (to 32 inches) has several stems.

Leaf-segments are five or seven, to 1 inch long, lanceolate or narrowly oblong, smooth. The spikes are dense, up to 6 inches long, long-stalked. The calyx is silky. The petals are small, white or pale yellowish.

June and July: on sandy river-banks and flood-plains from western Nebraska to northwestern Oklahoma. This is misnamed *P. compactus* by many authors, including the author of volumes 3 and 4 of this series. *P. compactus* proper has been generally known as *P. decumbens*, an earlier name. *Plate 134.* *P. pulcherrimus*, by some treated as a variety of the preceding species, is found in extreme southeastern Oklahoma. It has up to eleven segments. The hairs on the calyx lie flat. *P. microphyllus* also is found in our range only in extreme southern Oklahoma. It has from twenty-five to thirty-seven small segments about ⅕ inch long. The flowers are white, in spikes 1–2 inches long.

P. TENUIFOLIUS (1–2 feet) has a spike not more than ⅓ inch thick. The long points of the bracts project beyond the calyxes. On the high prairies of southwestern Kansas, adjacent Colorado, and northwestern Oklahoma.

P. PURPUREUS (1–3 feet) is the commonest species east of our area. The leaves have mostly five very narrow segments (some may have three). The plant is sparsely hairy. The leaves are borne well up on the stem. The flowers are rose or crimson ("purple"), in a very dense spike up to 2 inches long.

June to September: on prairies and dry hills from North Dakota and Montana to Oklahoma and eastern Colorado. *Plate 134.*

B. Three species with hairy calyx are found west of the continental divide.

P. SEARLSIAE (1–2 feet) is smooth. The leaves, mostly on the lower part of the stem, have from five to nine segments up to ½ inch long, elliptic or broader in the outer half. The spike is up to 4 inches long, on a stalk up to 6 inches. The petals are rose-pink.

April to June: in dry gravelly soil along our southern limits from southeastern California to southern Utah. *Plate 135.* *P. flavescens* has white flowers turning yellowish in age. The leaves have from three to seven thinly silky segments. In southeastern Utah. The crushed leaves are lemon-scented.

P. ORNATUS is much like *P. purpureus*. It is smooth.

The leaves have five or seven segments, broad between middle and tip. The spikes are 1–3 inches long. The flowers are pink or rose.

May to July: in sagebrush in eastern Washington and Oregon and the Snake River Plains in southwestern Idaho; also scattered in northwestern Nevada.

PLATE 135

Glycyrrhiza lepidota   *Hesselberg*

Dalea aurea   *Koch*

Dalea jamesii   *Koch*

Dalea formosa   *Hesselberg*

Hood

Petalostemon searlsiae

Amorpha nana   *W. Weber*

Johnson

Petalostemon villosus

Dalea lanata   *Morris*

Amorpha fruticosa   *Phelps*

INDIGO-BUSHES AND PEA-BUSHES (DALEA)

The numerous species of *Dalea* include herbs, shrubs, and even small trees. They are largely Mexican, but many enter our area. The leaves are mostly pinnately divided (in some species with few segments, palmately). Stems, leaves, and inflorescence are commonly covered with glands. The flowers are in spikes, heads, or racemes, varying in color from white to yellow, rose, and purple. Distinguishing marks are the narrow stalk-like bases of the petals (botanists call them "claws," I suppose because they hang on by them); the shape of the standard, often indented at the base, sometimes wider than long; and, except in some shrubby species, the union of the petals with the tube formed by the joined stalks of the stamens. The pod contains one or two seeds.

The genus is a difficult one in which to identify the species. They have been greatly confused in the standard manuals. For the relation of *Dalea* with *Petalostemon*, see the description of the latter genus.

I. *Two of our species are shrubby, with woody stems. These are barely within our southern limits.*

D. FORMOSA (1–4 feet) is smooth. The leaves are divided into seven or nine small, thick segments (or rarely up to fifteen). The petals are rose-purple. Barely in our range in southern Utah and Colorado. *Plate 135*. D. *thompsonae* has been found close to the Utah–Arizona border. It is a low shrub with orange glands. The flowers are rose-purple.

II. *Herbaceous species, with no woody stems.*

A. Two of these have yellow petals.

D. AUREA (1–2 feet) is silky and whitish. Leaf-segments are generally five, less commonly three or seven, about $\frac{1}{2}$ inch long. The spikes are dense, 1–2 inches long, with silky bracts. The pod also is silky.

May to July: on prairies from South Dakota and Wyoming to Colorado. *Plate 135*. D. *jamesii* is likewise silky, but with three segments about an inch long. The bracts may be purplish. In grassland in Kansas and Colorado. *Plate 135*.

B. The remaining herbaceous species have petals of other colors than yellow.

D. ENNEANDRA, with nine or fewer segments, has white flowers loosely disposed in curved racemes.

May to August: in dry soil from North Dakota to Oklahoma and eastward. The correct name is most likely to be D. *laxiflora*.

D. *lanata*, in southwestern Kansas, southeastern Colorado, and Oklahoma, and southward, has spreading, densely downy stems 1–2 feet long. The leaves have from seven to thirteen downy segments. The spikes are slender, up to 4 inches long, with many flowers. These are red or purple, or, rarely, white. In dry soil. *Plate 135*. D. *terminalis*, also densely downy, may have fifteen segments. The spikes are slender, the flowers red-purple. The calyx is smooth. In Utah.

D. LEPORINA (1–5 feet) has many smooth stems and branches, bearing smooth leaves with from nineteen to thirty-five segments. The spikes are dense, 1–2½ inches long, the petals blue or purplish with white bases. The pod is silky. This may be entirely south of our area, its place being taken as far north as South Dakota (and eastward) by D. *alopecuroides*, with white petals perhaps tinged with rose, and fewer segments (from fifteen to twenty-three).

D. *kingii*, in Nevada, has yellowish-green, sparsely hairy stems and leaves; the branches bear small spines. The leaf-segments are from two to seven, up to $\frac{2}{5}$ inch long. The flowers are purple.

FALSE INDIGOES AND LEADPLANTS (AMORPHA)

The botanical name signifies "formless," and refers to the flower which has only one petal (the standard). These are somewhat shrubby plants with leaves divided pinnately into numerous segments. The purple flowers are in long, dense, tapering spikes at and near the top of the plant, their yellow stamens projecting beyond the perianth. The pod has only one or two seeds; it projects from the calyx when ripe. For other false indigoes see *Baptisia*.

These are eastern plants, with one definitely shrubby exception.

LEADPLANT, A. CANESCENS (20–40 inches), has a dense covering of white hairs on the leaves. There are from fifteen to fifty-one segments $\frac{1}{3}$–$\frac{1}{2}$ inch long.

May to August: on prairies and in dry woodland from North Dakota to Oklahoma. A. *nana* (1–3 feet) is smooth, with from twenty-one to forty-one segments less than $\frac{1}{2}$ inch long. The flower-spikes are only about 3 inches long. In Kansas and Oklahoma. *Plate 135*. A. *fruticosa* is definitely shrubby ("fruticose"), almost smooth, with from eleven to thirty-five segments. From North Dakota to Oklahoma. *Plate 135*.

GLYCYRRHIZA

The leaves of *Glycyrrhiza* are divided pinnately into numerous narrow, sharp-pointed segments. The genus is named for the large, sweet-tasting rhizome (*glycy-* "sweet"; *rhiza*, "root," really a stem). The flowers are in dense, spikelike racemes. The stamens are alternately longer and shorter. The pod contains several seeds. It is generally covered with hooked prickles or glands, and does not split open.

WILD LICORICE, G. LEPIDOTA (1–3 feet), is covered at maturity with small scales (*lepidota*, "scaly"). The leaves have up to nineteen segments about an inch long. The flowers are yellowish-white.

May to July: mostly in moist soil, scattered in waste ground throughout our area. *Plate 135.*

G. glabra is widely cultivated for commercial licorice (a corruption of the scientific name), and may be found near our southwestern limits. It has ovate segments 1–2 inches long, and pale blue flowers. The pods lack prickles.

PARRYELLA

One, or possibly two species of *Parryella* may be found near our southern limits. They are really shrubs, but so small that the woody nature may not be apparent. The numerous leaf-segments are marked with glandular dots. The small, yellowish flowers are in spikelike racemes. The small pods contain one seed. The plants have been used by Indians in making brooms and baskets; and the seeds for toothache and killing insects.

P. filifolia has very narrow or even threadlike (*fili-*) segments. The racemes are loose, up to 6 inches long. *P. rotundata* is densely downy, with segments nearly as broad as long ("rotund"). The racemes are dense, less than an inch long.

The peanut, *Arachis hypogaea*, has been reported to grow in Kansas and Oklahoma, but is not currently listed. It may be known by four leaf-segments, on horizontal stems, and very small yellow flowers in spikes in the axils. To be expected in waste ground.

CROTALARIA

One species of *Crotalaria* is found in our area.

RATTLE-BOX, C. SAGITTALIS, owes its botanical name to the stipules of at least some leaves, which together form an arrowhead (*sagitta*, "arrow"). The leaf-blade has only one segment (i.e. is undivided). There are generally from two to four flowers in clusters opposite the leaves. The petals are yellow, and are scarcely longer than the calyx. The English name refers to the mature seed-pod, within which the seeds break loose and rattle as the plant is shaken. *Crotalus* is a rattlesnake. *Plate 136.*

STYLOSANTHES

One species of *Stylosanthes* is found in Kansas and Oklahoma. Pencil-flower, *S. biflora*, is more or less erect, 6–24 inches tall. The leaves are pinnately divided into three segments, each tipped with a minute spine. The uppermost leaf-stalks are surrounded by small bristly tubes formed from the stipules. The small yellow or orange flowers are clustered at the tips of stems. Both English and botanical names refer to the narrow and relatively long tube of the calyx, at the end of which petals and stamens are attached (the "pencil"; *stylo-*, "rod"). A small weed in dry woods, thickets, and old fields.

CORONILLA

Crown-vetch, *C. varia*, is cultivated in the East and is sometimes found growing wild. In our range it occurs only in South Dakota. It is bushy, up to several feet tall, the leaves divided pinnately into from eleven to twenty-five narrow segments. The pink flowers are in umbels on long stalks which grow from the axils.

PETERIA

We have one species of *Peteria*.

P. THOMPSONAE (8–16 inches) has from thirteen to
 twenty-one grayish leaf-segments ⅓–½ inch long,
more or less oval, with spinelike stipules. The flowers

are in several dense racemes. The yellow corolla is ⅔–1
inch long. The pods are narrow, flat, about 2 inches
long.

 May to July: on plains and foothills from southwestern Idaho to Utah and Nevada.

Lady's-fingers or kidney-vetch, *Anthyllis vulneraria*, has been
found in our range only in North Dakota, and only in one field, near
Fargo. It has downy stems 1–2 feet tall; leaves pinnately divided into

from five to thirteen narrow segments (except some lower leaves with
a single segment); a head of yellow or red flowers. The calyx is
densely hairy.

SWEET-VETCHES (HEDYSARUM)

The leaves of *Hedysarum* are pinnately divided
into many small segments. The flowers are in racemes
on stalks from the axils. The keel is noticeably longer
than the wings. The pods are flat, constricted between
seeds; when ripe they break into oval, one-seeded segments which do not open (compare *Desmodium*).

H. BOREALE (1–2 feet) has from nine to fifteen leaf-
 segments ½–1 inch long, nearly smooth. The
showy rose-purple flowers are in racemes from the
axils, ½–1 inch long. The pod has from two to five
sections ("joints").

 June and July: in cañons and valleys in Colorado
and northeastern Oregon. *Plate 136. H. gremiale*, in
the foothills of the Uintah Basin in northeastern
Utah, is similar. The pods are beset with bristles.

H. OCCIDENTALE (16–32 inches) has from nine to
 twenty-one leaf-segments ⅖–1⅕ inches long. The
flowers, from twenty to eighty in a raceme, are reddish
or purplish, nearly an inch long.

 June to September: at high altitudes from Washington to Idaho, Montana, and Wyoming. *Plate 136.
H. alpinum* is similar, with pods less than ¼ inch wide,
flowers less than ⅔ inch long. In northeastern Wyoming, Montana, and South Dakota. *Plate 136.*

H. SULPHURESCENS (1–2 feet) has from twenty to
 one hundred pale yellow or nearly white flowers,
½–¾ inch long, in a raceme.

 June to August: in open forest-land from the
Cascades in northern Washington to Montana and
Wyoming. *Plate 136.*

BUSH-CLOVERS (LESPEDEZA)

A number of species of *Lespedeza*, a genus of the
eastern states, are found in Kansas and Oklahoma.
The English name is misleading, since they do not
resemble the true clovers (and the botanical name was
a misprint for Cespedeza!). The leaves are pinnately
divided into three segments. The small violet, crimson, pink, or yellowish flowers are in heads, spikes, or
racemes, or singly in the axils. The seed-pods are
short, roundish, one-seeded. Some pods are formed by
flowers that do not open. Some species hybridize,
yielding plants difficult to name. Some are valuable
for forage.

I. *Species with violet, pink, or crimson flowers.*
 The first four creep or trail on the ground.

L. REPENS has violet flowers in small clusters near the
 tips of erect branches commonly 2–3 inches tall.
Plate 136. L. procumbens differs in being hairy and in
having flowers in racemes. Korean-clover, *L. stipulacea*, and Japanese-clover, *L. striata*, are cultivated

for forage and found wild chiefly on roadsides and in
waste ground. Both have conspicuous, relatively large
stipules, and small pink flowers. *L. striata:* Leaf-stalks
generally less than ⅛ inch. Kan, Okla. *L. stipulacea:*
Segments of younger leaves fringed with hairs. Kan.
Plate 136.

 The following five species grow mostly in dry
woodlands. The flowers are rose-pink or violet.

L. VIOLACEA (1–3 feet) has elliptic leaf-segments
 scarcely 2 inches long, on mostly numerous
branches. The flowers are in racemes mostly longer
than the leaves. Kansas and Oklahoma. *Plate 137. L.
virginica* (1–4 feet): Segments narrow, about 1 inch,
crowded; leaf-stalks short. Flowers crowded in the
axils, many of the leaves extending beyond them. Kan.
Plate 136. L. intermedia (6–24 inches): Segments ½–
1½ inches; leaf-stalks longer. Flowers as in the preceding. Okla. *Plate 137. L. nuttallii* (2–4 feet): Segments 1–1½ inches. Pink flowers at tips of branches

PLATE 136

Lespedeza repens *McDowell*

Crotalaria sagittalis *Hesselberg*

Lespedeza stipulacea *Johnson*

Lespedeza virginica *Ryker*

Hedysarum boreale *Korling*

Hedysarum occidentale *Uttal*

Hedysarum sulphurescens *Korling*

Hedysarum alpinum *Guppy*

Lespedeza stuevei *Johnson*

and clustered in axils. Kan, possibly Neb. *L. stuevii* (1–4 feet): Segments woolly or velvety underneath, oblong, $\frac{2}{5}$–1 inch. Flowers not so crowded. Kan, Okla. *Plate 136.*

II. *Species with yellowish or cream flowers.*

DUSTY-CLOVER, L. CAPITATA (2–4 feet), is named for the dense ("capitate") tufts of cream flowers whose petals are partly concealed by the long teeth of the hairy calyx and by the bracts; all in the axils of leaves. The leaf-segments are mostly narrow and thick.

July to September: in dry soil from Nebraska to Oklahoma. *Plate 137.*

L. hirta (2–5 feet) is similar, the calyx-teeth not so long, the flower-clusters rather less dense and borne on stalks projecting beyond the leaves. Segments 1–2 inches long. Plant with tawny or silvery hairs. se Kan, Okla. *Plate 137. L. cuneata* (3–5 feet): Segments less than 1 inch, tending to be wedge-shaped ("cuneate"). Flowers singly or in small clusters in the axils. se Kan. From Asia.

TICK-TREFOILS, BEGGAR'S-TICKS, OR STICKTIGHTS (DESMODIUM)

The English names well describe the most familiar characteristics of *Desmodium*. Every one who has walked much in fields and woods in the eastern half of this country, in late summer and autumn, knows them, even if he does not know what they are. The seed-pods are formed of rather triangular sections corner to corner or oval joints end to end, each containing a seed. These are detached at a touch and cling to clothing by the numerous tiny hooked hairs on their surface. The plants will certainly be classed as undesirable weeds by most persons. Yet the flowers are individually handsome and in some species make an attractive display which will interest the naturalist (see *D. canadense*).

The leaves of *Desmodium* are pinnately divided into three segments. The flowers, mostly purplish or rose, are in racemes which may be branched, or in a more ample inflorescence.

Our fifteen species are all eastern, in our range found only from North Dakota to Oklahoma. The genus is lacking in the vast area west of those states. Species are most easily identified by the shape of the pod-joints and the leaf segments.

Flowering is from July to September.

I. *Species with pod-joints flat on top, nearly triangular, joined by their upper corners, the connection very narrow.*

D. GLUTINOSUM has leaves with broad, ovate segments, all close beneath the inflorescence, which terminates the stem. The flowering branches are beset with minute hooked (therefore adhesive) hairs. From North Dakota to Oklahoma. *D. nudiflorum:* Our only species with the flowering stem leafless ("nude"). Leaves on other stems, near their tips. Kan, Okla. *D. pauciflorum:* Stems horizontal or erect. Flowers white, few (*pauci-*), on branches from the axils. Kan, Okla.

II. *Species with pod-joints not flat on top, oval, diamond-shaped, or elliptic, joined by a comparatively wide connection.*

D. ROTUNDIFOLIUM is our only species with prostrate stems; only the slender, few-flowered racemes stand erect. The leaf-segments are mostly round ("rotund"). In Kansas and Oklahoma. *Plate 137.*

The following four species have four or fewer joints to a pod. All are found in Kansas and Oklahoma.

D. marilandicum: Segments nearly round, less than 2 inches; leaf-stalks $\frac{1}{2}$–1 inch. *D. ciliare:* Segments $\frac{1}{2}$–$1\frac{1}{5}$ inches, ovate; leaf-stalk less than $\frac{1}{2}$ inch. *D. sessilifolium:* Segments $1\frac{1}{2}$–3 inches, narrow; leaf-stalk very short (the leaf almost "sessile"). Possibly also in Nebraska. *D. rigidum:* Stem downy. Segments ovate, 2–$2\frac{1}{2}$ inches; leaf-stalk less than 1 inch.

Two species, with more than four joints to a pod, have conspicuous ovate stipules $\frac{1}{2}$ inch long. Both from Nebraska to Oklahoma.

D. canescens: Stems generally hairy or hoary. Segments ovate or somewhat diamond-shaped, 2–5 inches. Pod-joints curved above and below, $\frac{1}{4}$–$\frac{1}{2}$ inch. *D. illinoense:* Similar. Segments smaller. Joints $\frac{1}{6}$–$\frac{1}{3}$ inch.

The remaining species, with more than four joints to a pod, have narrow stipules less than $\frac{1}{2}$ inch long.

D. canadense: Flowers many, on many branches, rose turning blue. Segments lanceolate or narrowly ovate. Joints curved less sharply above, with wide connection. ND to Okla. *Plate 138. D. cuspidatum:* Segments ovate, tapering to a point, 3–6 inches. Joints barely curved on top, with wide connections. Neb, Okla. *D. paniculatum:* Segments narrowly lanceolate, $1\frac{1}{2}$–4 inches; leaf-stalks 1 inch or longer. Inflorescence much branched ("paniculate"). Kan, Okla. *D. laevigatum:* Segments ovate, sharp-pointed, $1\frac{3}{4}$–$3\frac{1}{8}$ inches. Joints nearly diamond-shaped, angled above and below. Okla. *D. viridiflorum:* Hairy or woolly. Flowers pink turning green (*viridi-*). Segments diamond-shaped or triangular, blunt, 2–5 inches. Joints diamond-shaped. Okla.

PLATE 137

Lespedeza capitata *Gottscho*

Thermopsis montana *Lomax*

Desmodium rotundifolium *Johnson*

Thermopsis rhombifolia *Hoff*

Lespedeza hirta *Johnson*

Lespedeza violacea *Johnson*

Thermopsis divaricarpa *Uttal*

Lespedeza intermedia *Scribne*

THERMOPSIS

The yellow flowers of *Thermopsis* are in tall racemes. The leaves have blades divided palmately into three segments. The ten stamens are all separate. The pod is flat, with few seeds.

These plants are sometimes called false lupines, because of the superficial resemblance. The name refers to this, *Thermos* having been applied to plants now named *Lupinus*.

GOLDEN-PEA, T. DIVARICARPA (1–2 feet) has leaf-
    segments 1–2½ inches long.
April to July: in pine forests from Wyoming to Utah and Colorado. *Plate 137*.

T. RHOMBIFOLIA (4–12 inches) has leaf-segments ⅘–
    1⅗ inches long. The pod may form a half-circle or be even more curved.
April to June: on dry plains and slopes, especially where sandy, from North Dakota to Nebraska and Colorado; also in western Montana. *Plate 137*.

T. MONTANA (16–40 inches) has very narrow or elliptic leaf-segments up to 4 inches long. The softly hairy pod may be erect or horizontal.
May to August: on wet meadows or in well-drained soil from Washington to California and eastward to western Montana and Colorado. *Plate 137*.

BAPTISIA

The flowers of *Baptisia* are white, cream, yellow, or violet, in racemes. The plants are much branched, bushy, the leaves of most species divided palmately into three segments (in some the stipules seem like two more segments on the short leaf-stalk). In some species there is only one segment. The seed-pods are rather woody, thick, beaked, with a stalk above the level of the calyx. The leaves of most species turn black when they wither or are dried.

Our species come from the eastern states across our eastern boundaries. Several have been known as false indigo; in early days a blue dye, an inferior indigo, was extracted from them.

B. NUTTALLIANA (1–4 feet) tends to be downy. The
    branches are generally zigzag. The leaves have almost no stalks; the segments an inch long or longer. The stipules are inconspicuous. The petals are ⅕–⅗ inch long, yellow.
April to June: on prairies and in woodlands in Oklahoma. *Plate 138*.
    B. viridis generally has only two segments on the upper leaves; on some only one. The numerous flowers are in clusters up to a foot long. Petals about ½ inch,

cream. Okla. *Plate 138*. *B. sphaerocarpa:* Similar. All leaves with three segments. Okla.

B. LEUCOPHAEA (8–32 inches) has leaves with stipules ⅘–1⅗ inches long, and segments up to 4 inches long. The racemes, up to 8 inches long, slope downward. The flowers are white or cream.
May and June: on prairies and in woodlands from Nebraska to Oklahoma. *Plate 138*. *B. leucantha* (3–6 feet) has leaf-segments about 2 inches long. Stipules small, soon lost. Flowers in erect racemes up to 2 feet long. Petals white, the standard perhaps with purple marks, the wings almost an inch long. On prairies and in open woodland from Nebraska to Oklahoma.

B. MINOR (to 5 feet) is our only blue-flowered species.
    It is bushy. The leaf-segments may be 3 inches long; stipules about ½ inch.
May and June: in woodland and open places from Kansas to Oklahoma. *Plate 138*. This is considered by some to be a variety of *B. australis*, which grows farther to the east. It has smaller flowers and pods, larger leaf-segments.

SOPHORA

We have two herbaceous species of *Sophora* (most are woody). The flowers have ten separate stamens. The pods are narrow, constricted between seeds.

WHITE-LOCO, S. NUTTALLIANA (about 3 feet), has
    oblong leaf-segments nearly ½ inch long, smooth or nearly so. The flowers, in racemes, are white or yellowish.

April to June: on plains and prairies from South Dakota and Wyoming to Oklahoma and Utah. *Plate 139*. The plants may form dense colonies. The foliage is poisonous to livestock.
    S. stenophylla, in southern Utah, has very narrow (*steno-*) leaf-segments ½–1 inch long, downy on both surfaces. The plant is elsewhere velvety-woolly. The flowers are blue.

PLATE 138

Tephrosia virginiana   *Ryker*

Desmodium canadense   *Gottscho*

Baptisia leucophaea   *D. Richards*

Baptisia minor   *McIntyre*

Baptisia nuttalliana   *Mabel Nelson*

Baptisia viridis   *Johnson*

TEPHROSIA

Our species of *Tephrosia* are bushy, with flowers in spikes or spikelike racemes. The flowers mostly have a large standard. The pods are narrow and flat.

GOAT'S-RUE, T. VIRGINIANA (1–2 feet), has crowded flowers. The flowers have a pale yellow standard, the wings and keel pink or lavender. The plant may be silky-hairy. The leaves have from eleven to twenty-seven segments.

May: in sandy soil from South Dakota to Oklahoma. *Plate 138. T. onobrychoides* has segments up to 2 inches long. The flowers are widely spaced in long racemes. The petals are white turning rose in age. June and July: in sandy woods and on open ground.

DEER-CLOVERS, DEER-VETCHES, TREFOILS (LOTUS)

The leaves of *Lotus* are pinnately or almost palmately divided into small segments, mostly not numerous. The flowers of our species are yellow, with some red or turning red in age. They do not exceed $\frac{1}{2}$ inch in length. The stamens commonly have flat stalks.

The name suggests water-lilies, or the legendary plant of the "lotus-eaters" which induced visions and oblivion. But in classical times the word lotus was used for a number of different plants, including trees.

The genus is typically west-American. We have twelve species, only two at all widespread in our range.

I.   *Species whose leaves are divided into five or generally more segments.*

L. PINNATUS (8–16 inches) is stout; the leaves have from five to nine segments. The umbel, on a stalk 2–4 inches long, contains from three to twelve very short-stalked flowers. The standard and keel are yellow, the wings white.

May to July: in moist soil in Washington, Oregon, and Idaho. *Plate 139.*

Three species in this group barely come within our western boundary. *L. oblongifolius* (Calif, possibly Ore): From seven to eleven narrow, sharp segments. From one to five flowers; standard yellow, some with purple veins; wings pale. *Plate 139. L. tomentellus* (se Calif, w Nev): Prostrate, white-woolly. From four to eight thick, short segments. One or two flowers, yellow turning red. *Plate 139. L. crassifolius* (Columbia River; Calif): From seven to fifteen segments. From eight to fifteen flowers, greenish-yellow and reddish. *Plate 139.*

II. *Species whose leaves are divided into not more than five segments.*

   A. Plants with flowers at and near the tips of largely leafless stalks.

L. PURSHIANUS (6–30 inches) is bushy, hairy or smooth. The leaf-segments mostly number three.

The flower-stalks are about $\frac{1}{2}$ inch long. The petals are white, tinged or veined with pink, about $\frac{1}{4}$ inch long.

May to October: common in dry sandy and rocky places throughout our range. *Plate 139.* Known to many authors as *L. americanus.*

L. rigidus (1–3 feet) enters our area from the south, in Utah. Segments three or five. Flowers two or three together on a long stalk, yellow with some red or purple. *Plate 140. L. utahensis*, in southern Utah, has leaves almost without stalks, the segments (from three to six) thus simulating a group of small undivided leaves. Flowers two or three on a stalk longer than the leaves. This apparently hybridizes with *L. rigidus*, yielding plants which were long known as *L. longebracteatus*; in this concept *L. utahensis* was merged.

L. nevadensis is found along our western boundary, in Nevada. It is prostrate, forming mats of wiry branches. Segments three or five, broad. Flowers, one or more, on a stalk up to an inch long, yellowish, about $\frac{1}{4}$ inch long.

L. corniculatus, introduced from Europe and much planted in the Northeast to hold banks, has been found in Idaho, but otherwise seems to be entirely east and west of the area. Flowers from three to fifteen at the tip of a stem 1–5 inches long; such stems at the tips of rather sprawling leafy stems. Segments five, with two leaflike stipules. *Plate 139.*

   B. Plants with flowers in the axils of leaves, lacking conspicuous stalks.

L. WRIGHTII (8–16 inches) has flowers borne singly or two or three together. The petals are yellow or orange turning reddish. The leaves are almost without stalks, the segments (from three to six) palmately disposed or nearly so.

May to September: common in open pine forests in Utah and western Colorado. *Plate 139.*

L. denticulatus (8–20 inches) may be found within our western boundary in the Cascade Mountains. Leaves with two segments at the tip of the midrib and one or two at the side; they may be finely toothed

PLATE 139

Sophora nuttalliana

Wilson

Lotus oblongifolius

Myrick

Lotus corniculatus

Ryker

Lotus pinnatus

Gerdel

Lotus wrightii

Johnson

Lotus tomentellus

Hesselberg

Lotus humistratus

Johnson

Lotus purshianus

Finne

Lotus crassifolius

Korling

("denticulate"). Flowers whitish-cream, the standard purple-tinged on the back. *L. humistratus* has been recorded in the Intermountain Region, coming presumably from the south. It is prostrate or nearly so, densely and softly hairy. Flowers single. *Plate 139*. (*Humi-*, "soil"; *stratus*, "lying.")

INDIGOFERA

One species of *Indigofera* is barely within our range.

Scarlet-pea, *I. miniata*, has prostrate or upward-trending stems, to nearly 2 feet long. The leaves have from five to nine segments. The flowers, in short spikes, have salmon-pink (*not* scarlet!) petals and almost separate sepals. The narrow pod is not more than an inch long. On prairies in extreme southern Kansas and Oklahoma, flowering in May and June. *Plate 140*.

SESBANIA

Most species of *Sesbania* are shrubs. The leaves are divided pinnately into numerous segments. The flowers are yellow, in loose racemes. We have one herbaceous species.

S. MACROCARPA is smooth, with bright green leaves. The racemes have few flowers. The petals are pale yellow, commonly streaked and spotted with brownish-purple. The pods are up to 9 inches long but only ⅛ inch thick, with many seeds.

August to October: in bottomlands in eastern Kansas and probably elsewhere within our eastern boundaries. *Plate 140*. Named *S. exaltata* in the Southeast. Indians use the fibers for making fishing-lines.

THE LUPINES (LUPINUS)

If we were to recognize all the species (nearly 600 for North America) that have been proposed in the genus *Lupinus*, they would form perhaps our largest genus, and it would be quite impossible to get them into the same book as *Astragalus*, *Eriogonum*, and other monstrous assemblages (what we now call *L. argenteus* has over fifty names!). The difficulty is that the plants one finds seem not to be separable into groups by sufficiently sharp lines; they "intergrade." So one botanist's species is another's variety or subspecies, or a minor variant that deserves no name at all. The plants undoubtedly cross in nature (our garden varieties are hybrids), yielding plants of mixed heredities, which, when *they* reproduce, yield plants differing in minor characteristics. Modern workers have reversed the former proliferation of names and have assigned multitudes of forms to a smaller number of species. The descriptions and names here presented cannot pretend to be the last word; but they have at least tentative approval by Doctor David Dunn, the leading student of the genus.

So, instead of several hundred species in our area we recognize about seventy. Even this number is large enough to dismay the amateur. May he be consoled by the knowledge that professional botanists are also dismayed!*

The genus is easy to recognize. Its leaf-blades are divided palmately into five or more segments. Its flowers are in racemes which generally terminate the stems. The standard is mostly erect, in many species with its sides bent back. The calyx is commonly two-lipped (i.e. cleft at the sides so as to form an upper and a lower "lip").

I. *Species with no visible leafy-stem above ground.*

The leaves spring directly from ground level. *L. aridus* and *L. shockleyi* may be like this in places; see under II B. *L. grayi*, in II A, has leaves mostly near the ground. *L. caespitosus*, below, might be placed under II.

A. Species whose leaves are smooth on the upper surface.

L. BREVICAULIS has from five to eight leaf-segments; the leaf-stalks are at least ⅘–1⅗ inches long. The racemes are short, like heads. The flowers are about ¼ inch long, blue, or yellowish on the lower half. The upper lip of the calyx is almost lacking.

May and June: on sandy plains from the Sierra Nevada to eastern Oregon and western Colorado. *Plate 141*.

L. uncialis (tufts, not over 1 inch tall): Four or five segments; leaf-stalk ⅓–⅖ inch. Flowers in axils, ¼ inch, pale yellowish, the keel purple-tipped. Nev and perhaps adjacent states. *L. flavoculatus*: From seven to ten segments. Leaf-stalks and raceme-stalks

*We received 203 new transparencies for the genus in this volume, of which 53 are unidentified.

PLATE 140

Indigofera miniata *Siebel*

Lupinus lyallii *Korling*

Lupinus subvexus *Hickman*

Lupinus caudatus *Scribner*

Lupinus argenteus *Korling*

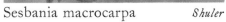

Lotus rigidus *Jarrett*

Sesbania macrocarpa *Shuler*

Lupinus latifolius *Johnson*

lying on the ground, bending up. Racemes 2–4 inches, dense. Flowers violet with a yellow center. sw Nev.

L. ODORATUS has from seven to nine leaf-segments, on a leaf-stalk $\frac{1}{3}$–$\frac{1}{2}$ inch long. The racemes are loosely flowered, $\frac{1}{4}$–$\frac{1}{2}$ inch long; the flowers about $\frac{1}{2}$ inch, blue with a yellow center.

April and May: on sandy slopes in western Nevada.

B. Species of group I whose leaves are silky or hairy on the upper surface. The leaves have generally from five to seven segments.

L. CAESPITOSUS has hairy leaves, with stalks 2–4 inches long. The stalk of the raceme is $\frac{2}{5}$–$\frac{4}{5}$ inch long, the racemes $\frac{4}{5}$–$1\frac{2}{5}$ inches; they are dense, with flowers in circles, pale blue, lilac, or whitish.

June and July: in gravelly valleys from eastern Oregon to Montana and southward to eastern California, Nevada, and Colorado. *Plate 141. L. lyallii*: Silky or roughly hairy. Leaf-stalks and raceme-stalks sprawling, the leaf-stalks $\frac{1}{6}$–$\frac{2}{5}$ inch. Racemes $\frac{2}{5}$–$\frac{4}{5}$ inch, dense. Flowers blue, perhaps with a pale center. High altitudes, from Wash to Ida and the Sierra Nevada and w Nev. *Plate 140.* The rough-hairy plants are in Nev and Ida. *L. lobbii*: Hairy. Leaf-stalks $\frac{1}{6}$–$\frac{1}{4}$ inch. Racemes 1–2$\frac{1}{2}$ inches. Flowers in circles about $\frac{1}{3}$ inch apart, violet with whitish center. On hillsides from e Ore to Mont, Utah, and Nev. *Plate 141.* Some botanists treat this and the following as varieties of *L. lepidus. L. cusickii*: Leaves hoary, on stalks about 1$\frac{1}{2}$ inches long. Racemes on stalks less than an inch. From one to three circles of blue flowers. From e Ore to Mont, Nev, and Utah.

II. *Species with evident leafy stems (in some, very short).*

A. Plants whose flowers are in distinct circles in the racemes, the lower circles at least $\frac{2}{5}$ inch apart.

1. Plants whose leaves are smooth or nearly so on the upper surface.

L. ARGENTEUS (8–28 inches) has from seven to nine leaf-segments. The racemes are 2–5 inches long, the circles of flowers about $\frac{1}{2}$ inch apart, blue, lilac, or whitish.

May to October: from dry slopes in northeastern California and Nevada to Montana, South Dakota, and Colorado. *Plate 140.* Several plants formerly listed as species, with foliage not smooth, are now shown to be so closely related to *L. argenteus* as to be perhaps treated as subspecies of that species. Chief among these are *L. rubricaulis* and *L. spathulatus. Plate 141. L. floribundus*: Segments of basal leaves broad near the

blunt tip. Flowers $\frac{1}{4}$ inch or less. Otherwise like *L. argenteus* and perhaps better considered a variety. se Ida, from s Mont to Colo. *Plate 143. L. caudatus* (see under 3) is closely related. *L. alpestris* is probably a hybrid between the two, which has finely downy leaves.

L. LATIFOLIUS (1–7 feet) has seven or nine segments to a leaf. The racemes are 6–18 inches long, the circles of flowers $\frac{1}{4}$–$\frac{3}{4}$ inch apart, blue or purplish or with some pink.

April to July: in dry places, on forested slopes, from Canada to northeastern California and Nevada. *Plate 140. L. superbus* (4–7 inches): Segments from five to eleven. Racemes 6–10 inches. Flowers in circles up to 1$\frac{1}{5}$ inches apart, blue, purple, or reddish. Flowers about $\frac{1}{2}$ inch. Wet meadows and stream margins from Canada to the Sierra Nevada, and to Wyo. *L. subvexus* (6–16 inches): Segments from five to nine. Racemes 2–6 inches. Flowers dark violet, lilac, or rose. With sagebrush, ne Calif. *Plate 140.*

2. Plants with hairs on the upper surface of leaf-segments; these may lie flat on the surface, or be downy, or hoary, or erect, but not silvery-silky (for which see under 3).

Most of these are not widespread in our range.

L. NANUS (4–16 inches) has from six to eight leaf-segments, finely downy. The racemes are 2–5 inches long, with from two to eight circles of blue flowers with a white or yellow center, up to 1$\frac{1}{5}$ inches apart.

April and May: in grassy and brushy places in northeastern Nevada. *Plate 141.* This is one subspecies, native in California, that has apparently been introduced farther east.

L. inyoensis (20–24 inches): Segments from seven to nine, downy. Racemes 2–4 inches. Flowers blue or violet. Sandy places, Sierra foothills, se Calif. *L. grayi* (4–7 inches): Stems horizontal, bending up. Leaves mostly basal. From eight to ten segments, hoary. Racemes 2–6 inches. Flowers purplish with yellow center. Dry slopes with pines, Sierra Nevada, L. Tahoe region. *Plate 141. L. sublanatus*: Similar; leaf-segments less than 1 inch. e of the Sierra Nevada. *L. pachylobus* (4–12 inches): From six to eight segments, hairy. Racemes 2–3 inches, few-flowered. Flowers blue with white center. Grassy slopes, e slope of the Sierra Nevada, c Calif. *L. malacophyllus* (4–6 inches): From five to seven segments, downy. Racemes 2–3 inches, with from three to nine circles. Flowers purplish. Sandy soil, w Nev, possibly e Calif. *L. evermannii* (6–8 inches): Tufts. From six to eight segments, downy. Racemes rather dense. s Ida, s Wyo, ne Nev. Rare.

L. sabinianus (2–4 feet): From eight to eleven segments, downy with fine hairs lying flat. Racemes 6–12 inches, with circles nearly an inch apart. Flowers

PLATE 141

Lupinus confertus   *Spellenberg*

Lupinus lobbii   *Johnson*

Lupinus minimus   *B. J. Cox*

Lupinus caespitosus   *Korling*

Lupinus spathulatus   *Fleak*

Lupinus grayi   *Spellenberg*

Lupinus brevicaulis   *Stockert*

Lupinus nanus   *Johnson*

yellow, occasionally tinged purple. Dry hills, se Wash, ne Ore. *L. volutans* (3–12 inches): Six or seven segments, hairy. Racemes 4–6 inches. Hillsides and sandy washes, se Ore, e and s Nev, Utah. *L. suksdorffii* (10–40 inches): From seven to nine segments, downy or hairy. Racemes 4–6 inches. Flowers blue or lavender. Dry hillsides, Columbia R in Wash and Ore. *L. vallicola* (6–16 inches): From six to eight segments, downy. Racemes $\frac{1}{2}$–5 inches, few-flowered. Grassy valleys and hills, Columbia R valley, Wash.

3.   Plants whose leaves are silvery-silky.

L. CAUDATUS (1–2 feet) has leaves with seven or eight segments (or ten in a subspecies). The racemes are 4–8 inches long (or 2 inches at high altitudes), with close circles of flowers. The upper lip of the calyx has a "spur" – a hollow extension – at the base (but in some subspecies this is not evident).

May to July: in forest and sagebrush from Oregon to Montana and southward to eastern California and Colorado. *Plate 140*. Plants of high altitudes in extreme Nevada form a subspecies, which has been known as *L. montigenus*. *L. minimus* (4–8 inches): From six to eight segments. Racemes 2–6 inches; circles of blue flowers $\frac{1}{5}$–$\frac{4}{5}$ inch apart. ne Wash. *Plate 141*. *L. greenei* (1–2 feet): Segments from seven to ten, rather narrow, broader towards the tip, with hairs flat on the surfaces, silvery. Racemes rarely over 4 inches. Flowers blue, violet, or purple. From Wyo to Nev and Colo. *Plate 145*. *L. palmeri* (1–2 feet): From six to nine rather elliptic, narrow segments silvery-silky on the upper surface. Flowers blue, with dark spot. s Nev, Utah. *L. confertus* (4–12 inches): Six or seven segments. Racemes 2–9 inches; circles $\frac{2}{5}$ inch apart. Flowers purple. Sierra Nevada, e Nev. *Plate 141*. *L. excubitus* (2–5 feet): Shrubby. From seven to nine segments. Racemes about 2 feet; circles about $1\frac{2}{5}$ inches apart. Flowers blue, violet, or orchid. e Calif, probably w Nev. *Plate 142*. *L. holmgrenianus* (18 inches): From six to eight segments. Flower-circles $\frac{3}{5}$–$\frac{4}{5}$ inch apart. Flowers purplish. se Calif, sw Nev. *L. bakeri* (2–3 feet): Flowers with a short standard and a white eye turning red or purplish. s Colo.

B. Species with racemes not bearing definite circles of flowers.
See also *L. caudatus, evermannii, minimus, pachylobus, vallicola*, whose racemes are variable in this respect.

1.   Plants whose leaves are smooth on the upper surface.
See also *L. wyethii* under 3.

L. ARBUSTUS (8–20 inches) has leaves divided into from seven to eleven segments. The racemes are

3–8 inches long, rather loose. The flowers are white or cream, or tinged variously, or rose or purple.

May to July: in pine forests, sagebrush, etc. from northeastern Washington and Oregon to Montana. *Plate 142*. This has generally been named *L. laxiflorus*. The paler-flowered plants are regarded by some as a distinct species, *L. calcaratus*. *Plate 142*.

L. burkei (18–36 inches): From seven to eleven segments. Racemes dense, at least 8 inches. Flowers small, blue or violet, the bracts long. From the Cascades to Ida and Wyo. *L. prunophilus* (about 2 feet): Segments from seven to eleven, smooth. Raceme dense, about 6 inches. Petals purple. From se Wash to Colo. *Plate 145*. *L. pusillus* (2–8 inches): Segments from five to seven. Racemes loose, about 3 inches. From Wash to s Nev, Utah, w Colo. *Plate 143*. *L. parviflorus* (1–1$\frac{1}{2}$ feet): Seven or eight segments. Racemes dense, 1$\frac{1}{2}$–3$\frac{1}{3}$ inches. Flowers blue or violet (or rarely whitish). Damp woods from Ida (and s Mont?) to Nev, Utah, Colo. *Plate 142*. By some authors placed in *L. argenteus* as a variety. *L. kingii* (2–8 inches): From five to seven segments. Racemes about 1 inch, headlike. Flowers blue or purplish. Open ground, e Nev, Utah, Colo. *Plate 143*. *L. polycarpus* (6–16 inches): Segments from five to eight. Racemes $\frac{1}{2}$–3 inches, loose. Flowers blue and white. Grassland, e Wash, e Ore. Has also passed as *L. micranthus*. *L. ammophilus* (8–10 inches): From six to nine segments. Racemes lax, 2–8 inches. Flowers blue or purple. May, early June. Mostly sandy (*ammo-*) soil, Colo, Utah, nw Nev. *Plate 142*. This with the two following form parts of a complex named *L. perennis*. *Plate 142*. *L. crassus*: Segments thick (*crassus*), succulent. Early April. w Colo. *L. onustus* (6–8 inches). From five to eight segments. Racemes 2–6 inches, loose. Dry slopes, ne Calif. Uncommon. *L. shockleyi* (4 inches, or in places stemless): From seven to ten segments. Racemes 1–2$\frac{1}{2}$ inches, loose. Flowers blue, purple, or pink. Sandy and gravelly soil, w Nev, e Calif. *L. arcticus* (one subspecies, 6–24 inches): From six to eight segments. Racemes 4–6 inches, the blue or lavender flowers with a slight tendency to be in distinct rings. High summits of the Cascades, Wash and Ore; barely in our range. *L. saxosus* (4–12 inches): From eight to twelve segments. Racemes 1–3$\frac{1}{2}$ inches, not dense. Flowers blue or violet. Gravelly plains, from e Wash to e Calif, w Nev. *Plate 142*. *L. plattensis* (8–40 inches): From seven to nine segments. Racemes 2–6 inches. Flowers blue with a dark spot. Plains and hills, Neb, Wyo, Kan, Colo. *Plate 143*. *L. polyphyllus* (20–40 inches): Rare in our range; west of the Cascades. From nine to thirteen segments (*poly-*, "many"). Racemes up to 8 inches. Flowers blue or violet. *Plate 143*. *L. leucanthus* is found only at Springdale, Utah.

2.   Plants whose leaves are silvery-silky on the upper surface.

PLATE 142

Lupinus calcaratus   *Fleak*

Lupinus arbustus   *Scribner*

Lupinus saxosus   *Spellenberg*

Lupinus ammophilus   *Roberts*

Lupinus parviflorus   *Korling*

Lupinus perennis   *Johnson*

Lupinus excubitus   *Johnson*

L. LEUCOPHYLLUS (2–4 feet) has leaves (*leuco-*, "white"; *phyll-*, "leaf") with from seven to ten segments. The racemes are 6–8 inches long, and dense (in one variety very slender). The flowers range from almost white, the standard and wings pale lavender, to entirely lilac.

June to August: from central Washington to Montana and southward to northeastern California, southern Nevada, and Utah. *Plate 143*.

L. *sulphureus* (16–32 inches): From nine to eleven segments. Racemes 2–6 inches, mostly loose. Flowers yellow, blue, or purplish. se Wash, Ida, ne Ore, Columbia R gorge. L. *sellulus* (3–6 inches): Segments six or seven. Racemes 1–4 inches, dense. Flowers blue or violet. Wash, Ore, Sierra Nevada, w Nev. L. *meionanthus* (8–20 inches): From six to eight segments. Racemes 1–3½ inches, dense. Flowers blue or violet with yellow center. From the Sierra Nevada to w Nev.

L. SERICEUS (8–20 inches) has from seven to nine leaf-segments. The racemes are loose, 4–6 inches long.

May to August: from Washington to California east of the Cascade Mountains, and from Montana to Colorado and Utah. *Plate 143*. L. *barbiger* (1–2 feet) has been found only in high mountain meadows in southern Utah. It has loose racemes 4–8 inches long. L. *amplus* is closely related, perhaps a subspecies. Segments about ten, 3–5 inches, smoother. Raceme 4–10 inches. Corolla large, dark purple. *Plate 145*. L. *jonesii* (to 4 feet): Segments from seven to nine, with dense yellowish hairs. Flowers numerous, white or pale yellowish with a faint brownish spot; on some plants in distinct circles. Utah.

3. Plants whose leaves are variously hairy, woolly, or downy on the upper surface.

See also L. *saxosus, sulphureus, leucophyllus*, which vary in this respect. Some subspecies of L. *argenteus* belong here.

L. ARIDUS (4–7 inches) forms tufts. The leaves have from six to eight yellowish, hairy segments. The racemes are 2–3 inches long, and dense. The flowers are pale lavender.

June to August: from south-central Washington and west-central Idaho to northeastern California and Nevada. *Plate 144*. This, with the silky-hairy and stemless L. *lobbii* and L. *lyallii*, has been treated as a subspecies of L. *lepidus*. That generally is west of our area (unless it just crosses the crest of the mountains on our western boundary). It may grow erect or form

mats of short stems. The leaves are grayish- or rusty-silky, or hairy.

L. BICOLOR (4–16 inches) has from five to seven downy leaf-segments. The racemes are up to 3 inches long. The flowers are blue, the standard with a white blaze which may be purple-streaked.

April to June: along the Columbia River in central Washington and Oregon. *Plate 144*. L. *ornatus* (6–18 inches), with silky leaf-segments, grows only on sandbars along Clearwater River in northwestern Idaho and in an area of Spokane, Wash. Flowers blue or lavender. *Plate 144*. L. *amphibius* (8–24 inches) grows on the banks of the Columbia River. It has silky leaf-segments. It may become extinct through the building of dams to control the river.

L. CONCINNUS (2–8 inches) has from five to eight short, broad, downy leaf-segments. The racemes are loose, 1–1½ inches long. The flowers are red-violet with a yellow spot. The stems are generally rusty-hairy.

April and May: in dry, open, gravelly places in southeastern California and southern Nevada. *Plate 144*. L. *nevadensis* (12–16 inches): From eight to ten hairy segments. Racemes 3–6 inches. With sagebrush, e Calif, w and se Nev. *Plate 144*. L. *duranii* (2–4 inches): Five or six woolly segments. Racemes 1–2½ inches, dense. In volcanic sand and gravel, e Calif. L. *andersoni* (1–3 feet): From seven to ten minutely downy segments. Racemes 2–8 inches, loose. Dry slopes. e Sierra Nevada, nw Nev. L. *christenae*, on the eastern slope of Mt. Lassen, with pale yellow flowers, has been treated as a variety of L. *andersoni*. L. *fulcratus* (12–16 inches): Closely related to L. *andersoni*, in the Sierra Nevada and sc Nev. Both may be recognized by leaflike stipules. L. *fulcratus* has from six to nine segments bearing short whitish hairs flat on the surface. Racemes 2 inches long, the flowers almost in distinct circles. *Plate 144*.

L. WYETHII (8–30 inches) has from nine to eleven leaf-segments clad with yellowish hairs lying flat. The racemes are 6–10 inches long, not dense.

May to July: with sagebrush and in mountain forests, and on ridges from Washington and Idaho to Nevada and from Montana to Colorado. *Plate 144*.

In Utah we have also L. *maculatus*, only in the Wasatch Mountains; the flowers with a spotted ("maculate") standard L. *obtusilobus*, a species of almost alpine situations in California, is found eastward as far as Mt. Rose, Nevada. *Plate 144*.

SPHAEROPHYSA

One species of the Asian *Sphaerophysa* is rapidly spreading as a weed in the arid lands of the West.

S. SALSULA (1–3 feet) is somewhat woody. The stems bear many leaves, which have from nine to

PLATE 143

Lupinus pusillus   *Hesselberg*

Lupinus kingii   *Johnson*

Lupinus floribundus   *Wilson*

Lupinus plattensis   *Roberts*

Lupinus polyphyllus   *Koepf*

Lupinus sericeus   *Dye*

Lupinus leucophyllus   *Uttal*

twenty-five segments $\frac{2}{5}$–$\frac{4}{5}$ inch long; the whole leaf being 2–4 inches long. The racemes arise in the axils, the loosely disposed flowers from four to twelve, about $\frac{1}{2}$ inch long, with brick-red or brownish petals. The pod is inflated, up to $1\frac{1}{5}$ inches long, and does not open.

May to July: mostly on alkaline and irrigated lands from eastern Washington to California and eastward to Colorado, and to be expected elsewhere.

CRAZY-WEEDS, LOCOWEEDS (OXYTROPIS)

In most species of *Oxytropis* the leaves all grow from ground level, the only stems above ground being the leafless flowering stems. The leaves are pinnately divided into numerous segments. The flowers are in dense spikelike or headlike racemes. The pod does not open when it is ripe, and may be inflated.

In many respects the genus resembles *Astragalus*, and indeed some authors have merged it with that genus. A technical distinction is the prominent beak on the keel of the corolla of *Oxytropis*.

The numerous species grow mostly at high altitudes or high latitudes around the world. A number of them are highly poisonous (compare *Astragalus*).

I.   *Species with not more than five flowers in a cluster; generally not more than three.*
      See also *O. deflexa, viscida, oreophila, lagopus* which generally have more than five flowers, but fewer may sometimes be found.

O. PARRYI ($\frac{1}{2}$–4 inches) forms grayish-silky cushions, the leaves up to 2 inches long with up to twenty-one very small segments. The racemes are headlike, with generally two flowers (less commonly one or three). The petals are purplish.

July and August: on high, alpine slopes and ridges from central Idaho to Nevada and California and eastward to Wyoming and Colorado.

O. MULTICEPS (1–4 inches) is silky, mostly forming cushions, the leaves with up to nine segments. The racemes generally have from one to three flowers (occasionally four).

May to August: on prairies, riverbanks, and foothills from Wyoming to northeastern Utah, western Nebraska, and Colorado. *Plate 146.*

O. PODOCARPA (1–2$\frac{1}{2}$ inches) has silky-hairy leaves with from eleven to twenty-seven tiny segments. There are one or two flowers in a cluster, the petals purple. The pod is bladdery-inflated.

July to September: on rocky ridges and slopes above timberline from Montana to Colorado and eastward to the Atlantic. *Plate 145.*

O. jonesii, only in Utah, may have up to five flowers in a raceme, with purplish petals. The leaves have from one to seven segments. The plants form cushions.

II. *Species with generally more than five flowers in a raceme.*

      A. The first four may have white or yellowish flowers (but two of them may be indistinguishable in flower color from B).
          See also *O. nana.*

O. CAMPESTRIS (1–12 inches) varies from smooth and green to densely silky-hairy. The leaves may have up to forty-one segments. The racemes have from five to thirty flowers, the petals white or yellowish, some with a purplish keel.

May to July: mostly at high altitudes around the world in the north; in our area southward in Washington, Oregon, Idaho, Montana, North Dakota, and to Colorado. *Plate 145.*

O. SERICEA (6–16 inches) is densely grayish-hairy. The leaves have from nine to twenty-one segments. The spikelike racemes have from ten to thirty-five flowers, the petals white or yellow, commonly tinged with pink and the keel tipped with purple.

June and July: on prairies and high slopes and meadows from Idaho to Montana and South Dakota and southward to Nevada, Utah, Colorado, and Oklahoma. *Plate 145.*

O. DEFLEXA (1–12 inches) is softly or thinly hairy. The leaves have from nine to forty-one segments. The racemes are from five- to twenty-five-flowered, almost headlike. The petals range from white to purplish. The pod points downward.

June and July: on meadows and by streams, from foothills to mountains from Washington to the Sierra Nevada and from Montana to Colorado and North Dakota; also in Siberia. *Plate 146.*

O. VISCIDA (2–10 inches) is smooth or nearly so. The leaves have from nineteen to thirty-nine segments. The racemes have from three to twenty flowers, with white, pale yellowish, or reddish-purple petals. Both leaves and inflorescence are glandular-sticky ("viscid").

June to August: on meadows and in sagebrush and on alpine summits, from Washington, Oregon, and the Sierra Nevada to the Rocky Mountains from Montana to Colorado. *Plate 146.*

PLATE 144

Lupinus aridus   *Fleak*

Lupinus ornatus   *Fleak*

Lupinus obtusilobus   *R. L. Nelson*

Lupinus wyethii   *B. J. Cox*

Lupinus nevadensis   *B. J. Cox*

Lupinus concinnus   *Buckalew*

Spellenberg

Lupinus fulcratus

Lupinus bicolor   *Myrick*

B. Species with flowers not white, cream, or yellow.

See also, under A, *O. deflexa*, *O. viscida*.

O. LAMBERTII (to 10 inches) is silky. The leaves have from nine to twenty-three narrow segments up to 1½ inches long. The spikelike racemes may be 6 or even 8 inches long. The flowers are purple.

May to July: on prairies from eastern Montana and North Dakota to Oklahoma. *Plate 145.*

O. SPLENDENS (4–14 inches) is silky-hairy. The leaves have most segments in bunches (from seven to fifteen); they are up to 1 inch long. The racemes have from twenty to eighty flowers, the petals rose or red-purple.

June to August: in meadowland and on gravel bars, on foothills and lower mountains from Montana to Colorado and North Dakota. *Plate 146.*

O. obnapiformis (2½–5 inches): Racemes 8–22-flowered, shorter than the leaves. Petals pink-purple with a pale veined eye. Pods inflated. ne Utah, nw Colo. *Plate 146*. *O. nana* (1–9 inches): Segments from seven to thirteen. Racemes with from five to fifteen crowded flowers. Petals purple or white with a purple-spotted keel. Calyx enlarged around the pod. Wyo.

O. LAGOPUS (to 5 inches) is erect or prostrate. It generally forms silky cushions. The leaves have from seven to fifteen segments. The racemes have from three to twenty flowers, crowded so that they are like heads. The petals are reddish-purple. The calyx enlarges around the pod.

May to July: on sagebrush plains and lower mountains in the Rocky Mountains from southeastern Wyoming, to Idaho and eastern Montana. *Plate 146*. *O. besseyi:* Similar. Racemes erect, on stalks to 8 inches. Calyx not enlarging, split by the growing pod. From Ida to Mont and nw Colo. *Plate 146.*

O. OREOPHILA generally forms cushions 4–12 inches across, with flowering stems up to 4 inches long, erect or prostrate. The leaves have from seven to seventeen segments up to ½ inch long. The racemes have from two to twelve flowers. The petals are pink or purple (rarely white). The pod is bladdery-inflated.

June to September: in dry gravelly and rocky places at high altitudes, and with sagebrush; from eastern California to Nevada and Utah. *Plate 146.*

O. riparia, from western Asia, is established in southwestern Montana. It has a leafy stem. The racemes tend to have all their flowers on one side. The flowers are purplish.

LOCOWEEDS AND MILK-VETCHES (ASTRAGALUS)

The genus *Astragalus* is the despair of most botanists — not to mention the amateur naturalist. Over two hundred species are found in our range, the differences among them largely technical. These present probably the most difficult problem in any of our six volumes. Indeed, without the published work and generous personal help of Rupert Barneby, no intelligible and usable treatment of this multitude would have been possible. Even so, I cannot promise that the following pages will provide the amateur with the means of identifying any milk-vetch or locoweed he may find. The diagnosis of species depends on combinations of varying characteristics which can only be described in the technical jargon of the professional botanist — and even he may be at fault. All we can hope for is that the assiduous reader may come close in putting a name on a plant.

The plants in almost all species have pinnately divided leaves (only three segments in some species, in some palmately disposed; none in others); their number, if observed in a number of plants, is often useful in identification. The same may be said of the number of flowers in the raceme. The character of the seed-pod (legume) is generally important: whether it is inflated (i.e. with more room inside than the seeds occupy), or bladdery (with thin walls); whether it is stalked above the level of the attachment of the calyx;

whether it is erect or pendulous. In the brief characterizations that follow, the absence of mention of the pod may be taken as meaning that it is not inflated, bladdery, pendulous, or stalked.

Many species are poisonous and when grazed by animals cause the nervous derangement which marks them as "crazy" or "loco"; the attacks may be fatal. Some species absorb and accumulate — without injury to themselves — the deadly element selenium.

To give the reader some slight chance of finding a name for the *Astragalus* he collects, the species are here arranged geographically within the area to which this volume is devoted. The regions are not mutually exclusive, since their boundaries are not sharply ecological, and many species cross them. But they nevertheless offer a means of eliminating species — providing that, as is probable, the collector knows where he is. For instance, if he is not in Utah, he can at once ignore some species in Region III that are found only in Utah. If he is in Oregon or Washington, he can dispense with all but one of the species of Region I. And so on.

Here are the four regions.

I. The high plains and valleys east of the Continental Divide (i.e. practically east of the crest and higher ridges of the Rocky Mountains from

PLATE 145

Lupinus amplus
Fleak

Oxytropis podocarpa
Guppy

Oxytropis lambertii
Korling

Oxytropis sericea
Roberts

Oxytropis campestris
Phelps

Lupinus greenei
Ure

Lupinus prunophilus
B. J. Cox

Montana to Colorado); including Oklahoma. Twenty-four species.

II. The Rocky Mountains from Montana to Colorado. Forty-one species.

III. The Intermountain Region, here interpreted as including all of the Great Basin; from the western slope of the Rocky Mountains to (but not including) northwestern Idaho, Washington, Oregon, and the Sierra Nevada in California. One hundred and twelve species.

IV. Washington and Oregon east of the Cascade Mountains, and northwestern Idaho. Twenty-four species.

In general, species are allotted to the regions where they seem (by scrutinizing Barneby's maps) most numerous. But in any region there will be many species from neighboring regions, necessitating many cross-references which must be taken into account. The boundaries between II and III are particularly vague, and the cross-references correspondingly many and important.

Because space must be a consideration in the preparation of these books, the treatment of species (especially those very restricted in range) is greatly abbreviated (for the abbreviations used, see the Introduction, in Part 1). Among the "shorthand" conventions I have adopted is to designate the hairiness or other vesture only of the upper surface of leaf-segments. "Smooth" means "Leaf-segments smooth on the upper surface."

And since photographs cannot show the particular details used in distinguishing species, and again for considerations of space, no attempt has been made to illustrate every species. The drawings can help to identify only the commoner species; but they also provide a means of acquainting the reader with the terms used and the types of variation among species.

I. *Species of the plains and valleys east of the Continental Divide.*

These are (in our range) the prairies and plains from North Dakota to Oklahoma and westward in Montana, Wyoming, and Colorado to the eastern foothills of the Rocky Mountains; including the valleys of the Missouri and Yellowstone Rivers, the North and South Platte Rivers, and the Arkansas River.

The following species of the Rocky Mountains (Region II) may also be found on the plains: with pods stalked and pendulous, *A. alpinus, aboriginum, americanus, tenellus, bodini, bisulcatus*; with pods, if stalked, not pendulous; plants forming mats or cushions, *A. kentrophyta, missouriensis*; plants with visible stems mostly spreading or prostrate, *A. vexilliflexus, adsurgens, agrestis.*

The wide-ranging *A. purshii* (region III) reaches North and South Dakota. *A. nuttallianus*, with central stem erect, is in Oklahoma.

A. Plants that form tufts, mats, or cushions, with short stems or none above ground.

1. Of these the following species have seven or more segments to a leaf, generally 1–2 inches long. The foliage is silky, woolly, or downy.

A. SHORTIANUS may rarely have stems up to 10 inches long. The petals are pink-purple with a pale eye.

May to July: on prairies, dry hills, and bluffs in southeastern Wyoming and Colorado; perhaps in western South Dakota. *Plate 147. A. mollissimus:* Raceme dense. Petals pink-purple or lavender or cream. From w SD to Okla, e Mont to e Colo. *Plate 147. A. lotiflorus:* Some leaves with as few as three segments. Raceme dense. Petals greenish or yellowish tinged lavender and tipped pink-purple. From ND to Okla, e Wyo, e Colo. *Plate 152.*

2. The remaining species of group A have three leaf-segments or fewer (but see *A. lotiflorus* under 1). Flowers also are few, mostly not more than five in a raceme or cluster. All these have silvery foliage.

A. GILVIFLORUS has generally two flowers in a cluster, the petals white with keel tipped pink or lilac.

April and May (and June at high altitudes): on barren hills and in badlands from North Dakota to western Nebraska, Montana, and eastern Wyoming; and in northern Utah. *Plate 147. A. hyalinus:* Flowers one or two together. Petals whitish with faintly lilac tips. From w SD to Neb, Wyo, ne Colo; possibly ND. *A. sericoleucus:* Stems prostrate, matted, up to 2 inches long. Flowers from three to five. Petals pink-purple with pale eye. w Neb, w Kan, e Wyo, ne Colo. *Plate 147. A. barrii:* Cushions or domes up to 20 inches across. From two to four flowers. Petals pink-purple with a pale eye. *Plate 147. A. aretioides:* Cushions 4–12 inches across. Silky. Flowers two. Petals pink- or magenta-purple, or blue- or reddish-violet, rarely white. w Wyo, extreme e Mont. *A. tridactylicus:* Generally forming cushions or mats. Silvery-hairy or silky. Segments three. Flowers from two to six. Petals pink-purple. Pod silky, seldom seen, probably like that of *A. sericoleucus.*

A. spatulatus: Leaves generally with only an end segment, this narrow. From two to nine flowers. Petals pink-purple with white tips. From w ND to Neb, ec Mont, n Colo, ne Utah, se Ida. *Plate 147. A. simplicifolius:* Leaves consisting of stalks only, i.e. undivided. From one to three flowers. Petals pink-purple with

PLATE 146

Oxytropis obnapiformis *W. Weber*

Oxytropis viscida *Korling*

Oxytropis deflexa *Wilson*

Oxytropis oreophila *Johnson*

Oxytropis multiceps *Hamilton*

Oxytropis besseyi *Phelps*

Oxytropis lagopus *Korling*

Oxytropis splendens *Roberts*

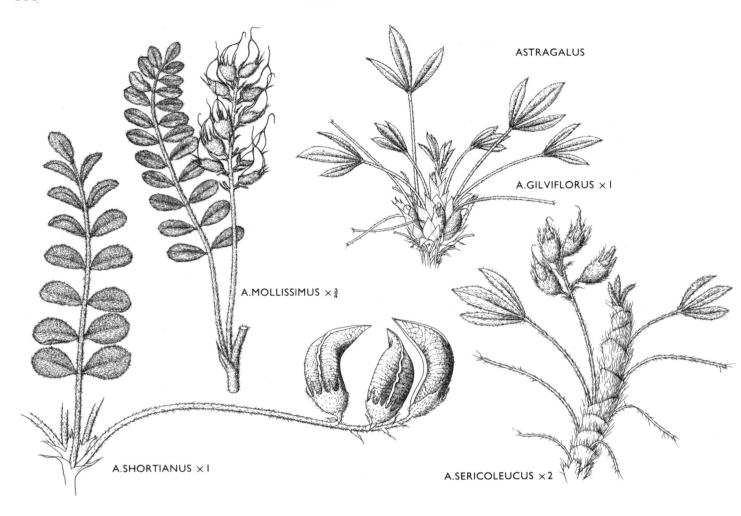

ASTRAGALUS

A.GILVIFLORUS × I

A.MOLLISSIMUS × ¾

A.SHORTIANUS × I

A.SERICOLEUCUS × 2

pale eye. Wyo, headwaters of N. Platte and Wind Rivers.

B. Plants with evident leafy stems, erect or more commonly horizontal with tips bending up. See also *A. shortianus* and *A. sericoleucus* under group A.

1. Plants with very narrow — even threadlike — leaf-segments 1–2 inches long or longer.

A. CERAMICUS has spreading, wiry stems bending up from a prostrate base, 1–12 inches long. The foliage is grayish or silvery. The flowers are from two to fifteen, the petals white or flesh-color. The pod is pendulous and bladdery, on a stalk above the calyx.

April to July: in sandy soil from western North Dakota to Oklahoma, eastern Montana, Colorado, and southeastern Utah. *Plate 147. A. pectinatus:* Gray-green. Stems 6–24 inches. Raceme dense, up to thirty flowers. Petals yellowish. Pod long-pointed. From ND to Kan, e Colo, w Mont, Wyo. *Plate 147. A. gracilis:* Green or grayish. Stems 6–16 inches. Up to forty flowers. Petals pale lilac or purple. From w ND to Okla, s Mont, e Wyo, Colo. *A. puniceus:* Finely

hairy. Stems 8–20 inches, spreading, forming wide clumps. Petals pink-purple. Pod somewhat inflated, lying on the ground. se Colo, nw Okla.

2. Plants with broader leaf-segments.

The first two of these have silky or hairy leaf-segments, generally gray-green; and hanging pods. The remaining species have smooth or downy segments or these beset with small hairs lying flat. The last two have hanging pods.

A. PLATTENSIS has stems loosely entangled, ½–8 inches long. The petals are pink- or lilac-purple. The pod is spongy.

March to July: on clay or sandy prairies and in old fields and on roadsides from North Dakota to Oklahoma, eastern Wyoming, and Colorado.

A. racemosus: Some plants erect, to 2 feet tall. Racemes dense. Up to seventy flowers. Petals whitish or yellowish tinged or tipped lilac or pink. From ND to s Okla and sw Wyo and Colo. *Plate 147. A. drummondii:* Erect, to 2 feet. Petals white or cream with lilac-tipped keel. From w ND to Colo, w Mont, se Ida, Utah. *Plate 148. A. canadensis:* Erect, to 3 feet. Up to thirty-five segments. Racemes dense. Flowers

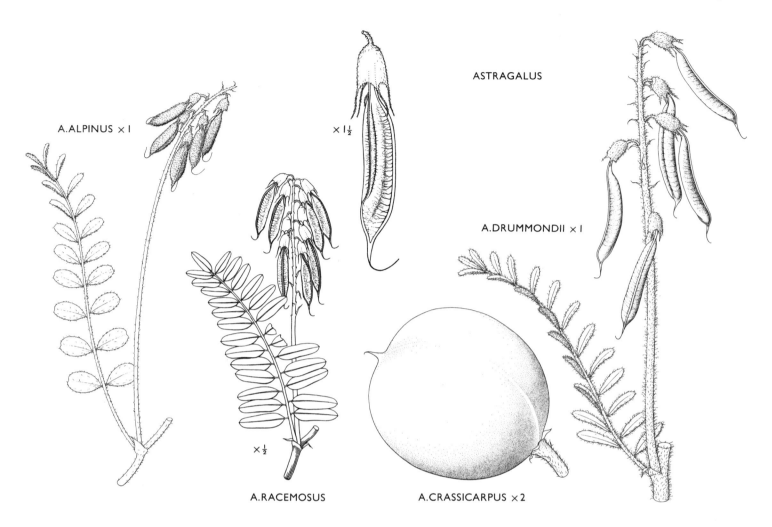

A.ALPINUS ×1

ASTRAGALUS

×1½

A.DRUMMONDII ×1

×½

A.RACEMOSUS

A.CRASSICARPUS ×2

many, the petals greenish-white, cream, or straw-color. Throughout our area and most of the country. *Plate 148. A. eucosmus:* Stems erect or bending up, 4–16 inches. Foliage smooth or nearly. Racemes compact. Petals purplish, purplish-tipped or -margined, pinkish-gray, or whitish. From sw Mont to Colo, w Mont, w Wyo, se Ida. *A. flexuosus:* Stems bending up, 24 inches. Petals white, cream, suffused with lilac or purple. From ND and e Mont to w Neb, Colo, and se Utah. *A. crassicarpus:* Stems bending up, 4–24 inches. Racemes dense. Flowers up to thirty-five. Petals purple, lilac, or white with keel purple-tipped. Pod fleshy ("ground-plums"). From ND to Okla and Colo and the Rocky Mountains. *Plate 148. A. sparsiflorus:* Stems prostrate or bending up, 3–12 inches. Segments $\frac{1}{12}$–$\frac{3}{5}$ inch, rather broad. From two to ten flowers. Petals white, pink-veined, the keel tipped pink or purple. e Colo.

II. *Species of the Rocky Mountains.*

The boundary between the mountains proper and the headwaters of the Yellowstone River, the North and South Platte Rivers, and the Arkansas River, cannot be arbitrarily fixed. The species included here are those which are related to the western territories rather than the eastern. The boundary between the Rocky Mountains and the Intermountain Region is likewise vague.

A. canadensis (see under I) ranges across the entire country.

Of the other species here assigned to region I, the following may be found westward in the Rocky Mountains: *A. spatulatus* (essentially stemless); *A. ceramicus, pectinatus, drummondii, flexuosus, crassicarpus* (all with evident leafy stems).

Of the species placed in region III, these may be found eastward in w or c Colo: Dwarf plants with short stems or none: *A. purshii, naturitensis, megacarpus* (also in sw Wyo), *humillimus, calycosus, eastwoodae.* Plants with at least some stems longer than 6 inches: *A. lentiginosus, nuttallianus, oophorus, asclepiadoides, praelongus, cibarius, microcymbus, convallarius, humistratus.*

A. Plants whose pods are stalked (above the level of attachment of the calyx) and hang down or lie on the ground. The flowers are whitish, cream, or pale yellow except as otherwise noted.

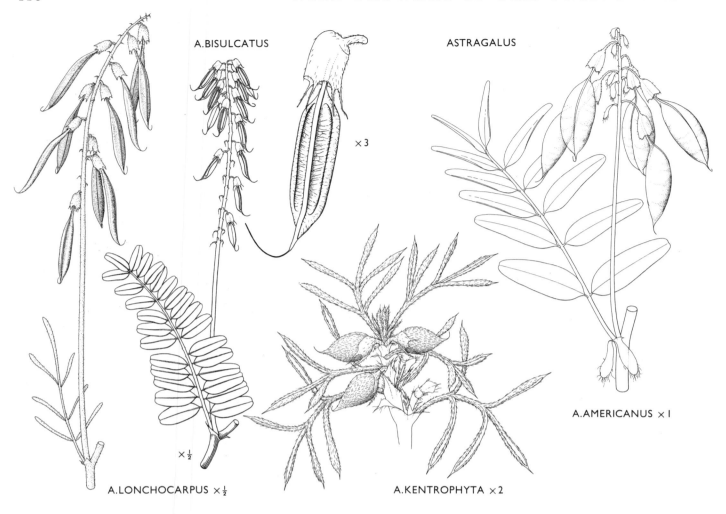

A.BISULCATUS

ASTRAGALUS

×3

A.AMERICANUS × 1

A.LONCHOCARPUS ×½

×½

A.KENTROPHYTA ×2

The stems of these species spread sideways with ends bending up except as otherwise described. The character of leaf-surface stated means that of the upper surface; when not mentioned, the surface bears small hairs lying flat.

The references to SD indicate the Black Hills, whose species are related to those of the Rocky Mountains.

A. ALPINUS: Erect. Leaf-segments up to twenty-five, $\frac{1}{10}$–$\frac{4}{5}$ inch, hairy. Up to twenty-five flowers in a raceme. Petals variously margined and veined with purple, some plants with purple wings. Pod three-faced. Rockies from Mont to Colo; w SD; n Wash, ne Ore, Ida, Nev. *Plate 148. A. aboriginum:* Erect, spreading, or trailing. Leaf-segments densely silky, hairy, downy, or smooth, $\frac{1}{8}$–1 inch, elliptic or narrower. Up to thirty flowers. Nearly the same range as *A. alpinus. A. americanus:* Erect, up to 2 feet. Segments smooth, up to thirteen, $\frac{1}{2}$–$2\frac{1}{2}$ inches. Up to thirteen flowers. Pod bladdery. w Mont, n Wyo, w SD. *Plate 148. A. molybdenus* ($\frac{1}{5}$–$2\frac{1}{5}$ inches): Stems mostly prostrate. Greenish or grayish; black hairs in the racemes. Flowers from three to six. Petals pink-purple,

lilac, or whitish with standard suffused and veined lilac. c Colo. *A. robbinsii:* Stem may trail. Black hairs in the raceme. Segments from seven to seventeen, $\frac{1}{5}$–$1\frac{1}{3}$ inches. Up to twenty-one flowers. Petals on some plants pale pink with whitish stalks, or whitish with pink tips. w Mont, w Wyo, Colo; n Wash, ne Ore, Ida. Has been confused with *A. alpinus. A. scopulorum:* Segments smooth, up to twenty-nine, $\frac{1}{6}$–$\frac{4}{5}$ inch. Flowers from ten to twenty-two. Pods may curve. Colo, e Utah. *A. proximus:* Some plants erect. Segments up to eleven, very narrow, $\frac{1}{4}$–1 inch. Up to forty flowers in a very loose raceme. Petals lilac-tipped. sw Colo. *A. schmollae:* Erect, 1–2 feet. Raceme black-hairy. Segments downy, up to twenty-one, $\frac{1}{4}$–1 inch. Flowers up to twenty-eight, loosely disposed. Pod three-angled. sw Colo. *A. lonchocarpus:* Some plants erect, 1–2 feet. Segments hoary or silky, not more than nine, up to 1 inch. Flowers up to thirty-five, loosely disposed. sw Colo, Utah, e Nev. *Plate 148. A. tenellus:* Erect (to 18 inches), or prostrate. Segments to twenty-one, $\frac{1}{8}$–1 inch. Flowers from one to twenty. Petals of some tipped or veined or suffused with lilac, of others all pink-lavender. Mont to Colo; s Ida, Nev, Utah; ND to Neb. *A. bodini:* Prostrate or

PLATE 147

Astragalus shortianus

Blecher

Astragalus barrii

Stockert

Astragalus gilviflorus

Stockert

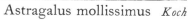

Astragalus mollissimus *Koch*

Astragalus spatulatus

Roberts

Astragalus sericoleucus

W. Weber

Astragalus racemosus

Roberts

Astragalus pectinatus

McRae

Astragalus ceramicus

Roberts

bushy. Segments smooth, up to seventeen, $\frac{1}{10}$–$\frac{3}{5}$ inch. Flowers from three to fifteen. Petals pink-purple or reddish-lilac. s Wyo, c Colo, c Utah, w Neb. *A. oster-houti*: Erect, to 18 inches, in clumps. Segments smooth, very narrow, to $1\frac{1}{2}$ inches. Flowers up to twenty-five. Pod long-stalked. w Colo. *A. bourgovii*: Segments almost smooth, up to nineteen, $\frac{1}{8}$–$\frac{4}{5}$ inch. Flowers up to thirteen, pink-purple. w Mont, n Ida. *A. ripleyi*: Erect, to 2 feet. Segments smooth, up to seventeen, $\frac{1}{3}$–1 inch. Flowers up to forty-five, pale lemon-yellow. Pod three-angled, long-stalked. s Colo. *A. bisulcatus*: Some plants erect, to 20 inches. Segments smooth, up to thirty-five, $\frac{1}{5}$–$1\frac{1}{5}$ inches. Flowers up to eighty in a dense raceme. Petals rose-purple, whitish, or pale yellowish or straw-color, some suffused with purple. Mont to Colo, ND, w SD, Neb, and w Kan; Utah. *Plate 148*.

B. Plants whose pods, if stalked above the calyx, do not hang down.

1.　Plants forming cushions with scarcely any visible stems, or mats of prostrate stems. Leaf-segments three or fewer. Flowers fewer than seven in a cluster.

The distinction in manner of growth is not clear, many species being variable in this respect.

A. KENTROPHYTA: Variable in stature – prostrate, matted, cushion-forming, or bushy. Surface from smooth to downy, soft-hairy, or silky. Segments from three to nine, $\frac{1}{20}$–$\frac{3}{4}$ inch. Flowers from one to three. Petals whitish with keel tipped pink or purple, or all pink-lilac, or with pale wings. Pod small. Almost throughout our range from w ND and w Neb to e Ore, Colo to e Calif. *Plate 148*. The distinctive features of this widespread complex are the small number of leaf-segments, and the very small flowers (petals not more than $\frac{1}{3}$ inch) in small clusters in the axils. *A. drabelli-formis*: Dwarf, mats or cushions. Silvery or hoary. No segments except the end one. Flowers from one to four. Petals pink-purple with a pale eye. Pod three-angled. w Wyo. *A. detritalis*: Similar in aspect. Segments none or up to seven, almost hairlike. Flowers from two to six. Petals pink-purple. Pod more or less erect. nw Colo, ne Utah. *A. proimanthus*: Tufts or cushions. Silky-hairy. Segments three (rarely only the end one), $\frac{1}{5}$–$\frac{2}{5}$ inch. Flowers in pairs in axils. Petals whitish, pod erect, leathery. sw Wyo. *A. lutosus* (1–4 inches): Tufts or mats. Hoary. From fifteen to twenty-seven segments. Petals white, more or less pink-veined, the keel tipped lilac. Pod bladdery. nw Colo, ne Utah. Very rare.
　　See also *A. molybdenus, brandegei, leptaleus*.

2.　Plants with visible stems, in some species forming mats or tufts, in others spreading and bending up, none strictly erect. Leaf-segments mostly numerous (generally from seven to twenty-one).

a. Species with few flowers (mostly from one to seven), generally loosely disposed.

A. VEXILLIFLEXUS: Stems slender, prostrate or spreading. Segments from seven to thirteen. Flowers from three to seven in dense racemes. Petals pink-purple with pale eye and tips. w ND, w SD to Ida, ne Wyo. *A. leptaleus*: Spreading or in tufts. Smooth. Segments to twenty-three, $\frac{1}{8}$–$\frac{1}{2}$ inch. Flowers from one to five, white with bluish keel-tip. Pod hanging. w Mont, e Ida, Colo. *A. brandegei*: Wiry. Smooth. Segments from five to fifteen, narrow, even threadlike, $\frac{1}{4}$–1 inch. Flowers from one to five, whitish with lilac veins and tips. Pod hanging. Colo, e Utah. *Plate 149*. *A. cerussatus*: Stems up to 10 inches. Finely soft-hairy. Segments to twenty-one, narrow, $\frac{1}{6}$–$\frac{1}{2}$ inch. Flowers from three to seven. Petals pale lilac or whitish with lilac tips and pale purple veins. Colo. *A. wetherilli*: Stems to 10 inches. Smooth. Segments broad, from seven to fifteen, $\frac{1}{5}$–$\frac{3}{5}$ inch. Flowers from two to nine. Petals whitish, tinged or veined with lavender. Pod inflated. w Colo, e Utah.
　　See also *A. agrestis, molybdenus*, some plants of which may have fewer than seven flowers. *A. linifolius*, under 3, generally has two or three.

b. Species with more than seven flowers (from two to fifty, mostly from ten to thirty; see also *A. wetherilli*).

A. ADSURGENS: To 1 foot. Surface densely downy or silky or smooth. Segments up to twenty-five, $\frac{1}{3}$–1 inch. Flowers from ten to fifty, magenta-purple, reddish-lilac, slate-blue, or whitish. Pod erect, beaked. ND to w Neb, w Mont to Colo, Ida, e Wash. *Plate 148*. *A. agrestis*: Weak. Smooth or downy, the raceme softly hairy. Segments from thirteen to twenty-one, $\frac{1}{6}$–$\frac{4}{5}$ inch. Flowers and pod much as in *A. adsurgens*, but pod hairy. Almost throughout our range from ND to w Neb to e Wash, Ore; Colo to ne Calif. *Plate 149*. *A. parryi* (4–14 inches): Softly hairy. From fifteen to twenty-seven segments. From four to nine flowers. Petals white or rose. Pod curved. From Mont to s Wyo. *Plate 149*. *A. pattersonii* (4–20 inches): Clumps red-tinged, with a bloom. From fifteen to twenty-five segments. From ten to twenty-five flowers. Pods erect. w Colo. *A. flavus*: Tufts. Smooth or nearly so. Segments from eleven to nineteen, $\frac{1}{4}$–$\frac{4}{5}$ inch. Flowers from ten to thirty. Petals lemon- or pale yellow or straw-color, whitish, or pale lilac. Pod erect. sw Wyo, w Colo, e and s Utah. *Plate 149*. *A. grayi* (8–14 inches): Segments leathery, smooth, from four to ten. Flowers from nine to twenty-seven. Petals cream. Pod erect. s Mont, Wyo. *A. nelsonianus*: Clumps, to 1 foot. Smooth or downy. Segments from five to nine, $\frac{1}{2}$ to 2 inches. Flowers from eight to twenty. Petals white. Pod woody. sw Wyo, nw Utah. *A. miser* ($\frac{1}{2}$–7 inches): In tufts or branching. From seven to twenty-one

PLATE 148

Astragalus bisulcatus

Roberts

Astragalus kentrophyta

Scribner

Astragalus canadensis *Johnson*

Kravig

Astragalus crassicarpus

Astragalus alpinus *Green*

Astragalus adsurgens *Stockert*

Astragalus lonchocarpus *Wilson*

Astragalus americanus *Uttal*

Astragalus drummondii *Korling*

segments, on some plants threadlike. From three to twenty flowers. Petals whitish or pale yellowish, more or less lilac-veined. w Wyo, Mont, w Nev, Utah, e Colo. *Plate 152. A. hallii* (6–20 inches): Stems more or less prostrate. From thirteen to twenty-seven segments. Flowers from ten to twenty-eight. Petals red-violet, pink-purple, or dull lilac or whitish with purple tips. Colo. *A. wingatanus:* Slender, wiry, to 16 inches. Smooth. Segments from three to fifteen, narrow, even hairlike, $\frac{1}{6}$–$\frac{3}{4}$ inch. Flowers from ten to thirty-five, loosely disposed. Petals lilac purple with white tips, or whitish suffused or veined with lilac. Pod hanging. w Colo, e Utah. *A. chamaeleuce* (to 1$\frac{1}{2}$ inches): Stems, if any, prostrate. Segments from five to fifteen. Flowers from four to eleven. Petals pale yellowish with purple tips or tinge, or pink-purple with a pale eye. sw Wyo, e Utah, nw Colo. *Plate 149. A. anisus* (to 2 inches): Silvery. Segments from eleven to fifteen. Flowers from three to seven. Petals pink-purple. Pod spongy. Gunnison R valley, Colo. *A. missouriensis* (0–6 inches): Mostly prostrate. Silvery or greenish-gray. From eleven to seventeen segments. Flowers from five to fifteen. Petals pink-purple with a pale eye. From Mont to Colo, ND to Okla. *Plate 150. A. iodopetalus:* Low tufts, the stems prostrate. Nearly smooth. Segments from seven to thirty-one, $\frac{1}{8}$–$\frac{3}{4}$ inch. Flowers from twelve to twenty, close-packed. Petals reddish-violet with pale center. Pod leathery or woody. sw Colo. *A. geyeri* (4–12 inches): Erect or prostrate. Greenish. From three to thirteen segments. From two to eight flowers in a loose raceme. Petals whitish with lilac tips, or all lilac. Pod bladdery. From se Ore to s Ida, sw Wyo, w Nev, Utah, Colo. *Plate 149.*

3. One species of entirely different aspect, the plants rushlike.

A. LINIFOLIUS: Erect. Leaves mostly without segments (some perhaps with two on the sides), yellow-green, rushlike. Flowers from six to ten, generally two or three, loosely disposed, white with pink-tipped keel. Pod erect, woody. Northwestern Colorado.

III. *Species of The Intermountain Region.*

Many species here assigned to region II are found also in the Intermountain Region. Of these, the following (mostly in Colorado) have pods stalked (above the calyx) and pendulous (or lying on the ground): *A. alpinus, aboriginum, americanus, robbinsii, scopulorum, proximus, schmollae, lonchocarpus, tenellus, bodini, osterhoutii, bourgovii, ripleyi, bisulcatus.* Plants whose pods, if stalked, are not pendulous: *A. kentrophyta, detritalis* (stemless or mat-forming); *A. vexilliflexus, brandegei, wetherillii* (stems evident; racemes few-flowered); *A. adsurgens, agrestis, flavus, nelsonianus, wingatanus* (stems evident; more than seven flowers).

And from region IV, *A. curvicarpus.* From regions I and II *A. canadensis.*

A. Dwarf species, lacking visible stems above ground, or with stems up to 6 inches long (rarely more).

1. Species not limited to Utah (ten of them do occur there); in general ranging through parts of Idaho, Wyoming, and Nevada (with adjacent territory in other states; eight are in Colorado, five in eastern Oregon, two in eastern Washington, three in eastern California).

A. PURSHII is the most widespread of these species, occurring throughout the Intermountain Region and across the Rocky Mountains. It consists of tufts of leaves without visible stems, or matted stems up to 4 inches long, mostly softly hairy or woolly. The petals are whitish, pale yellow, pale pink, or pink-purple.

April to June: on dry hills, plains, and mesas throughout our range except Nebraska, Kansas, and Oklahoma. *Plate 149.* Very variable in number of flowers per raceme and their size and color.

A. newberryi: Stemless.* Leaves finely silky-woolly. Petals generally pink-purple with a pale eye (on some plants white with pinkish tips or margins. se Ore, s Ida, Nev, w Utah. *A. uncialis:* Stemless. Leaf-segments from three to five, silvery. Flowers from one to three. Petals pink or violet with a pale eye. Nev. *A. utahensis:* Stems commonly prostrate, up to 6 inches. Leaves densely woolly. Petals pink-purple with a pale eye. se Ida, sw Wyo, e Nev, s Utah. *Plate 149. A. argophyllus:* Stemless or stems up to 4 inches; dense hairs either lying flat or standing out. Petals pink-purple, some tinged with purple. se Ida, Nev, Utah. *A. callithrix* ($\frac{1}{2}$–2 inches): White-hairy. Flowers large. Petals pink-purple. Pod rough-hairy. e Nev. *A. marianus* (0–2 inches): Silvery. From three to ten flowers. Petals pink-purple, the standard commonly purple-margined and wings and keel purple-tipped. e Nev, sw Utah. *A. tephrodes* (0–6 inches): Stems, if any, prostrate. Petals pink-purple or lilac, or dirty white with margin of standard and tip of keel purple. Extreme sw Utah, se Nev. *A. desperatus:* Stems none or to 1$\frac{1}{5}$ inches. Leaves silvery or hoary. Petals pink-purple or lilac, some wing-tips white. se Utah, w Colo. *Plate 150. A. deterior:* Stems up to 1$\frac{1}{5}$ inches. Hoary. From two to five flowers per raceme. Petals pale yellowish, the keel spotted purple. sw Colo. *A. naturitensis:* Stems none or to 1$\frac{1}{5}$ inches. Hoary. Standard whitish or suffused with lilac; wings and keel-tip purple. sw Colo. *Plate 151. A. amphioxys* ($\frac{1}{2}$–3 inches): Stems prostrate or nearly so. Silvery with stiff hairs lying flat. From four to ten flowers. Petals pink-purple, the standard with a large, veined eye. s Nev,

---

*This expression, as used in these pages, means "lacking a visible leafy stem above ground."

PLATE 149

Astragalus agrestis   *Korling*

Astragalus purshii   *Spurr*

Astragalus chamaeleuce   *Scribner*

Astragalus utahensis   *Scribner*

Astragalus flavus   *Roberts*

Astragalus geyeri   *Nichols*

Astragalus brandegei   *Korling*

Astragalus parryi   *Roberts*

s Utah, w Colo. *Plate 150. A. megacarpus:* Stems $\frac{2}{5}$–2 inches. Nearly smooth. From three to five flowers. Petals pink-purple or white with pink veins. Pod bladdery. ne Nev, sw Wyo, nw Colo. *A. platytropis* (to 1 inch): Silvery-grayish-silky. From four to nine flowers. Petals whitish suffused with lilac. Pod bladdery. e Calif, Nev. *A. humillimus:* Stems less than $\frac{1}{2}$ inch. From one to three flowers. Petals "pallid." sw Colo. *A. nyensis* (up to 1 inch): Central stem erect. Roughish-hairy. From one to four flowers. Petals whitish, the standard faintly lilac-veined. s Nev. *A. calycosus:* Stems less than 1 inch. Hoary or silvery. Flowers from one to eight. Petals whitish, pink, blue, or purple, the wing-tips pale, the keel-tip mostly spotted. sw Wyo, sw Colo. *Plate 150. A. austinae:* Tufts or mats, the stems none or to 4 inches. Silvery-hairy. Petals whitish, tinged or veined lilac. Region of Lake Tahoe. *A. didymocarpus:* Stems 1–1$\frac{2}{5}$ inches, spreading or prostrate. Petals whitish tinged lavender, or pink-purple with pale wing-tips. Nev, Calif. *A. chamaemeniscus* (1–5 inches): Stems prostrate, radiating. Smooth. Flowers from five to ten. Petals red-violet, or rose with a pale eye. e Calif, w Nev. *A. obscurus:* Stems 2–6 inches, commonly prostrate. Petals pale yellowish or dirty-white, commonly suffused with lilac. se Ore, sw Ida, ne Calif, n Nev. *A. conjunctus:* Stems $\frac{1}{2}$–4 inches, erect. Petals whitish with purple keel-tip, or suffused with purple. ne Ore, w Ida. *A. eastwoodae:* Stems 1–4 inches, bending up. Smooth. From three to seven flowers. Petals pink-purple. Pods stalked above the calyx, inflated. Utah, w Colo. *A. jejunus:* Stems none or up to 1 inch. From three to seven flowers. Petals pink- or lavender-purple with pale wing-tips. Pod bladdery. sw Wyo, ec Nev, Utah. *A. arthuri:* 1–6$\frac{1}{5}$ inches, tending to erect. Smoothish. Petals pale yellowish. Pod hanging, stalked above the calyx. ne Ore, s Ida, ne Wash. *A. sterilis:* 2–6$\frac{1}{5}$ inches, wiry, zigzag. From six to ten leaf-segments. From two to five flowers. Petals pale yellowish. ne Ore, sw Ida.

2. Species limited, in our range, to Utah.

A. CASTANEIFORMIS has stems up to 1$\frac{1}{5}$ inches long.

The leaves are gray or silvery. The petals are whitish, more or less suffused with purple.

May and June: on gravelly and stony knolls, bluffs, and hillsides in southern Utah. *A. cymboides* (ec): Stems, if any, prostrate and less than 1 inch. Hoary or silvery. From four to nine flowers. Petals whitish or yellowish, the wings commonly lilac-tipped, some all suffused with lilac, rarely all pink-purple. *A. monumentalis* (se): Stems $\frac{1}{5}$–1$\frac{2}{5}$ inches. From three to nine flowers. Petals pink-purple. *A. cottami* (se): Similar. Flowers $\frac{4}{5}$–1 inch. Pod more curved, $\frac{1}{2}$–$\frac{3}{4}$ inch. Petals rose-purple, the standard perhaps paler. *A. eurekensis* (c): Stemless. From five to eleven leaf-segments. From three to seven flowers. Petals pale yel-

lowish, perhaps veined or suffused with purple. *A. ampullarius* (sw): Stems 1–3 inches. Smooth. Petals pale yellowish or purple with white wing-tips and pale eye. Pod erect, stalked, inflated. *A. zionis* (s): Stems $\frac{1}{2}$–3 inches. Densely soft-hairy, generally silvery. From three to eleven flowers. Petals purple, pale at the base. *A. perianus* (c): Stems 1–3 inches. Hoary. From three to six flowers. Petals whitish or rose. Pod bladdery. *A. striatiflorus* (s): Stems $\frac{1}{2}$–2 inches. Finely hairy. From two to five flowers. Petals whitish commonly suffused with lilac, purple-veined and -tipped. *A. desereticus* (c): Stems 1–2 inches. Densely hairy, silvery. Petals whitish. *A. loanus* (c): Stemless. Hairy. From three to nine segments. From two to seven flowers. Petals white, the keel lavender-tipped. *A. limnocharis* (sw): Stems $\frac{2}{5}$–1$\frac{1}{5}$ inches. Nearly smooth. From four to eight flowers. Petals pale yellowish. *A. chloödes* (ne): Stemless. Gray or silvery. Leaves consisting only of a stalk with a narrow end segment. Petals pink-purple. *A. serpens* (c): Stems 1–6 inches. Tufts of many stems. Flowers from three to nine. Petals greenish-purple, the standard with darker veins. Pod bladdery.

B. Species with at least some stems longer than 6 inches, erect, or prostrate, or bending up from a horizontal base, or diffusely branched.

1. Species of general distribution in our range (compare groups 2–4).

A. LENTIGINOSUS (4–40 inches) is prostrate, green or silvery-silky. The raceme may be loose, or so short as to simulate an umbel. The petals, in our range, are whitish or purple. The keel may be spotted. In most varieties the pod is inflated.

April to August: on dry plains and hillsides, open gravelly crests and rock slopes, etc. from Washington to Idaho and southward to California and Colorado. *Plate 150.* Barneby writes: "The freckled milk-vetch, *A. lentiginosus,* is hardly a species in any conventional sense of the term. As circumscribed here, it is an excessively polymorphic complex . . ." embracing an almost unmanageable range of variation. He recognizes thirty-six varieties; many of these occur in our area.

A. hornii (3–12 inches): Erect or nearly so. Variously hairy or smooth. Up to thirty-five flowers. Petals whitish or cream. Pod bladdery. w Nev. *A. iodanthus* (2–14 inches): Stems prostrate or bending up. Petals purple, whitish with purple keel-tip, or cream. se Ore, s Ida, Calif, Nev. *A. pubentissimus* (1–10 inches): Loose tufts, the stems bending up. Greenish or hoary. Petals pink-purple, the standard striped. sw Wyo, w Utah. *A. nuttallianus* (1–12 inches): The central stem erect. Smooth or with small hairs lying flat. Petals whitish, pink-lilac, or pink-purple with a pale eye. se Calif, s and e Utah, w Colo, Okla. *Plate 150.* Many varieties,

PLATE 150

Astragalus calycosus   *Scribner*

Astragalus oophorus   *W. Weber*

Astragalus lentiginosus   *Rickett*

Astragalus nuttallianus   *Henze*

Astragalus desperatus   *W. Weber*

Astragalus missouriensis   *Wilson*

Astragalus lentiginosus   *Finzel*

Astragalus amphioxys   *W. Weber*

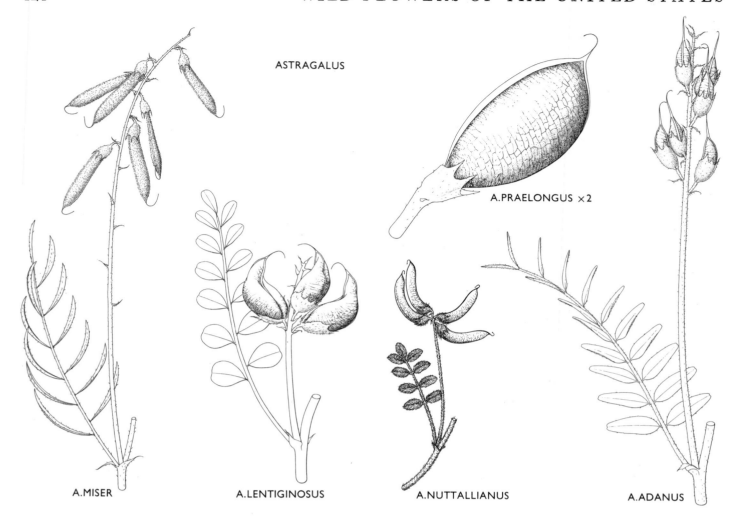

ASTRAGALUS

A.PRAELONGUS ×2

A.MISER   A.LENTIGINOSUS   A.NUTTALLIANUS   A.ADANUS

most in Texas. *A. lemmoni* (4–16 inches): Stems prostrate. Petals whitish or lilac-tinged; the standard may be purple-veined. sc Ore, ne and e Calif. *A. sabulonum* ($\frac{1}{2}$–10 inches): Erect or bending up. Hairy or silky. Flowers from two to five. Petals pale yellowish, tinged or veined lilac or purple. Pod somewhat inflated. se Utah, s and w Nev. *A. aquilonius:* Stems more or less horizontal and bending up, 8–14 inches. Flowers from five to nine. Petals greenish-white commonly tinged or veined with lilac. Pod bladdery. ec Ida. *A. oophorus* (6–10 inches): Stems bending up. Smooth. Petals purple with white wing-tips, or pale yellowish with or without a lilac tinge. Pod bladdery. From Calif through Nev to w Utah; w Colo. *Plate 150. A. beckwithii* (1–14 inches): Stems bending up or nearly erect. Smooth. Petals pale yellowish or purple with white wing-tips. e Ore, w and s Ida, se Wash, Nev, w Utah. *A. tetrapterus* (4–12 inches): Stems erect or bending up (except in fruit). Silvery or smooth and green. Petals white tinged lilac, yellowish tinged pink, or pink-purple with pale tips. Pod hanging, crescent- or ring-shaped. se Wash, e Nev, sw Utah. *A. nudisiliquus:* Stems mostly prostrate, 2–10 inches, in mats. White-woolly. From four to eight flowers. Petals

pink-purple with a pale eye. se Wash, sw Ida. *A pterocarpus* (6–14 inches): Wiry, rushlike, many erect stems. Silvery-hoary. Segments from three to seven. Petals purple or whitish with purple tips, with a pale eye. Pod pendulous, with a thin wing (*ptero-*) all round. nw Nev. *A. inflexus:* Stems prostrate, 4–14 inches. White-woolly or greenish. Petals pink-purple with pale eye. Pod rough-hairy. se Wash, ne Ore, wc Ida, w Mont. *Plate 151. A. malacus* (1–8 inches): Erect. Rough-hairy. Petals reddish-violet with pale eye. Pod bent down, curved (up to a half-circle). se Ore, sw Ida, ne Calif, Nev. *A. terminalis* (2–6 inches): Stems horizontal, bending up, zigzag. Silky-hoary, the hairs lying flat. Petals white, perhaps suffused lilac. Pod erect. s Ida, sw Mont, w Wyo. *A. arrectus* (8–16 inches): Erect. Smooth (black hairs may be seen in the inflorescence). From thirteen to thirty-three flowers. Petals pale yellowish. Pod erect, short-stalked. e Wash, sw Ida. *A. eremiticus* (4–20 inches): Erect. Smooth. Petals pale yellowish, pale purple, or pink-purple with white wing-tips. Pod erect, stalked above the calyx. se Ore, sw Ida, Nev, sw Utah. *A. porrectus* (10–40 inches): Erect, bushy. Smooth. Up to thirty-three flowers. Petals white. Pod short-stalked. c Nev. Rare.

A. ASCLEPIADOIDES (3–14 inches) is remarkable for its undivided leaves, the blades ovate or nearly round, ½–2 inches long, practically without stalks, smooth with a bloom. Stems are erect. Petals greenish-yellow with pale wing-tips and purple keel-tip, or all purple with white wing-tips. Pod erect, stalked above the calyx, inflated. Eastern Utah, western Colorado. *Plate 151*.

A. preussii (4–14 inches): Erect or nearly so. Smooth. Flowers from four to sixteen. Petals pink-purple suffused with lilac towards their tips. Pod inflated. s Nev, s Utah. *A. praelongus* (8–24 inches): Erect. Smooth or with small hairs lying flat. Petals pale yellowish. Pod erect or spreading, inflated. se Nev, s and w Utah, w Colo. *Plate 151. A. paysonii* (8–18 inches): Stems bending up. Smooth. Petals whitish. Pod hanging. c Ida, w Wyo. *A. scaphoides* (6–16 inches): Erect. Smooth. Petals pale yellowish. Pod stalked. se Ida, sw Mont. *A. atratus* (1–12 inches): Stems weak, radiating, wiry, sparsely leafy. Petals whitish or pale lilac. Pod hanging. e Wash, sw Ida, e Calif, Nev. *A. mulfordae* (4–10 inches): Stems bending up, branching. Nearly smooth. Petals whitish. Pod hanging, stalked above the calyx. sw Ida, e Ore. *A. minthorniae* (4–12 inches): Erect. Nearly smooth; black hairs in the raceme. Flowers from seven to thirty-five. Petals pale yellowish tinged purple, or wine-purple with paler or white wing-tips. Pod erect. e Calif, s Nev, sw Utah. *A. cibarius* (2½–8 inches): Stems bending up. Smooth. Petals purple with white wing-tips, bluish-white, or yellowish tinged lavender. se Ida, w Wyo, sw Mont, ne Nev, w Utah, nw Colo. *A. toquimanus* (3–10 inches): Wiry, curving up. Hairs lying flat. Petals pale yellowish-veined and suffused with lilac. Pod pendulous, very short-stalked. c Nev. *A. toanus* (10–20 inches): Robust, sparsely leafy, bushy, rushlike. Grayish or green. Segments of lower leaves from one to four pairs, mostly threadlike; of upper leaves commonly none. From seven to thirty-five flowers. Petals pink-purple with pale or white wing-tips. Pod erect. From se Ore to s Mont, w Wyo, e Nev, nw Utah. *A. oocalycis* (10–16 inches): Bushy. Smooth. From thirty-five to sixty flowers. Petals pale yellowish. s Colo. *A. fucatus* (3–12 inches): Stems spreading and bending up. Grayish or green. Petals reddish- or magenta-purple, the standard with a pale eye and striped. Pod inflated. se Utah, sw Colo. *A. subcinereus* (6–28 inches): Stems prostrate or spreading. Nearly smooth. Petals whitish or yellowish commonly veined or suffused with lilac or purple. Pod inflated. e Nev, sw Utah. *A. microcymbus* (10–24 inches): Stems prostrate, bending up, or bushy. Grayish. Petals whitish with lilac tinge, the keel purple-tipped. Pod hanging. Gunnison R Valley, w Colo. *A. convallarius* (6–30 inches): Stems erect, bending up, or rarely prostrate, much branched. Grayish or smooth. Many leaves without segments, others with up to six pairs of narrow segments. Petals pale yellowish, with or without purple veins or tinge, less commonly rose-purple. Pod hanging. se Ida, w Wyo, e Nev, Utah, nw Colo. *A. diversifolius* (8–20 inches): Stems branching. Smooth or downy. From one to five leaf-segments. Petals greenish-white. se Ida, nw Utah. *A. pinonis* (6–24 inches): Stems weak, erect or straggling, sparsely leafy. Downy. Petals greenish-white or pale yellowish, commonly lilac-tinged and the standard lilac-veined. c Nev, w Utah. *A. filipes* (10–20 inches): Sparsely leafy, erect. Smooth. Petals whitish, greenish-white, or cream. Pod hanging, stalked above the calyx. e Wash, e Ore, ne Calif, s Ida, n Nev. *A. whitneyi* (8–12 inches): Stems branching. Smooth or hairy. Petals pale yellowish, pinkish-white, lilac, or pink-purple. Pod hanging, stalked above the calyx, bladdery. se Wash, e Ore, sw Ida, n and w Nev, ne and e Calif. *A. microcystis* (2–16 inches): Branching, forming tufts. Smooth or nearly so. Flowers from four to twelve. Petals pink or magenta or whitish with pink tips and the standard with purple veins. e Wash, n Ida, w Mont. *A. humistratus* (7–24 inches): Stems prostrate or spreading and branching, perhaps forming mats. Smooth or downy. Petals greenish- or pinkish-white, pale yellowish, or magenta purple. se Nev, sw Utah, s Colo. *A. coltoni* (4–16 inches): Almost leafless, erect. Green or grayish. Segments up to 17 in one variety, or none in upper leaves of one variety, all commonly narrow. Petals pink-purple. Pod pendulous, stalked. s Utah, sw Colo.

2. The following species are found, in our range, only in Idaho.

A. AMBLYTROPIS (4–16 inches) has prostrate or trailing, branching stems. The leaves are grayish or silvery. From six to ten flowers. The petals are straw-colored, perhaps suffused or veined with lilac. The pod is bladdery.

May to July: along the Salmon River. *A. amnisamissi* (4–10 inches): Smooth. Stems pointing up. Petals whitish suffused with purplish. Pod inflated. In the Lost River (amnis amissus) Mountains. *A. adanus* (10–18 inches): Robust, leafy. Smooth. Petals pale yellowish. *A. atropubescens* (6–12 inches): Erect. Smooth. Petals white or cream. Pod erect. *A. oniciformis*: Stems mostly prostrate, 4–10 inches. Smooth or nearly so. From six to twelve flowers. Petals pale yellowish or whitish, perhaps suffused with lilac. Pod erect. *A. camptopus* (8–12 inches): Erect. Up to fifteen flowers. Petals pink-purple. Pod stalked and coiled into a ring.

3. A number of species are found only in eastern California, or in eastern California and western Nevada.

A. ANDERSONII forms tufts 4–8 inches tall. The stems

and foliage are gray-hairy. There are from twelve to twenty flowers per raceme, the petals whitish or pale yellowish, on some plants tinged or veined lavender.

April to July: in sandy and gravelly places.

A. monoensis (3–8 inches): Prostrate or pointing up, slender. Silvery-silky or hairy. Flowers crowded. Petals whitish, perhaps lavender-tinged. Only Mono Co., Calif. *A. pseudiodanthus:* Stems prostrate, matted, 8–12 inches. Smooth. Flowers from twelve to twenty-five. Petals reddish-lilac with a pale eye. Pod forms a ring. Rare. *A. casei* (6–16 inches): Wiry, mostly erect. Hoary. Petals pink-purple with white wing-tips. *A. serenoi* (6–18 inches): Erect or nearly so. Silvery. Petals lilac or purple with white wing-tips, or pale yellowish with purplish wing- and keel-tips. Pod erect. *A. inversus:* Stems bending up, 8–20 inches. Hairy or smooth. Petals yellowish. Pod pendulous, stalked. Only ne Calif. Rare. *A. gibbsii:* Stems prostrate or bending up, 6–14 inches. Grayish-green. Flowers from ten to thirty. Petals dull yellow. Pod pendulous, stalked. *A. pulsiferae:* Stems mostly prostrate, 4–10 inches. Gray-hairy. Flowers from three to thirteen. Petals whitish with lilac veins and tips. Pod bladdery. ne Calif, w Nev (and one place in s Wash).

4. Species of group 8 limited, in our area, to Utah.

a. A number of these have more than eight leaf-segments.

See also *A. saurinus, sabulosus,* under b.

A. PARDALINUS (2–12 inches) forms loose tufts, the stems bending up. There are from three to eight flowers in a raceme. The petals are pink or purple. The pods are inflated.

May and June: on sandy plains and bluffs in the Colorado Basin.

A. wardi (sc): Stems in loose clumps, bending up, 4–12 inches. Smooth. Petals whitish or greenish with pink veins. Pod more or less hanging, bladdery. *A. bryantii* (sc): Stems 14–32 inches, erect. Leaf-segments yellowish, smooth on top. Petals purple with lighter or white wing-tips. *A. cronquistii* (se): Stems 8–16 inches, bending up, diffuse. Smooth or nearly so. Petals pink-purple with paler wing-tips. Pod hanging or sloping down. *A. duchesnensis* (ne): Stems erect or straggling, 6–14 inches, wiry, sparsely leafy. Becoming smooth. Leaf-segments narrow, even thread-like. Standard and keel pink or red-purple with a pale eye, the wings white: *A. sesquiflorus* (se and sc): Stems prostrate, matted, 1–7 inches. Hoary. From one to three flowers per raceme. Petals pink-purple. *A. moencoppensis* (se and ec): Stems many in broomlike tufts, sparsely leafy, 3–10 inches. Petals red-lilac or purplish. *A. malacoides* (s): Stems branching, bending up, not more than 5 inches. Finely hairy. Petals purplish. Pod with a stalk (above the calyx) up to ⅛ inch.

b. The remaining species of group B in Utah have fewer than eight leaf-segments.

A. EPISCOPUS is wiry and apparently leafless, green or yellowish-green. Most or all leaves are nothing but the grooved midrib; a few, generally low on the stem, may have up to four rather narrow segments. The petals are whitish with a pink tinge.

May and June: in sandy clay and on rock slopes (and petrified forest) in east-central Utah. *A. lancearius* (s and se): Aspect similar, wiry, nearly leafless, 8–18 inches. Segments none or from one to six. Petals whitish or faintly tinged pink or lilac. *A. nidularius* (se): Stems wiry, sparsely leafy, 6–12 inches. From five to nine narrow leaf-segments up to ½ inch long. Petals pink-purple, the stalks paler. Pod hanging, stalked above the calyx. *A. harrisonii* (c): Stems in a bushy clump, sparsely leafy or leafless, 16–28 inches. From three to seven narrow segments up to ⅛ inch. From four to twelve flowers. Petals pale purple. Pod hanging, stalked. *A. hamiltoni* (ne): Erect, 10–16 inches. Silvery or hoary. From three to five segments up to an inch long. Petals pale yellowish. Pod hanging, stalked. *A. rafaelensis* (ec): Stems apparently leafless, coarse, 16–22 inches. Smooth. One or two pairs of narrow, even threadlike segments, or none. Petals pink-purple with pale wing-tips, or white. *A. saurinus* (ne): Stems erect, 8–12 inches, sparsely leafy. Downy. From three to eleven narrow, even threadlike segments. Petals pink-purple with white wing-tips. *A. woodruffi* (ec): Stems erect, coarse, 1–2 feet. Silvery-silky. From one to seven narrow, even threadlike, well-spaced segments. Up to forty-five flowers in dense racemes. Petals pink-purple with a pale eye in the striped standard, the wing-tips paler. Malodorous. *A. sabulosus* (c): Stems robust, tending upward, branching, 4–12 inches. Downy or silvery-silky. From five to eleven segments (except the youngest leaves). Petals straw-colored. Pod hanging, somewhat inflated. *A. musiniensis* (ec): Stems short, almost lacking. Grayish or silvery. Leaf-segments three or five (or on some leaves, one). From one to four flowers. Petals pink-purple with a paler eye in the striped standard. Pod spongy.

IV. *Species of eastern Washington, northwestern Idaho, and eastern Oregon.*

The following species of the Rocky Mountain (Region II) are found also in this northwestern area: *A. americanus, adsurgens, aboriginum, kentrophyta, lotiflorus, robbinsii, tenellus;* also the wide-ranging *A. canadensis* (Region I); and from the adjacent Intermountain Region we have dwarf species with scarcely visible stem: *A. newberryi, purshii, obscurus, conjunctus, sterilis;* and species with at least some stems over 6 inches tall: *A.*

PLATE 151

Astragalus inflexus

Spellenberg

Astragalus asclepiadoides   *W. Weber*

Astragalus naturitensis   *Roberts*

Astragalus succumbens   *Spellenberg*

Astragalus leibergi   *Spellenberg*

Astragalus cusickii   *George*

Myrick

Astragalus praelongus   *Rose*   Astragalus curvicarpus   Astragalus collinus   *Guppy*

lemmoni, *lentiginosus*, *atratus*, *eremiticus*, *filipes*, *beckwithii*, *tetrapterus*, *iodanthus*, *nudisiliquus*, *malacus*, *mulfordae*, *whitneyi*.

A. Species with pods on a stalk extending above the level of attachment of the perianth.

In most of these species this pod-stalk ranges from $\frac{1}{5}$ to $\frac{4}{5}$ inch; in three it does not exceed $\frac{1}{5}$ inch and is partly concealed by the calyx.

1. Species whose pods hang (in some they may extend horizontally).

These are plants mostly with horizontally spreading stems bending up and branching (prostrate in one), at least some of which exceed 6 inches.

A. COLLINUS (6–16 inches) is finely hairy. The stems may be erect. Flowers are numerous, the petals cream, pale yellow, or lemon-yellow. May to July: southeastern and north-central Washington, northeastern Oregon, northwestern Idaho. *Plate 151*.

A. curvicarpus (6–16 inches): Similar. Some plants smooth. Fewer flowers (to twenty-five). Petals white, pale yellowish, or lemon-yellow. sw Ida, s and se Ore, nw Nev. *Plate 151*. *A. sclerocarpus* (8–20 inches): Stems wiry, straggling. Leaf-segments narrow, even threadlike. Petals whitish with lilac tips, the keel spotted. Columbia R valley, Wash, adjacent Ore. *A. sinuatus* (8–18 inches): Leafy. Finely hairy. Petals whitish. Pod on some plants more or less horizontal. c Wash. *A. speirocarpus* (4–14 inches): Hoary. Petals whitish or lilac-tinged and keel purple-tipped. Pod on some plants more or less horizontal. sc Wash. *A. alvordensis* (6–12 inches): Erect, wiry, the branches forming a sort of triangular plane. Grayish or almost smooth. From five to fourteen flowers. Petals pale lilac, or whitish or yellowish veined and suffused with lilac, the keel-tip commonly purplish. Pod stalked, pendulous. se Ore, nw Nev. *A. solitarius* (12–18 inches): Erect, wiry, sparsely leafy. Grayish-hoary. From five to nine segments. Up to thirty flowers. Petals pale lilac. Pod pendulous, stalked. se Ore. *A. applegatii* (12–16 inches): Erect, slender, branching. Smooth. From seven to eleven segments. From ten to eighteen flowers. Petals whitish, the standard and keel-tip faintly lilac-tinged. Pod stalked. s Ore, just e of the Cascades. *A. howellii* (3–8 inches): Erect. Finely hairy. Petals pale yellowish. nc Ore. *A. misellus* (2–10 inches): Stems of some plants prostrate. Petals yellowish or greenish-yellow, the standard lilac-veined. e Wash, e Ore. *A. cusickii* (1–2 feet): Slender, sparsely leafy, rushlike. Smooth or nearly so. Segments mostly very narrow, few on upper leaves. Flowers from four to fourteen. Petals white, cream, or purplish. Pod bladdery. ne Ore, w Ida. *Plate 151*.

2. One species with more or less hanging pods has scarcely any stem above ground, but forms tufts.

A. SALMONIS ($\frac{2}{5}$–2 inches) is smooth or nearly so. The racemes have from two to eight flowers. The petals are whitish tinged or suffused with lavender, the keel-tip purple. The pod hangs down or lies on the ground (doubtless because the ground is so close).

April to June: on dry slopes and in stiff clay in east-central Oregon and southwestern Idaho.

3. Two species have erect pods.

They are mainly plants of the Columbia River valley. Their stems, if any, are erect or nearly so.

A. TWEEDYI (14–32 inches) tends to be finely hairy. The petals are pale yellowish. Columbia River and tributaries, central Oregon, adjacent Washington. *A. leibergi* (2–4 inches): Silky. Petals whitish. c Wash. *Plate 151*.

B. Species with pods not visible on a stalk above the calyx (a very short stalk may be concealed in the calyx).

1. Two of these are very short-stemmed, forming tufts. The pods are erect.

A. RIPARIUS ($1\frac{1}{2}$–6 inches) is nearly smooth. Leaf-segments are many (up to thirty-three). The petals are greenish-white or cream.

April to June: on dry bluffs and banks in southeastern Washington and northwestern Idaho. *A. reventiformis* (1–5 inches): Almost stemless. Petals white. c Ore.

2. The remaining species have at least some stems longer than 6 inches.

A. HOODIANUS (2–12 inches) is erect, silvery. The leaves have from twenty-five to thirty-seven segments. The flowers are cream. The pod is erect.

March to June: on dry gravelly and grassy hillsides and branches in the Columbia River valley, in north-central Oregon and adjacent Washington. *A. reventus* (3–8 inches): Stems short, forming tufts. Leaf-segments from twenty-three to forty-one. Petals white or cream. ne Ore, se Wash. *A. sheldoni* (2–15 inches): Stems erect, pale green or straw-color. Finely hairy. From twenty-five to thirty-five segments. Petals white or cream. se Wash, ne Ore, nw Ida. *A. vallaris:* Stems spreading on the ground, 4–12 inches. Smooth. From five to seven flowers. Petals whitish. Along the Snake River, w Ida, ne Ore. *A. peckii* (2–8 inches): Stems prostrate or in tufts, densely leafy. Leaves up to $1\frac{1}{2}$ inches long with segments not more than $\frac{1}{4}$ inch. From five to nine flowers. Petals pale yellowish, the standard purple-veined. Pod turned down. sc Ore. *A. tegetarioides:* Stems threadlike, prostrate. Leaves $\frac{1}{2}$–$1\frac{1}{2}$ inches. From three to six tiny flowers. Petals whitish. Pod commonly on the ground.

A. columbianus (6–14 inches): Leaf-segments from five to thirteen. From two to ten flowers. Petals whitish. Pods probably on the ground. Columbia R valley, c Wash. *A. diaphanus* (2–12 inches): Stems prostrate or diffusely branched. Petals whitish with standard lavender-veined and keel purple-tipped. Pod turned down, somewhat inflated. On sand and gravel and barrens in Washington and Oregon.

A. SPALDINGII (4–14 inches) has prostrate stems, or
    with tips bending up, forming tufts or mats. The petals are whitish, some tinged or veined with lavender. The pod is horizontal.

May to July: on dry hillsides and prairies, and in sagebrush, in eastern Washington and northeastern Oregon. *A. tyghensis* (6–22 inches): Similar. Densely hairy-woolly. Up to forty flowers. Petals pale yellow. Pod horizontal. c Ore. *A. lyallii* (6–16 inches): Petals whitish tinged lavender, the standard striped. Pod bent down. sc Wash. *A. succumbens* (6–16 inches): Erect, bushy. Rather rough-hairy. Leaf-segments from twenty-five to thirty-five. Standard and keel pink-purple, the wings whitish. Pod rather erect. Bend of the Columbia R, n Ore and Wash. *Plate 151.* *A. caricinus* (6–12 inches): Erect. Petals whitish tinged lavender. Pod turned down. s Wash, s Ida.

ONOBRYCHIS

One species of *Onobrychis* is in our area.

O. VICIAEFOLIA (8–16 inches) has leaves divided into
    from eleven to seventeen (or on some plants to twenty-seven) narrowly elliptic segments $\frac{2}{5}$–$\frac{4}{5}$ inch long. The racemes have from ten to fifty flowers, with brownish bracts. The flowers are about $\frac{1}{2}$ inch long, pink or lavender veined with reddish-purple; the wings are not more than half as long as the keel. The pods are ovate, $\frac{1}{4}$–$\frac{1}{3}$ inch long, downy, short-spined.

June to August: introduced from Europe in Washington and western Montana.

THE TOUCH-ME-NOT FAMILY (BALSAMINACEAE)

The *Balsaminaceae* comprise only one genus in North America.

JEWELWEEDS, SNAPWEEDS, OR TOUCH-ME-NOTS (IMPATIENS)

The curious flower of *Impatiens* cannot be confused with any other. There are (in our species) three sepals; the flower hangs on its stalk and the lowest sepal is much larger than the other two, saclike and colored like a petal; it projects backwards under the flower-stalk; the other two sepals are small. The petals emerge from the large sepal; there are apparently three, all separate, but those on the sides are two-lobed and each is probably two petals joined. There are five stamens. The fruit is a narrow capsule; it opens at a touch, the five pieces coiling and explosively ejecting the seeds, and thus giving two English names to the genus. The leaves are without lobes or segments, but are toothed.

A large number of species grow in India.

JEWELWEED, I. CAPENSIS (2–5 feet), has orange petals and lower sepal, generally marked with reddish-brown. The spur of the sepal is bent so as to point forward.

June to September: in moist shady places from North Dakota to Oklahoma and Colorado (and reported, perhaps incorrectly, from Idaho). *Plate 152.*

I. pallida is found in eastern Kansas and possibly in North Dakota. The flowers are yellow. The spur of the sepal points straight down.

I. ecalcarata has an orange flower without spots. The large sepal lacks a spur. From Oregon to Montana. *I. noli-tangere* has yellowish flowers which may be mottled with crimson or reddish-brown. Leaves are more coarsely toothed. From Oregon to Idaho.

THE VIOLET FAMILY (VIOLACEAE)

Except for our two species of *Hybanthus*, the *Violaceae* are represented in our area only by species of *Viola*. The flowers of *Hybanthus* may be recognized as allied to the violets, in spite of their small greenish petals, by their pistil and stamens.

THE VIOLETS (VIOLA)

The flowers of the violets have a flat lower petal which provides a landing-place for insects, two side petals or "wings," and two upper petals. The lower petal is generally prolonged backward into a hollow sac or tube, a "spur." The five stamens closely surround the pistil, only the short style and stigma generally being visible. The two lower stamens bear nectaries, bodies that exude nectar, which extend into the spur. The whole arrangement makes self-fertilization almost impossible but favors cross-fertilization. Many violets also form flowers that fertilize themselves without opening, and these may be responsible for most of the seeds. The fruit is a small capsule which splits into three parts, each bearing a row of seeds.

The species are numerous and some of them, which are distinguished by only minor details, hybridize freely in nature, making identification almost impossible; this is particularly true of the "stemless blue violets" (see below). In fact it has been said that there are no true species in this group, or that they all form one vast and heterogeneous species. However, the descriptions below will enable the reader to name at least some of the plants he finds; perhaps most of them.

All the violets are spring-flowering. If, however, frosts are long delayed in the autumn until the days are again short as in early spring, flowers may be seen in this season also.

The majority of our species are those of the eastern United States, which just reach our northeastern area, or, by way of Texas, enter our southeastern states.

I. *The so-called stemless violets, whose leaves and flowers spring from an underground stem (rhizome).*

A. Species whose leaves are not lobed or cleft, with generally blue, violet, or purple flowers. Some species have white-flowered forms. Runners are not found in most species.
See also *V. triloba*.

V. PAPILIONACEA is the commonest "stemless" violet of the Northeast. The leaves are heart-shaped with blunt teeth. The wings have tufts of hairs — "beards." The flowers vary from deep violet to white.

In moist places from North Dakota and eastern Wyoming to northern Colorado and Oklahoma. *Plate 152. V. sororia:* Similar, but stems, leaf-stalks, and flower-stalks hairy or downy. e Kan, Okla. *V. cucullata:* Flowers on long stalks above the leaves. Hairs on wings tipped by little knobs. e Kan, Neb. *V. affinis:* Leaf-blades narrower, tapering. Lowest petal bearded like the wings. se Kan. *V. septentrionalis:* Downy. Wings and lowest petal bearded. From ND to Neb.

V. fimbriatula: Leaf-blades lanceolate with longer teeth near the base. Okla. *V. villosa:* Leaf-blades roundish, hairy. Wings and lowest petal bearded. Okla. *V. missouriensis:* Leaf-blades triangular. Petals pale violet with white base. From Neb to Okla. *V. nephrophylla:* Lowest petal hairy, wings bearded. Leaf-stalks and flower-stalks smooth. ND, Kan. *V. sagittata:* Leaf-stalks longer than the blades; blades lanceolate, commonly with prominent teeth or even lobes at the base. Flowers purple with a white center and dark veins. Flower-stalks equal to or longer than the leaves. Kan, Okla. *V. emarginata:* Similar. Leaves variable, rarely lobed at the base. Petals commonly notched. Kan, Okla. *V. palustris:* Smooth, with creeping stems. Spur of lowest petal short. Petals pale lilac with darker veins. From Mont to Colo, Okla, and Utah; Wash and Ore. *Plate 152.*

B. Stemless species with leaves not lobed or cleft whose flowers are always white (in several species marked with purplish veins).
Most of these have runners.

V. PALLENS spreads by runners. The leaves are broadly ovate, heart-shaped, blunt, smooth. The flowers are veined with purple. The wings lack beards.

May to August: in wet soil in Montana and North Dakota. *Plate 152.* Some treat this as a variety of the western *V. macloskeyi. V. primulifolia* has oblong or ovate leaf-blades which taper at the base to a broad, thin stalk. The three lower petals are purple-veined. The wings may have a few veins. Okla.

C. Stemless violets whose leaves are lobed or cleft.

V. TRILOBA is hairy. The leaves present at flowering time have blades cleft palmately into three or more lobes. These variously toothed or lobed. The earliest leaves are unlobed, as are those formed after flowering and lasting into summer. At such times the plants closely resemble *V. sororia* (see under A); and for this reason some have merged the two species and included *V. palmata* (see below). The petals are violet; the lowest copiously hairy.

In woods, in Kansas and Oklahoma. *V. palmata:* Hairy. Leaves deeply cleft into from five to eleven lobes. In other respects like *V. triloba.* Kan, Okla. *V. viarum:* Smooth. Leaves with triangular blades deeply cleft at the base into pointed lobes. Petals deep violet. Lowest petal notched and rolled into a tube, not bearded; wings bearded. Neb. *V. pedatifida:* Smooth. Leaf-blades cleft or divided into many narrow lobes: three main segments each deeply cleft. Petals generally pale violet, the lower three bearded. Kan, Okla, Colo. *Plate 152.*

PLATE 152

Viola palustris

Kravig

Viola pedatifida

Blecher

Viola papilionacea

Rickett

Viola pallens

Johnson

Astragalus lotiflorus

Stockert

Astragalus miser

Uttal

Viola pedata

Rickett

Impatiens capensis

Rickett

Bird's-foot violet, *V. pedata*, the most beautiful of all violets, is found in eastern Kansas and Oklahoma. The leaf-blades are divided and cleft into a number of narrow parts. The upper petals flare outward and backwards, exposing the yellow tips of the stamens. In one variety the upper two petals are deep violet-purple, the lower three lilac; in another all petals are lilac (but some may be marked with purple). *Plate 152*.

II. *Species with visible leafy stems above ground.*
    Many of these are found in our western areas.

A. Species with white, blue, or violet flowers.

V. ADUNCA has thickish leaf-blades, mostly ovate. The petals are violet, the wings with white beards, the three lower whitish at the base. The spur is nearly half as long as the lower blade and may be hooked at the tip.
    March to August: in meadows and woods through most of our area (apparently not in North Dakota, Kansas, or Oklahoma). *Plate 153*.

V. CANADENSIS has rather narrow, tapering leaf-blades; the stipules are lanceolate. The petals are white, or in some plants lavender-tinged; the wings with beards. The lowest petal (and perhaps the wings) has a yellow base and brownish lines.
    April to September: in moist meadows and woods in the Rocky Mountains from Montana to Colorado and Utah. *V. rugulosa* is by some identified with *V. canadensis*. *Plate 153*. The difference is chiefly the formation of many branching rhizomes. The leaves are more wrinkled ("rugulose") and hairy. Rocky Mountains and westward.

V. BECKWITHII has leaf-blades cleft into three primary lobes each twice pinnately cleft into narrow lobes. The two upper petals are red-violet, the three lower lilac, yellow at the base, with dark veins. The wings have yellow beards.
    March to May: in dry soil, as in brush and pine forest, from Idaho and Oregon to the eastern slope of the Sierra Nevada in Mono County and eastward to Utah. *Plate 153*. *V. trinervata*, in eastern Washington

and Oregon, has leathery, smooth leaf-segments. The petals are much as in the preceding species. *Plate 153*.
    V. rafinesquii has hairy leaf-blades tapering to the stalk; stipules are cleft into narrow lobes, like a cockscomb. The flowers are small, from cream to blue-violet, commonly marked with yellow. Kan, Okla. The name Johnny-jump-up is applied to this species and to the following two, as well as several others. *V. arvensis:* Petals yellow, commonly marked with lavender. *V. tricolor:* Two upper petals purple. Ancestor of pansies. These are European species, commonly cultivated, interbreeding and yielding all color-combinations. *Plate 153*. *V. striata* may be found in southeastern Kansas. Stipules toothed. Flowers cream with brown-purple lines. Wings bearded.

B. Species with yellow flowers.

V. NUTTALLII has leaves nearly 3 inches long, with lanceolate blades. The petals are slightly hairy; they may be tinged with purple on the back.
    April and May: on plains and hills from Washington and Oregon to North Dakota and southward to Colorado, Utah, and Oklahoma. Includes a number of varieties. *Plate 153*. *V. charlestonensis:* Leaves gray-downy. Named for the Charleston Mts of sw Nev; also in Utah. *V. orbiculata:* Stems 2 inches or less. Leaf-blades nearly round. Wings bearded. From the Cascades in Washington to Montana. *Plate 153*. *V. purpurea:* Leaves purple-tinged. Two upper petals purplish on the back; the three lower purple-veined. Wings bearded. From Wash to Mont, s to Colo, Utah. *Plate 153*. *V. biflora:* Leaves with roundish blades. Stems prostrate or bending up. Petals streaked with purplish-brown. From Alaska to Colo. *Plate 153*. *V. pensylvanica:* Smooth. From one to three long-stalked basal leaves with heart-shaped blades. Petals with purplish veins. The wings with beards. In one variety the pods white-woolly. Kan, Okla. *V. pubescens:* Similar. Stems softly hairy. One or no long-stalked basal leaf. SD, Nev. *V. sheltonii:* Leaves blue-green, divided into three, the segments palmately cleft and lobed. Petals lemon-yellow with brown-purple veins, the upper two brown-purple on the back. Barely entering our range in the west.

THE GREEN-VIOLETS (HYBANTHUS)

The relationship of *Hybanthus* to *Viola* is not evident at first glance. The small, not brightly colored flowers are borne singly or in small clusters in the axils of leaves on an erect stem. The petals and sepals are about equal in length. But the lowest petal is slightly larger and slightly cup- or sac-like; the stamens are joined into a sheath around the pistil, from which the broad, bent-down end of the style emerges; and the

lower two stamens bear glands at the base; all much as in *Viola*.

H. VERTICILLATUS has leaves only $\frac{1}{4}$ inch wide or less, and without stalks. The petals are $\frac{1}{8}$–$\frac{1}{6}$ inch long; the upper four are greenish, rosy, or purplish; the lowest whitish or yellowish commonly with a red spot near the tip.

PLATE 153

Viola beckwithii   *Shaw*

Viola adunca   *Johnson*

Viola rugulosa   *Uttal*

Viola tricolor   *Rickett*

Viola orbiculata   *Korling*

Viola nuttallii   *George*

Viola biflora   *Blecher*

Viola purpurea   *Korling*

Viola trinervata   *Spurr*

April to September: on prairies and mesas and in disturbed soil in Kansas and Colorado. *Plate 154.* In recent works named *H. linearis.*

H. concolor (1–3 feet) has leaves which taper at the base to a sort of stalk; they may be toothed. The stem is generally downy. The petals are $\frac{1}{5}$ inch long or less, all greenish. An eastern species reaching north-eastern Kansas. *Plate 154.*

THE RHATANY FAMILY (KRAMERIACEAE)

The *Krameriaceae* contain only the genus *Krameria.*

RHATANY OR PRAIRIE-BURS (KRAMERIA)

One species of *Krameria* is found in our area.

PRAIRIE-BUR, K. LANCEOLATA, has stems trailing on the ground or curving upward, up to 2 feet long. The leaves are narrowly elliptic or lanceolate, hairy on the under side. The flowers have five crimson sepals and five small petals, the three upper stalked, the two lower gland-like. There are four stamens, partly joined. The fruit is a round bur, covered with a white down from which rise delicate spines; containing one seed.

April to August: on prairies and slopes in Kansas and Oklahoma. *Plate 154.*

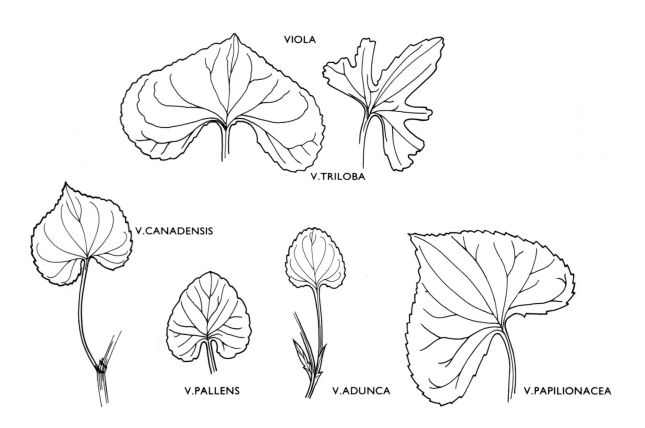

GROUP X

Sepals four or five; petals four or five, joined at least at their base, and radially symmetric (or very nearly so); stamens of the same number or twice as many. Leaves all at the base or in pairs or circles on the flowering stems, mostly undivided. Ovary superior.

Exceptions: The flowers of *Trientalis* commonly have six or seven of each part. *Glaux* has no petals. *Menyanthes* may have six; and its leaves are divided. Some species in the primrose, dogbane, milkweed, phlox, and heath families have leaves borne singly on the stems; and a number of species in the phlox family have lobed, cleft, and divided leaves.

I.   *Plants all of whose stamens are opposite the midlines of petals:* primrose family.

II.   *Plants at least half of whose stamens are opposite the line of junction of adjacent petals.*

    A. Plants with milky sap.

1.   Plants with two ovaries joined to a single style and stigma, or to a stigma with no style: dogbane family.

2.   Plants with two ovaries and two styles which share a single stigma, to which the tips of the stamens are attached: milkweed family.

    B. Plants without milky sap.
      One species of the milkweed family lacks "milk."

1.   Plants with four or five petals; an ovary with a single chamber containing many ovules; and a two-lobed stigma: gentian family.

2.   Plants with five petals; an ovary with three chambers; and a style with three stigmas (two in some species of *Navarretia*): phlox family.

3.   Woody plants with four or five petals; a generally bell-shaped or urn-shaped corolla; stamens with terminal pores through which the pollen is shed; and an ovary with two or more chambers: heath family.

THE PRIMROSE FAMILY (PRIMULACEAE)

In most families whose petals and stamens are of the same number the stamens alternate with the petals; that is, each stamen stands opposite the gap between two adjacent petals, or the line of junction of two joined petals. In the primrose family (and a few others), each stamen stands opposite the middle of a petal.

There are generally five petals in our species, either joined so as to form a distinct tube with flaring lobes at the end, or joined only at the base and so appearing separate. The one pistil has a single style. A further characteristic, which demands expert dissection to determine, is that the ovules within the ovary are borne on a column that rises from the base of the ovary and does not reach the tip of the cavity.

Our species of *Primulaceae* have undivided and mostly unlobed leaves. The flowers in several genera are in umbels; in others, on stalks from the axils.

Guide to Genera of Primulaceae

I.   *Genera with no leaves on the flowering stems.*

    A. Plants whose corolla is a definite tube crowned with spreading lobes: *Primula* (leaves all at the base of the stem); *Douglasia* (leaves on a mat or cushion of stems).

    B. Plants whose corolla has no very evident tube: *Dodecatheon* (flowers pointing down with corolla-lobes bent sharply upward); *Androsace* (flowers minute, white).

II. *Genera with leaves on the flowering stems.*

    A. Plants with leaves in pairs or circles: *Steironema* (flowers on stalks from the axils; petals yellow, joined only at the base; stamens separate, each, in the bud, enfolded by a petal); *Lysimachia* (flowers and petals as in *Steironema*; stalks of the stamens joined around the ovary); *Naumburgia* (petals as in *Steironema*; flowers in dense tufts in the axils); *Trientalis* (leaves in one circle just beneath a terminal umbel); *Glaux* (succulent; flowers minute; no petals; leaves small, in pairs); *Anagallis* (flowers blue or salmon, on threadlike stalks in the axils).

    B. Plants with leaves borne singly: *Samolus* (flowers in racemes; corolla cup shaped, small, white or pink); *Centunculus* (plants small; flowers minute, in the axils; corolla-lobes pink, commonly four).

PRIMROSES (PRIMULA)

The true primroses, not to be confused with evening-primroses or primrose-willows, are easily recognized. The leaves are all at the base of the flowering stem, which bears at its summit an umbel of flowers. The calyx is angular, with five teeth. The corolla forms a tube with five notched or cleft lobes. The stamens are attached to the corolla-tube and do not project.

The genus *Primula* is best developed in Asian highlands, and species from Asia have given us most of our garden varieties.

P. PARRYI (to 1 foot) is one of the best reasons for climbing mountains. The stems may be nearly 2 feet tall, crowned by umbels of vivid magenta-pink flowers with yellow centers, nearly an inch across the petals. The leaves are erect, long and relatively narrow.

June to August: among rocks and on meadows and stream-banks from Idaho and Montana to Utah and Colorado. *Plate 154.*

P. *nevadensis* (to 5 inches) has leaves longer than the flowering stems; they may be toothed near the tip. The corolla-lobes are violet with a purple ring at the base; the tube yellow or orange. In the mountains of east-central Nevada.

P. *angustifolia* (to 3 inches) has narrowly lanceolate leaves ½–2 inches long. The stem bears one or two flowers, the corolla scarcely 1 inch across, rose with yellow center. May and June: southeastern Utah. *Plate 154.* P. *maguirei:* Leaves broad at the tips, up to 3 inches. Stem to 4 inches, with from one to three flowers up to 1 inch across, red. ne Utah. P. *cusickiana:* Corolla violet or purplish. c Ida, ne Ore.

P. INCANA (to 16 inches) has a rosette of leaves 1–2 inches long, broadest at the tip, finely toothed. The stem has from three to twelve lilac flowers, the petals deeply cleft. The plants are mealy.

May to July: on stream-banks and in moist meadows from southeastern Idaho to Montana, Colorado, and Utah.

P. *specuicola* (to 10 inches) has flowers not ½ inch across. se Utah.

DOUGLASIA

Two species of *Douglasia* may be found in our area. They form cushions or mats from which rise leafless flowering stems. The flowers are pink or red, the petals forming a tube flaring into five lobes at the end.

D. MONTANA forms small cushions, with narrowly lanceolate leaves up to ⅓ inch long. The flowering stems are up to 1 inch tall, each generally with one pink or rose-violet flower.

May to July: on foothills and rock slopes from Idaho to Montana and northern Wyoming. *Plate 154.*

D. NIVALIS forms mats of grayish-downy, narrow leaves ⅖–1⅕ inches long. The flowering stems are ½–3 inches tall, bearing from two to eight flowers in an umbel. The corolla is bright red or magenta-purple.

April to August: from sagebrush slopes to alpine ridges in central and eastern Washington. *Plate 154.*

PLATE 154

Primula angustifolia

Korling

Krameria lanceolata

Johnson

Douglasia nivalis

Spurr

Primula parryi

Korling

Douglasia montana

Spurr

Todsen

Hybanthus verticillatus

Hybanthus concolor

Johnson

THE SHOOTING-STARS (DODECATHEON)

The species of *Dodecatheon* are among the most charming of our wild flowers in high mountains as well as in our prairies. They owe their English name to their hanging flowers with sepals and petals bent sharply back. The stamens form a dark-colored cone emerging from their midst. The leaves are all at ground level, at the base of the flowering stems.

I. *Species whose stigma is at least twice as wide as the style.*

D. ALPINUM (2–6 inches) has flower-parts in four's.
    The bent-back lobes of the corolla are lavender or magenta; the short joined part ("tube") is yellowish with a reddish ring at the base. The tips of the stamens are purplish and wrinkled. The leaves are narrow and without teeth.
    June and July: on mountain meadows and by streams from the Cascade Mountains of Oregon and the Sierra Nevada to northeastern Oregon and Utah. *Plate 155.*

D. JEFFREYI (6–24 inches) has flower-parts in four's or five's. The corolla-lobes are from purplish to pinkish-lavender or even light yellow or whitish, the joined part cream or yellow with a red band. The leaves are generally more than ⅖ inch wide and may be glandular-downy, the margins plain, scalloped, or finely toothed.
    June to August: on wet ground in the Cascade Mountains and the Sierra Nevada and eastward to Montana. *Plate 155.*
    D. *redolens* (10–24 inches) has flower-parts in five's. The corolla-lobes are lavender or magenta, the joined part yellow. The plant is glandular-downy. At high altitudes from the Sierra Nevada to Utah.

II. *Species whose stigma is about as wide as the style.*

D. DENTATUM (4–14 inches) has thin ovate leaf-blades, with toothed ("dentate") or wavy edges, on long stalks, up to 10 inches long overall. The flowers are white, from one to seven making an umbel.
    June to August: in moist forest soil in Washington, northern Oregon, and central Idaho. *Plate 155.*

D. PULCHELLUM (2–20 inches) has very variable leaves, the blades with or without small teeth, lanceolate or widest near the tip, tapering to a flat ("winged") stalk, up to 10 inches overall. The flowers, from one to twenty-five, have corolla-lobes from white to purplish, the joined part yellowish with a basal purplish line.
    April to August: in meadows and swamps and by streams throughout our range from the Rocky Mountains west. This very variable species has received more than thirty names. *Plate 155.*
    D. *conjugens* (3–10 inches): Smooth. Leaves without teeth. Corolla-lobes from white to magenta, the joined part yellow with a maroon base. From the Cascades in Washington and Oregon to Montana and Wyoming. *Plate 155.*
    D. *poeticum* (4–16 inches): Leaf-blades lanceolate, or broader between middle and tip, coarsely toothed or almost without teeth. Corolla-lobes from bright pink to orchid, the joined part yellow with a red ring. Wet soil, on the eastern slope of the Cascades in southern Washington and northern Oregon.
    D. *meadia* (6–20 inches) is an eastern species found within our limits from North Dakota to Oklahoma. Leaf-blades smooth, elliptic or oblong, without teeth, tapering to the stalk, generally red at the base. Corolla-lobes from pink to lilac. *Plate 155.*

ANDROSACE

The genus *Androsace* consists of diminutive plants which often form tufts or rosettes of leaves on the ground, the tiny white flowers being borne on leafless erect stems, in umbels, with a circle of bracts — an involucre — beneath the radiating flower-stalks. The corolla is funnel-shaped, scarcely longer than the calyx.

A. OCCIDENTALIS has a rosette of narrow, pointed leaves less than an inch long, from which rise the one or more stems, up to 4 inches tall, which bear the umbels. The bracts of the involucre are lanceolate.
    April to June: from the Rocky Mountains eastward; also in the Sierra Nevada. *Plate 156.*

A. SEPTENTRIONALIS has leaves in a dense tuft; they are up to 1½ inches long, and may be toothed. The flowering stems are up to a foot tall. The bracts of the involucre are very narrow.
    May to August: in the Arctic around the world, southward in mountains to California and Colorado. *Plate 155.*

A. FILIFORMIS (1–4 feet) has many delicate stems rising from rosettes of finely toothed, stalked leaves. The umbels have flowers about $\frac{1}{10}$ inch long.
    June and July: from the Columbia River Valley in Washington to Montana and in the Rocky Mountains to Colorado. *Plate 155.*

PLATE 155

Dodecatheon conjugens   *Dilley*

Androsace septentrionalis   *Johnson*

Androsace filiformis   *Frost*

Dodecatheon conjugens   *Engels*

Dodecatheon meadia   *Johnson*

Dodecatheon alpinum   *Redfield*

Dodecatheon jeffreyi   *Johnson*

Dodecatheon pulchellum   *Nichols*

Dodecatheon dentatum   *Dye*

A. LEHMANNIANA has prostrate stems each ending in
a rosette of leaves, all forming mats up to 4 inches
across. The leaves are gray-hairy. The umbels are 2–8-
flowered; the corolla white, with a yellow eye, about $\frac{1}{4}$
inch across.

June and July: in the Arctic and southward to
the high mountains of Colorado and Utah. *Plate 156*.
A. carinata: Similar. Leaves lanceolate. Corolla white
or cream with a yellow, orange, or pink eye. *Plate 156*.
From Montana and Wyoming to Utah and Colorado.

LOOSESTRIFES (STEIRONEMA, LYSIMACHIA, AND NAUMBURGIA)

The two genera *Steironema* and *Lysimachia* are by
some authors united, under the latter name. However,
a magnifier will reveal that in the plants named
Steironema the stamens are entirely separate, and in
the bud each petal is folded around its stamen; while
in *Lysimachia* the stalks of the stamens are joined so as
to make a sleeve around the ovary. Both genera have
yellow petals joined only at the base. The leaves are in
pairs or circles.

The flowers of *Steironema* and *Lysimachia* are at
the tips of stalks growing from the axils, or borne
singly in the axils. In *Naumburgia* they are in dense
tufts in the axils.

The English name is a translation of the Greek
Lysimachia. This is thought to refer to the Thracian
King Lysimachos; there are various legends connect-
ing the plant with the ending of strife. The name
loosestrife is also used for species of *Lythrum*.

FRINGED LOOSESTRIFE, S. CILIATUM (1–4 feet),
derives its name at least partly from the leaf-stalks
which are fringed with hairs ("ciliate"). The flowers,
at the tips of many branches, face outwards and downwards. The broad petals are toothed and pointed on
the outer margin.

June to August: in wet meadows and thickets
from Washington and Oregon to North Dakota,
Utah, Colorado, and Kansas. *Plate 156*.
S. lanceolatum is similar. The leaf-blades are narrower, no more than lanceolate, and shorter, no more
than 4 inches, with stalks not abundantly fringed. The
corolla is smaller, the lobes rarely more than $\frac{1}{3}$ inch
long. In swamps and damp meadows in central Washington and barely within our eastern boundaries. *Plate
156*. The Washington plants form a variety by some
authors referred to a distinct species, *S. hybridum*.

MONEYWORT or CREEPING-JENNY, L. NUMMU-
LARIA, has creeping stems with pairs of almost
round leaves (the "money"). The petals are marked
with dark dots. June to August: an European species
naturalized in damp soil in scattered places in our
range. *Plate 157*.

N. THYRSIFLORA (8–30 inches) has narrow petals,
commonly six or seven, the stamens of the same
number. May to July: in swamps, bogs, and ditches
almost throughout our range. *Plate 156*.

TRIENTALIS

Two species of *Trientalis* may be found in our
area. They are easily recognized by the crowding of
the leaves at and near the tip of the stem. The flowers
are on slender stalks from the axils of these leaves.

T. LATIFOLIA (4–10 inches) has leaves generally more
than 2 inches long. The flowers are pinkish, $\frac{1}{3}$–$\frac{1}{2}$
inch across.

April to July: in woods and on prairies in northern Idaho (and mostly west of the Cascade Mountains). *Plate 157*.
T. arctica (2–8 inches), perhaps a subspecies of
T. europaea which circles the world in the far north,
has leaves less than 2 inches long and mostly white
flowers $\frac{1}{2}$–$\frac{2}{3}$ inch across. In bogs and swamps in
northern Idaho. *Plate 156*.

GLAUX

The genus *Glaux* consists of a single species.

SEA-MILKWORT, G. MARITIMA (1–11 inches), is a
small succulent plant of salty places around the
world. The small, narrow leaves are paired. The flowers are minute, single in the axils. Petals are lacking;
the sepals range from white to crimson, to $\frac{1}{5}$ inch long.
The stamens are opposite the gaps between sepals.
May to July: in moist salty soil in marshes and
meadows.

PLATE 156

Androsace occidentalis *Love*

Androsace lehmanniana *Guppy*

Samolus parviflorus *D. Richards*

Naumburgia thyrsiflora *Houseknecht*

Steironema ciliatum *Rickett*

Androsace carinata *Uttal*

Trientalis arctica *Spurr*

Steironema lanceolatum *Becker*

ANAGALLIS

Only one species of *Anagallis* occurs in the United States.

SCARLET PIMPERNEL, A. ARVENSIS, is a small, branched plant, commonly spreading horizontally, with pairs of small leaves, and single flowers on threadlike stalks in their axils. The English name is only partly appropriate, since some plants have blue flowers, and others, white; in fact, the petals are rarely scarlet, more commonly salmon. Calyx and corolla are deeply cleft, so that sepals and petals may seem to be separate.

March to July: a common weed on roadsides and in waste ground in California, less common in Oregon, and comparatively rare in western Washington. *Plate 158*. The name pimpernel is a corruption of a Latin word meaning "featherlike," or, botanically, pinnately cleft or divided. It has been applied to a number of species, often with some such qualifying word as "false" and without reference to cleft or divided leaves (e.g. *Samolus parviflorus*). Another name for *A. arvensis* is poor-man's-weatherglass, because the flowers close in humid weather. Also John-go-to-bed-at-noon, shepherd's-clock, red-bird's-eye, ladybird, and others.

SAMOLUS

The flowers of *Samolus* are small, cup-shaped, in racemes on tall stems. The leaves are large, at the base and borne singly on the stem.

S. EBRACTEATUS (up to 1 foot) has white or pink flowers about ¼ inch across. The leaves are widest between middle and tip.

Through the year: in low ground in Nevada. *S. parviflorus* (to 2 feet) has white flowers not more than ⅛ inch across. It is found in shallow water, mud, wet sand, through the southern half of our range. *Plate 156*.

CENTUNCULUS

The one species of *Centunculus* is in our range.

CHAFFWEED, C. MINIMUS, is an insignificant plant rarely exceeding 4 inches in height. The small oblong leaves, which have no stalks, are mostly borne singly in the branching stems. The minute flowers are in their axils, practically without stalks. The petals are pink; they mostly number four.

April to July: in pools and moist soil practically throughout the United States.

THE GENTIAN FAMILY (GENTIANACEAE)

The species of *Gentianaceae* are various in appearance but uniform in detail of the flowers. The stamens are attached to the corolla and alternate with its lobes. The ovary has one cavity with ovules in two lines on its inner surface, or all over it. The stigma is generally two-lobed. The fruit is a capsule which splits into two parts.

The leaves are mostly paired or in circles; they lack teeth or lobes, and are undivided in all but one of our genera. The flowers are large or small, with corolla-lobes spreading at the end of a tube which is in some so short that they seem to be separate petals; in others long and slender; or with a funnel-shaped corolla bearing relatively short lobes. The color ranges from white to greenish to pink, purple, and blue.

Guide to Genera of Gentianaceae

I. *Genera whose petals are joined through most of their length (the corolla-tube equal to or longer than the corolla lobes).*

A. Plants with mostly funnel-shaped flowers, from blue and purple to white and yellowish: *Gentiana*.

B. Plants with slender corolla-tube crowned with spreading lobes, from rose and reddish to white: *Centaurium*.

II. *Genera whose petals are joined only at the base, the corolla-tube much shorter than the lobes.*

  A. Land-plants, with undivided leaves: *Swertia* (except one species, with four corolla-lobes, a conspicuous gland on each); *Bartonia* (four or five yellowish corolla-lobes, very small; the leaves are small scales); *Halenia* (five greenish corolla-lobes, with spurs); *Lomatogonium* (four or five blue corolla-lobes with two small scales at the base of each); *Sabatia* (flowers rose or pink, with five lobes); *Eustoma* (flowers red-purple).

  B. Plants of water and bogs with leaves divided into three: *Menyanthes*.

THE GENTIANS (GENTIANA)

The gentians, genus *Gentiana*, contribute to the beauty of the landscape in most of the United States, but are especially conspicuous in the Rocky Mountains, carpeting valleys with blue, and adding to the diminutive flora of high mountain meadows and tundra. They have a funnel-shaped (or bottle-shaped) corolla, the four or five lobes with or without a plaited membrane joining them. The stamens are joined to the corolla. The pistil has an ovary with one chamber, the seeds-to-be attached in two lines or all over the inner surface. The style is very short; the stigma two-lobed. The leaves are in pairs, lacking stalks.

I. *Species whose corolla-lobes are not joined by membranes; the calyx-lobes are separated by V-shaped gaps.*
  The membranes of other species, even if present, may be inconspicuous. See particularly *G. andrewsii, flavida, rubricaulis* in group II. Most of these species have calyx-lobes separated by V-shaped gaps.

G. THERMALIS (4–16 inches) has numerous leaves in a tuft at the base of the stems. The flowers are borne singly on long stalks at the tips and from the axils. The corolla has generally four lobes, deep blue or purplish, irregularly toothed.

  July and August: in meadows and bogs around the world at high latitudes extending southward to Idaho, Montana, and South Dakota. *Plate 157*. Some authors treat this, with other plants (e.g. *G. holopetala*), as varieties of a species named *G. detonsa. G. tonsa* is similar but has corolla-lobes not or scarcely fringed. In North and South Dakota.

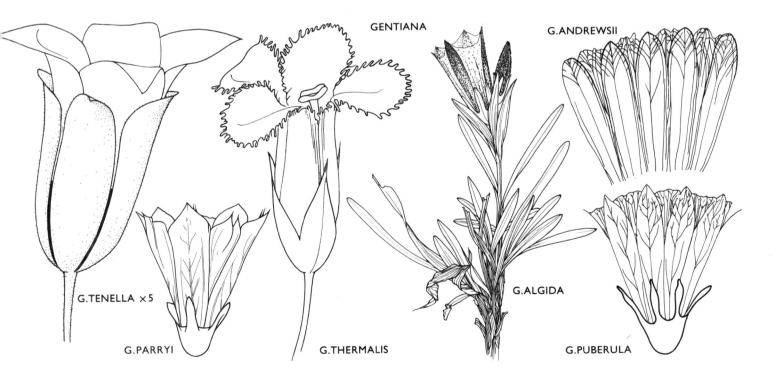

GENTIANA

G.ANDREWSII

G.TENELLA × 5

G.PARRYI

G.THERMALIS

G.ALGIDA

G.PUBERULA

G. TENELLA (about 3 inches) forms dense rosettes of
    basal leaves. The leaves on the stem are about $\frac{1}{5}$–$\frac{3}{5}$
inch long. The flowers are $\frac{1}{3}$–$\frac{3}{5}$ inch long, from white
to purplish, mostly four-lobed.

    July and August: in the Rocky Mountains from
Wyoming to Colorado, in the Sierra Nevada and
White Mountains of Nevada, and reported in Idaho
and Montana. *Plate 157.*

    G. simplex (2–8 inches): Leaves narrow, 1 inch
long or less. Flower single at the end of the stem,
mostly four-lobed, blue, 1–1½ inches long. Cascades
of Oregon, eastward to Idaho, southward to the Sierra
Nevada. *Plate 157. G. holopetala* (2–16 inches): Corolla blue or purple, 1–2 inches long, four-lobed.
Flowers single at the tips of stems. Sierra Nevada. See
under *G. thermalis. Plate 157. G. barbellata* (2–6 inches): Leaves 1–2 inches long. Corolla 1–2 inches long,
deep blue, yellowish inside. Wyoming, Utah. *Plate
157. G. propinqua* (about 4 inches): Leaves indented
at the base, $\frac{2}{5}$–1$\frac{3}{5}$ inches long. Flowers accompanied
by leaflike bracts, the upper nearly an inch long, the
lower less. Corolla light purple, with four spreading
lobes. Montana. *Plate 157. G. procera* (1–2 feet):
Corolla-lobes toothed. Leaves narrow. North Dakota.
Plate 158.

FELWORT, G. AMARELLA (2–20 inches), has mostly
    lanceolate leaves. The numerous flowers are at
the tip of the stem and in the axils. The small (less than
an inch) corolla has a rather slender tube, fringed inside, with commonly four pale violet or lilac (or even
cream), spreading lobes.

    June to September: in moist soil from Washing-
ton to California and eastward to the Rocky Mountains and North Dakota. *Plate 157.* The fringed hairs
just below the corolla-lobes provide a transition to the
membranes of the species in group II.

II. *Species whose corolla-lobes are joined by membranes,*
     commonly plaited and toothed.

        To see these, it may be necessary to slit the
    corolla lengthwise. Most of these species have
    wide gaps between narrow calyx-lobes.

G. PUBERULENTA (8–20 inches) has stiff leaves with
    rough edges. The stem is minutely downy ("pu-
berulent"). The corolla-lobes are purple, pointed,
longer than the plaited membranes between, which
may be fringed, or cleft into two. The calyx-lobes are
narrow, with a wide curved gap between.

    September and October: on prairies and in sandy
and rocky places from North Dakota to Kansas. *Plate
158.* This is the species described in volume 1 as *G.
puberula.* A recent study has shown that *G. puberulenta*
is the correct name.

    G. rubricaulis (1–3 feet): Stems commonly tinged
red (*rubri-*). Leaves lanceolate or ovate with round

bases. Calyx teeth narrow, with a straight (square) gap
between. Corolla blue-violet, the lobes longer than the
membranes and scarcely spreading apart. Neb. *G.
andrewsii*, closed or bottle gentian (1–3 feet): Flowers
in a terminal cluster and perhaps also in the upper
axils. Corolla blue-violet (or pink or white), its lobes
not separating. Membranes longer than the lobes,
toothed. North Dakota to Kansas. *Plate 158. G. flavida*
(2–3 feet): Leaves ovate, with basal lobes around the
stem. Calyx-teeth separated by V-shaped gaps. Corolla yellow-white or greenish, the erect lobes much
longer than the minutely toothed membranes. Kan.
Plate 158.

G. AFFINIS (6–16 inches) has ovate, lanceolate, and
    elliptic leaves about an inch long. The flowers
are in the upper axils, an inch long or longer, each with
two bracts, the corolla blue-purple, with short lobes
and the membranes still shorter. The narrow lobes of
the calyx are spaced around the rim of the cup.

    July to September: in meadows and valleys, and
on foothills from California to Colorado and in North
and South Dakota. *Plate 158.*

    G. parryi (4–16 inches): Leaves thick smooth,
from very narrow to ovate. Calyx-teeth broad with
narrow stalks under the rim of the cup. Corolla blue
or purplish, about 1½ inches long, the membranes
shorter than the lobes. From Wyoming to Utah and
Colorado. *Plate 159.*

MOSS GENTIAN, G. PROSTRATA (1–6 inches) is a
    diminutive plant of high mountains. The moss-
like leaves are only $\frac{1}{5}$–$\frac{2}{5}$ inch long. The flowers are
single at the tips of the stems. The corolla is narrow,
funnel-shaped, ½–1 inch long, greenish-blue or purplish, the pale edges of the lobes joined by folded
membranes about as long.

    July and August: in wet, boggy mountains from
central Idaho to Montana and southward to Nevada,
Utah, and Colorado. *Plate 159.* In volume 4 this was
named *G. fremontii*, but, according to recent authors,
there is no valid basis of separation between the two
supposed species.

G. CALYCOSA (2–12 inches) forms a cluster of stems
    each tipped by a single flower or a group of three.
The calyx-lobes are narrow, attached just outside the
apparent rim of the cup. The corolla is 1–1½ inches
long, deep or pale blue, or mottled with green, or yellowish. The membranes are commonly cleft into from
two to four narrow teeth, about equal to the lobes.

    July to October: in meadows and swamps and by
streams from the Cascade Mountains and the Sierra
Nevada to the Rocky Mountains. *Plate 158.*

G. ALGIDA (2–8 inches) forms small tufts at high alti-
    tudes. The basal leaves are very narrow, up to 5

PLATE 157

Lysimachia nummularia
D. Richards

Scribner

Gentiana propinqua

Gentiana thermalis
Phelps

Gentiana amarella
Roberts

Gentiana tenella
Niehaus

Gentiana barbellata
Schooley

Trientalis latifolia
Mansfield

Gentiana simplex
Niehaus

Gentiana holopetala
Johnson

inches long; those on the stem up to 2 inches. Leaves are crowded under the flowers. The narrow calyx-lobes are below the apparent rim of the cup. The corolla is greenish-white or pale yellowish, blotched and streaked purplish, the membranes folded between the short tips of the very short lobes.

June to August: in alpine bogs and meadows from Montana to Colorado (and in Alaska and Siberia). *Plate 158*.

G. newberryi (1–5 inches): Stems bending up from an horizontal base, each tipped with a flower. Calyx-teeth narrow, $\frac{1}{4}$–$\frac{1}{2}$ inch long. Corolla greenish with pale blue or deep violet lobes, inside white dotted with green, 1–2 inches long, joined by slenderly toothed membranes. From the Sierra Nevada to western Nevada and southern Oregon. *Plate 159*.

G. glauca (2–6 inches): Leaves broadest near the tip, less than 1 inch, forming small rosettes. Flowers crowded. Corolla dark blue, $\frac{2}{5}$–$\frac{4}{5}$ inch. Tundra and alpine meadows. Montana. *Plate 159*.

CENTAURIES (CENTAURIUM)

The centauries are scarcely 2 feet tall, with pink or purple flowers, not more than $\frac{1}{2}$ inch across, in inflorescences at the tip of the stem. The leaves are in pairs, rarely more than an inch long. The corolla has a relatively long, slender tube crowned by five spreading, pointed lobes.

The flowers of the first two species have no visible stalks, and are in dense clusters. The others have stalked flowers.

The correct name of the genus may be *Erythraea*.

C. UMBELLATUM (4–20 inches) has very narrow stem-leaves. The flowers are in a flat cluster. The corolla is rose-purple, the tube ($\frac{1}{3}$ inch) slightly longer than the lobes but not twice as long.

July and August: in moist open ground from Washington to Idaho. A native of Europe. *Plate 160*.

C. muhlenbergii extends eastward through the Columbia River Gorge to eastern Washington. It generally has a single stem, up to a foot tall; no conspicuous rosette of basal leaves. The corolla is yellowish or salmon, the tube nearly twice as long as the lobes, which are $\frac{1}{6}$–$\frac{1}{4}$ inch. *C. curvistamineum* (1–8 inches) may have flower-stalks up to $\frac{1}{2}$ inch long. The corolla is pink, the tube twice as long as the lobes. In eastern Washington and northwestern Nevada.

C. EXALTATUM (2–10 inches) has leaves about an inch long, the basal with one main vein, not forming a conspicuous rosette. The flowers are on long stalks at the tips of branches and in their forks. The corolla is pale salmon or almost white, the tube about $\frac{1}{3}$ inch long, at least twice as long as the lobes.

June and July: in moist ground (especially near hot springs and alkaline lakes) from the Cascade Mountains in Washington to Nebraska and southward to eastern California, Nevada, Utah (perhaps to Colorado).

C. nuttallii (3–12 inches) has pink flowers on long stalks forming a loose inflorescence. The corolla-lobes are up to $\frac{1}{4}$ inch long, a little shorter than the tube. In southern Idaho, Nevada, and Utah.

C. CALYCOSUM (to 2 feet) has leaves 1–2 inches long, the lower generally widest between middle and tip. The corolla-lobes are rose with a white base, nearly as long as the tube, which averages about $\frac{1}{2}$ inch.

March to November: in moist ground in Utah and western Colorado. *Plate 160*.

C. texense has a corolla-tube which scarcely emerges from the calyx, its rose or whitish lobes not more than $\frac{1}{4}$ inch long. Southeastern Kansas and Oklahoma.

SWERTIA

The leaves of *Swertia* are mostly in pairs or circles. The flowers are mostly greenish or yellowish (in three of our species they may be blue). The corolla has four lobes (in one of our species, five). Each lobe bears one or two conspicuous glands near its base; these are pits bounded by a raised and generally cleft or fringed scale. In some species there is a circle of hairs or scales – a corona – just outside the stamens. The stamens may be joined near the base. The stigma is two-lobed; the style may be long and slender or almost lacking.

Some botanists have divided the genus and recently our species have been assigned to *Frasera* (largely because of number of chromosomes). There seem to be no visible, constant differences to warrant such separations.

I.   *Species with leaves on the stem mostly in pairs.*

FELWORT, S. PERENNIS (2–20 inches), is our only species with five corolla-lobes (some flowers have four); they are narrow, bluish variously spotted with

PLATE 158

Anagallis arvensis

Korling

Gentiana andrewsii

Rickett

Gentiana flavida

Beesley

Gentiana calycosa

Spurr

Gentiana algida

Roberts

Gentiana puberulenta

Johnson

Gentiana affinis

Roberts

Gentiana procera

Johnson

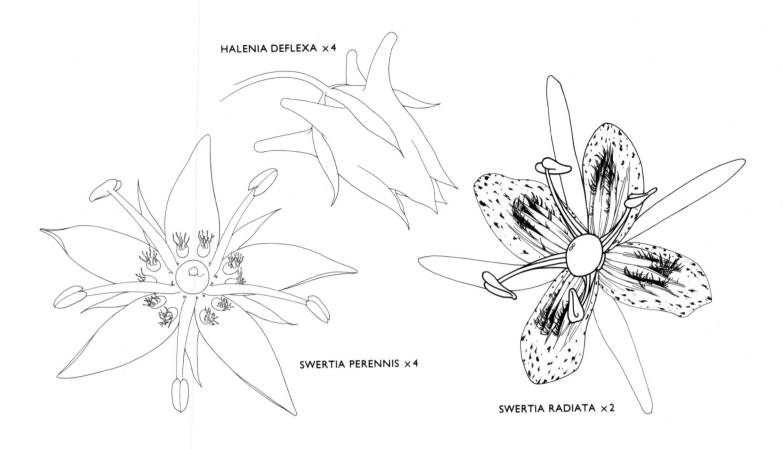

HALENIA DEFLEXA ×4

SWERTIA PERENNIS ×4

SWERTIA RADIATA ×2

green or white. The glandular pits are surrounded by fringed scales. The style is very short. Most of the leaves are at and near the base of the flowering stem.

July to September: in meadows and damp soil generally from the Cascade Mountains and the Sierra Nevada to the Rocky Mountains. *Plate 159*.

S. ALBICAULIS (4–28 inches) has prominently three-veined leaves with white margins. The corolla ranges from white to dark blue, on some plants mottled. Each lobe has one gland with a narrow fringe; and a ring of toothed scales near the stamens.

May to July: on dry slopes from Washington to California and eastward to western Montana and Idaho. *Plate 159*.

S. *coloradensis* (to 8 inches): Forming tufts. Leaves to 8 inches, thick, white-margined, narrow. Corolla cream, not spotted. se Colo. S. *utahensis* (40–80 inches): Leaves narrow, with white margins. Corolla yellowish-green, purple-spotted. s Utah. S. *puberulenta* (not more than 1 foot) is finely downy. The leaves have white margins. The corolla-lobes are greenish-white with purple dots, about ⅓ inch long. Eastern slope of the central Sierra Nevada; White and Inyo Mts. S. *montana* (to 2 feet) also has white-margined leaves. The corolla is clear white or cream. Central and west-central Idaho. *Plate 160*.

II.   *Species with leaves in circles.*

S. RADIATA (3–7 feet) has from three to seven leaves at each level; they are 4–10 inches long. The numerous basal leaves are 10–20 inches long. There are four petals, their lobes over ½ inch long, greenish-white with dots or streaks of purple, and two glands. The fringed edges and the corona of cleft scales are conspicuous.

June to August: in open pine forests from Washington to North and South Dakota and southward to California, Utah, and Colorado. *Plate 159*. The correct name may be S. *speciosa*, depending upon the exact date in 1837 or 1838 on which another species received that epithet. First come, first served!

S. *fastigiata* (to 5 feet) generally has one stem, with a narrow, crowded inflorescence. The corolla is pale or dark blue. In moist woods and meadows from northeastern Oregon to northeastern Idaho. *Plate 160*.

S. ALBOMARGINATA (8–20 inches) has white-margined leaves (like those of several other species). The leaves are three or four in a circle, those at the base stalked and with crisped edges. The flowers have no corona and each petal has one gland.

May to July: in dry rocky places in Colorado and Utah.

PLATE 159

Swertia radiata   *Jarrett*

Swertia perennis   *Korling*

Gentiana newberryi   *Korling*

Gentiana parryi   *Messinger*

Gentiana glauca   *Scribner*

Swertia albicaulis   *Spellenberg*

Swertia radiata   *Johnson*

Gentiana prostrata   *Rickett*

BARTONIA

One species of *Bartonia* comes into Oklahoma from the Southeast. *B. paniculata* has a stem 2–18 inches tall which generally bends and may twine. The leaves are minute, greenish or purple, narrow scales.

The flowers also are tiny, on short branches near the tip of the stem. Calyx and corolla are yellowish, about $\frac{1}{4}$ inch long or less. In wet meadows, bogs, and swamps.

HALENIA

We have one species of the mainly tropical American genus *Halenia*.

SPURRED-GENTIAN, H. DEFLEXA (4–36 inches), has paired leaves with five main veins. The flowers

are in branching clusters near the top of the plant. The corolla is purplish-green or bronze, with four lobes and four spurs.

July to September: in moist woods in Montana and North and South Dakota. *Plate 160.*

LOMATOGONIUM

One species of *Lomatogonium* is in our range.

L. ROTATUM (1–10 inches tall) may be bushy or the stems may be unbranched. The leaves are succulent, up to $1\frac{1}{8}$ inches long. The flowers are on slender stalks in the axils. They have from two to five sepals

nearly as long as or longer than the corolla. The corolla is blue (or white), the lobes $\frac{1}{5}$–$\frac{3}{5}$ inch long. The pistil lacks a style; there are two stigmas on the ovary.

July to September: in wet and saline soil, from Canada southward to Idaho, Wyoming, and Colorado. (Also in Siberia.) *Plate 160.*

SABATIA

Our two species of the mainly southern genus *Sabatia* have five pink petals, joined only at the extreme base. There are five stamens and a style cleft into two branches.

ROSE-PINK or BITTER-BLOOM, S. ANGULARIS (to 3 feet) is generally bushy-branched. The leaves, paired, have basal lobes embracing the stem. The fragrant pink flowers have a yellow eye. The ends of the

corolla-lobes are blunt and broad. In fields and open woodlands in extreme southeastern Kansas, and Oklahoma. *Plate 161.*

S. campestris is similar, not so tall, not so branched. The yellow eye of the corolla has lines running out on the petals. The calyx has wings running up to the gaps between teeth. On prairies and in fields and woodland in southeastern Kansas and Oklahoma. *Plate 160.*

EUSTOMA

One species of *Eustoma* is found in our range.

PRAIRIE-GENTIAN, E. GRANDIFLORUM (1–2 feet), has paired leaves $1\frac{1}{2}$–4 inches long. The elliptic basal leaves mostly have three veins. The flowers have

a blue or purple corolla 2–3 inches across, the lobes joined only at the base and so appearing separate.

June to August: in grassland on high plains and prairies, in Nebraska, southwestern Kansas, Colorado, and Oklahoma. *Plate 162.*

MENYANTHES

The genus *Menyanthes* consists of one species.

BUCKBEAN, M. TRIFOLIATA, grows in bogs and shallow lakes, the stem generally submerged and only

the leaves and flowers visible. The leaf-blades are divided into three segments. The flowers are in racemes on leafless stems up to a foot tall. Calyx and corolla are cleft nearly to the base, each with five or six lobes. The

PLATE 160

Sabatia campestris   *Merkle*

Menyanthes trifoliata   *Gottscho*

Lomatogonium rotatum   *Scribner*

Swertia montana   *MacPhail*

Swertia fastigiata   *George*

Halenia deflexa   *Johnson*

Centaurium calycosum   *Johnson*

Centaurium umbellatum   *Spurr*

corolla is white or tinged pink, and densely bearded. May to August: in northeastern Oregon; and in the Rocky Mountains from Montana to Colorado. *Plate 160.*

THE DOGBANE FAMILY (APOCYNACEAE)

The *Apocynaceae* are distinguished by their milky juice, seen when a leaf or stem is broken. This "latex" may be poisonous. The flower is remarkable for having two ovaries but only one or no style and one stigma; two seed-pods (follicles) are formed from each flower. The other parts of the flower are in fives, the petals joined to form a tube or bell. The leaves are undivided and without lobes and teeth; they have short stalks or none.

THE DOGBANES (APOCYNUM)

The dogbanes are generally erect, branched, with many small, bell-shaped or cylindric flowers in loose inflorescences at the ends of branches. Just beneath each of the five lobes of the corolla a hand magnifier reveals a small appendage. The large stigma is attached to the tips of both ovaries, no style intervening. The follicles are long and thin. The seed has a tuft of silky hair.

The names of the genus both suggest a danger (a "bane") to dogs; but the name *Apocynum*, of which dogbane is a rough translation, was originally given to some other plant. These plants apparently offer no threat to dogs.

SPREADING DOGBANE, A. ANDROSAEMIFOLIUM (8–16 inches), generally has a repeatedly forking system of stems rather than one main stem. The leaves have ovate blades on short stalks. The flowers are fragrant; many hang on curved stalks. The corolla is pale pink with darker pink lines inside; the five teeth curve out. The pods are 3–8 inches long.

June to August: in dry soil practically throughout the country. *Plate 161.*

A. pumilum (4–16 inches) is generally similar in its forking stem, though smaller. The leaves commonly droop. The corolla is pink; the teeth spread but are not curved outward. Flowering from June to August on dry slopes from Washington to California and eastward to Montana and Colorado. *Plate 161.*

INDIAN HEMP, A. CANNABINUM (1–2 feet), has mostly paired or clustered branches. The leaves have ovate or lanceolate blades, somewhat downy underneath, those on the main stem short-stalked. The flowers are in clusters at the tips of stems and branches. The corolla is greenish-white; the teeth are not curved. The pods are 5–8 inches long, slightly curved.

June to September: in fields and thickets and on roadsides, a common weed throughout the country. *Plate 161.* Very variable; a number of varieties have been named, some once treated as species. It also interbreeds with *A. androsaemifolium*, producing a confusing array of plants which cannot be assigned to either species. Plants long known as *A. medium* (and many other names) are now suspected to be the result of this crossing. They have the general aspect of *A. cannabinum* with the bell-shaped (but white) corolla of *A. androsaemifolium*. Another closely related species (if it is a species) is *A. suksdorfii* (16–30 inches). The corolla is whitish or greenish, cylindric, less than $\frac{1}{6}$ inch long. The leaves are short-stalked.

A. SIBIRICUM (8–20 inches), in spite of its name, is found practically throughout our area. The leaves have practically no stalks and many of them have a base extending around the stem. There are conspicuous bracts. The corolla is roundish, very small, white.

June to August: mostly by streams, in rocky ground.

AMSONIA

The flowers of *Amsonia* are in a mostly dense inflorescence at the tip of the stem. Their shape is generally what the botanist calls "salverform": a relatively slender corolla-tube crowned by mostly spreading lobes. The color in our species is light blue or white. The leaves are borne singly, but in some species they are so crowded as to appear to be in circles. The two ovaries have in common a threadlike style, ending in a round stigma with a cuplike membrane underneath.

This is chiefly a genus of southern parts; in our area mostly from southeastern California to western Colorado.

PLATE 161

Amsonia eastwoodiana   *Todsen*

Apocynum pumilum   *Myrick*

Amsonia tabernaemontana   *Horst*

Asclepias amplexicaulis   *V. Richard*

Amsonia illustris   *Roche*

Apocynum cannabinum   *D. Richards*

Jarrett

Apocynum androsaemifolium

Sabatia angularis   *Johnson*

I.   *Species whose stigma is not lobed.*
Only in Kansas and Oklahoma in our range.

A. ILLUSTRIS (2–4 feet) has narrowly lanceolate, shining leaves, the blades tapering both ways, short-
stalked; they are smooth and somewhat leathery. The
inflorescence is ample. The calyx is hairy. The corolla-
tube (tending to buff at the base) is $\frac{1}{4}$–$\frac{1}{3}$ inch long, the
lobes spread about as wide.

April to July: mostly on rocky and gravelly
stream-banks. *Plate 161. A. tabernaemontana* (12–40
inches) has ovate leaves and a smooth calyx. The inflorescence is not so large. Barely within our limits.
Plate 161. (In previous volumes these two were confused, the illustration of *A. illustris* labeled *A. tabernaemontana.*) *A. ciliata* (2–5 feet) is known by its very
narrow leaves, which are downy. The corolla-lobes are
about $\frac{1}{3}$ inch long; the pods about 4 inches. April to
June: in woods. Only in Oklahoma.

II.   *Species whose stigma is two-lobed.*

A. BREVIFOLIA (6–14 inches) is named for its short
leaves. The blades are ovate or lanceolate, about
an inch long. The corolla-lobes are $\frac{1}{6}$–$\frac{1}{4}$ inch long;
pods 2–3 inches.

March to June: on deserts and mountain slopes
in southern Nevada and southwestern Utah.

A. tomentosa (12–16 inches) is named for the
woolly ("tomentose") stem and leaves. The leaves are
ovate or lanceolate, 1–1$\frac{1}{4}$ inches long. In southern
Nevada.

A. JONESII (8–16 inches) has ovate leaves with a whitish bloom, the blades up to 2 inches long. The
flowers are numerous.

April to June: in rocky gorges and cañons in
southeastern Utah and southwestern Colorado.

A. eastwoodiana (1–2 feet) is distinguished by a
corolla-tube $\frac{2}{5}$–$\frac{4}{5}$ inch long. (The lobes, however are
small, $\frac{1}{6}$–$\frac{1}{4}$ inch.) The leaves are lanceolate, the upper
ones narrowly so, 1–2 inches long. By streams and in
ravines in Utah. *Plate 161.*

THE MILKWEED FAMILY (ASCLEPIADACEAE)

The milkweed family derives its English
name from the thick white sap which oozes from
any broken surface of most of the plants. But
such "milk" is found also in other families; the
distinctive characteristics of this family are in the
extraordinary structure of the flower. The tips of
the five stamens are joined with a broad disk
which is supported by the two styles of the two
ovaries. The pollen of each stamen forms two
waxy masses of microscopic grains. The fruit of
each flower is a pair of follicles – but one may

fail to develop. The seeds are generally tipped
with long silky hairs. The leaves are mostly paired. A corona of sacs, cups, or scales surrounds
the stamens.

The arrangement of the numerous species
into genera has proved peculiarly difficult. Many
genera have been named which are, when all
the species of the world are studied, impossible
to separate. The classification here adopted is not
in accord with the best botanical researches, but
is convenient for the recognition of our species.

Guide to Genera of Asclepiadaceae

I.   *Plants growing erect without support.*

A. A genus with a corona of cups or sacs each
generally with a horn; petals mostly bent
down: *Asclepias.*

B. Genera whose corona lacks horns: *Acerates*
(corona a ring of sacs, the open sides against
the stamens; petals bent down); *Asclepiodora* (corona of sacs reclining on the spreading corolla,
the tips bending up).

II.   *Plants with climbing or trailing stems.*

A. Genera whose corona is evident (not a circle
of scales): *Matelea* (corona a thick cup or ring
around the stamens; pollen-masses horizontal);
Gonolobus (like *Matelea* but stamens with winglike appendages); *Sarcostemna* (corona a ring of
inflated sacs).

B. A genus whose corona is a circle of small
scales, or lacking: *Cynanchum.*

PLATE 162

Asclepias verticillata   *Johnson*

Asclepias syriaca   *Johnson*

Asclepias sullivantii   *Rout*

Asclepias purpurascens   *Werking*

Asclepias ovalifolia   *Johnson*

Asclepias arenaria   *Uttal*

Eustoma grandiflorum   *Roberts*

MILKWEEDS (ASCLEPIAS)

The three names *Asclepias*, *Acerates*, and *Asclepiodora* (and some others) properly belong to one genus, *Asclepias*; when all the species so named are considered, the differences among these supposed genera fade out. Earlier botanists, with fewer species known to them, separated the three supposed genera, and others; and the distinctions, which are fairly valid for species of the eastern United States, were maintained in the first two volumes of this series. Even in the area treated in the present volume, it is convenient for elementary identification to keep the three separate. The distinguishing characteristics, though not scientifically valid, are fairly evident for the species of the area.

The corolla of *Asclepias* (in the narrow sense of that genus) is deeply cleft into five lobes which are generally turned down so sharply as to hide the calyx. Just above the junction of the lobes and from the tube formed by the stamens rise five cups, forming the crown or corona of the corolla. In most species, from within each cup rises a curved horn, the point directed towards the stigma. This apparatus, the corona, is commonly the most conspicuous part of the flower. The flowers of many species are sweetly fragrant.

Adjoining masses of pollen are attached to a cleft gland. Insects alighting on the stigma may get their feet in this; if they are large enough they can pull it out and fly away with two masses of pollen dangling — to be deposited on the next stigma visited. Many insects cannot exert enough pull and die in the trap.

I. *Species found in our range only east of the Rocky Mountains.*

Seven species with wider ranges may also be found in this area: *A. hallii, incarnata, involucrata, latifolia, speciosa, subverticillata, tuberosa*; these are treated under II.

A. Species with leaves in pairs.

A. SYRIACA (3–7 feet) has ovate or elliptic leaves up to a foot long, grayish-downy underneath. The petals are greenish- or rose-purple. The follicles are ribbed and warty.

June to August: on roadsides and in fields and thickets from North Dakota to Kansas. *Plate 162. A. purpurascens* (about 3 feet): Petals deep rose or even brick-red (not "purple"), with a corona of tall hoods. Flowers borne only at the tip of the stem. From e SD to Okla. *Plate 162. A. sullivantii* (2–5 feet): Leaves oval, blunt. Flowers from purplish to nearly white, with tall hoods. Pods smooth. From ND to Kan. *Plate 162. A. ovalifolia* (1–2 feet): Leaves downy underneath. Petals greenish-white with yellowish corona.

Pods tapering, downy. ND, SD, Neb. *Plate 162. A. amplexicaulis* (1–4 feet): Leaves with wavy edges, and basal lobes around the stem. Flowers large, greenish suffused with rose. Hoods short and broad. *Plate 161. A. meadii* (1–3 feet): Leaves with basal lobes around the stem, tapering to the tip, with a whitish bloom. Flowers greenish-yellow. Kan. *A. variegata* (1–3 feet): Leaves oblong, blunt. Flowers white with purplish centers. Hoods cuplike. Pods slender, tapering. Okla.

A. ARENARIA (1–2 feet) has broad, almost squarish leaves, or broadest in the outer half, $2\frac{1}{2}$–$3\frac{1}{2}$ inches long, generally white-woolly. The corolla is pale green. The hoods are cuplike and two-lobed.

May to August: in sandy soil (*arena*, "sand") from South Dakota to Oklahoma and Colorado. *Plate 162.*

B. Species with leaves borne singly or in circles.

A. UNCIALIS has a cluster of stems only about an inch long. The leaves are still shorter, the lower ovate, the upper narrower. The few flowers have rose petals about $\frac{1}{8}$ inch long. The hoods are cream, cup-shaped, with tongue-like horns.

May and June: in sandy soil from Wyoming and North Dakota to Colorado. *Plate 163. A. pumila* (6–12 inches): Leaves threadlike. Petals white faintly suffused with rose or yellowish, up to $\frac{1}{8}$ inch. Hoods oval, blunt, the horns twice as long. Pods erect. From ND, Mont, and Wyo to Colo and Okla. *Plate 163.*

A. VERTICILLATA (6–36 inches) has a generally unbranched stem, with commonly three or four leaves in each circle; these very narrow (the edges rolled underneath), stiff, 1–$2\frac{1}{2}$ inches long. The corolla is greenish-white (on some plants purplish underneath).

April to August: on prairies and dunes and in open woods and thickets. From North Dakota to Oklahoma. *Plate 162. A. quadrifolia* (1–3 feet): Leaves four at each lower level, commonly some in pairs above, ovate or lanceolate. Petals pale pink, corona white. se Kan, Okla.

II. *Species found from the Rocky Mountains westward.*

Including those found *also* eastward.

A. Species with pink, red, orange, or violet petals; not white, greenish, or yellowish. Some species under B may have pink petals and most have a flush of pink or rose on the back. See *A. involucrata, subverticillata, macrosperma.*

PLATE 163

Asclepias speciosa   *Wooden*

Asclepias fascicularis   *Mackintosh*

Asclepias tuberosa   *Johnson*

Asclepias subulata   *Horst*

Asclepias pumila   *Oldemeyer*

Asclepias erosa   *Stackhouse*

Asclepias uncialis   *Broeske*

Asclepias hallii   *Roberts*

A. SPECIOSA (2–4 feet) is densely white-woolly on the stem and under side of leaves. The leaf-blades are up to 8 inches long, ovate, blunt. The flowers are large, the rose corolla about ½ inch long, the hoods pointed and spreading. The pods also are white-woolly; on some plants spiny or warty.

May to September: on roadsides and in fields and elsewhere throughout our area. *Plate 163*. *A. hallii* (8–20 inches); Leaves to 6 inches, short-stalked. Corolla rose, the lobes ¼–⅓ inch. Hoods elliptic, pointed, the horn short, curved. From Nev to Colo. *Plate 163*.

A. FASCICULARIS (16–40 inches) has the principal leaves up to 5 inches, mostly in three's and four's, short-stalked, narrow-bladed. Clusters ("fascicles") of short branches are in the axils, with crowded small leaves. The corolla is grayish-pink, the lobes ⅛–⅙ inch. The hoods are shallowly cup-shaped with long horns. The pods are erect, on erect stalks.

June to August: commonly along streams from Washington to California, Idaho, and Utah. *Plate 163*. *A. tuberosa* (1–3 feet): Leaves narrow, pointed, roughly hairy, mostly borne singly, in some forms with indented base. Juice not milky. Corolla commonly bright orange, but varying to red or yellow in some forms. From ND to Okla and from Colo to Calif. *Plate 163*. *A. ruthiae* (2–5 inches): Leaves paired, ovate, stalked, to 2 inches, with a whitish bloom. Flowers few in a terminal cluster. Corolla-lobes pale violet, about ¼ inch. c Nev, Utah. *A. cutleri* (2–6 inches): Leaves threadlike, to 3 inches. Flowers few in a terminal cluster. Corolla-lobes pale greenish-rose, about ⅕ inch. se Utah.

A. INCARNATA (1–5 feet) has many rather small, pink flowers commonly in several clusters. The corona is paler than the petals; both may be white. The pods are slender, on erect or nearly erect stalks.

May to September: in moist soil from Wyoming and North Dakota to Colorado, Utah, and Oklahoma. *Plate 164*.

B. Species with white, greenish, or yellowish petals. Several have a tinge of pink or rose on the under side of the petals.

A. INVOLUCRATA (1–10 inches) has clustered, branching stems. The leaves are narrowly lanceolate, tapering to a fine point, up to 5 inches long. The flowers have pale green or pink petals tinged with purple on the back, the lobes about ¼ inch long.

March to July: on gravelly hills and plains in southern Utah. *Plate 164*. *A. subverticillata* (6–48 inches): Leaves mostly from three to five in each circle, or some in pairs; their blades narrow, up to 5 inches, short-stalked. Petals white (rarely suffused with greenish-purple), the corolla-lobes ⅛–⅕ inch. Hoods cup-like, blunt-pointed, with long horns. Pods erect on erect stalks. Colo, Utah. *Plate 164*. *A. macrosperma* (2–6 inches): Leaves ovate, 2½ inches, finely woolly. Flower pale green, some corolla-lobes tinged with purple on the back. Hoods short. Utah. *A. macrotis* (4–12 inches): Bushy, twiggy; leaves almost threadlike. Corolla pale greenish-yellow, its lobes about ⅕ inch. Hoods tapering to a long point; horns shorter. Pods erect on bent-down stalks. Okla, Colo. *Plate 164*. *A. labriformis* (8–20 inches): Leaves narrowly lanceolate, 2–6 inches. Corolla pale yellowish-green, the lobes ⅓ inch. e Utah.

A. EROSA (2–4 feet*) has large paired, ovate leaves which may embrace the stem between basal lobes; when young they are cobwebby-woolly; when mature, pale green. The corolla is greenish-yellow, the lobes about ⅖ inch long. The hoods are bluntly pointed, the horns about equal.

April to October: in cañons and washes from southern California to Utah. *Plate 163*. *A. eriocarpa*, a Californian species, may just cross our western boundary. Leaves usually three or more at each level, finely white-woolly when young. Corolla cream, perhaps with a purplish tinge. Hoods broad and short. *A. latifolia* (8–24 inches): Barely in our range, in eastern California. Leaf-blades very broad (*lati-*), the end roundish, up to 6 inches. Corolla pale green, perhaps purple-tinged on the back, the lobes about ½ inch. Hoods short, broad. *A. subulata* (3–5 feet): Perhaps in our range, in eastern California. Leaves threadlike, 1–2 inches, soon falling. Corolla pale greenish-white. Hoods longer than the stamens, dilated at the tip. *Plate 163*.

GREEN-MILKWEEDS (ACERATES)

The name means "without horns," and this was the original distinguishing characteristic. However, as more species of milkweeds became known, it was evident that in many species of *Asclepias* the horns of the hoods are no more than ridges; in short the distinction does not hold. A better distinction, taken together with the absence of horns, is the character of the hoods; they stand erect with the opening against the stamens, or even without an opening. At least this forms a means of identification for our species.

GREEN-MILKWEED, A. VIRIDIFLORA (7–36 inches), has leaf-blades from very narrow to almost round;

* The "3–7 feet" of volume 4 was a misprint that went undetected.

PLATE 164

Asclepias macrotis   *Todsen*

Asclepias involucrata   *Korling*

Cynanchum laeve   *D. Richards*

Asclepiodora asperula   *Johnson*

Asclepiodora viridis   *Rickett*

Acerates latifolia   *Ure*

Asclepias subverticillata   *Johnson*

Asclepias incarnata   *Roberts*

they are paired or irregularly grouped. The flowers are many, with a pale green corolla, the lobes about $\frac{1}{4}$ inch long. The hoods taper upwards. The pods stand on stalks which are bent down.

April to August: on prairies, plains, and hillsides, and in glades from Wyoming and North Dakota to Oklahoma and Colorado. *Plate 165*. *A. hirtella* (16–40 inches), with spreading stems, and a covering of short stiff hairs, barely enters our range in eastern Kansas and Oklahoma.

A. LANUGINOSA (3–8 inches) is finely hairy, with lanceolate leaves up to $2\frac{1}{2}$ inches long. The flowers are in a terminal cluster; the corolla pale greenish-yellow, perhaps tinged with purple on the back.

May and June: on prairies, sandhills, and railway embankments from North Dakota to Kansas.

A. STENOPHYLLA (8–30 inches) has narrow (*steno-*) leaves up to 6 inches long and $\frac{1}{6}$ inch wide. The few flowers are from greenish-white to pale yellow, the corolla-lobes about $\frac{1}{4}$ inch long. The hoods have a two-lobed tip, and a ridge on the surface which corresponds to the horn of *Asclepias*. The pods stand on erect stalks.

June to August: on prairies from South Dakota to Oklahoma. *A. rusbyi*, in Utah, is similar, with shorter hoods. *A. engelmanniana* may reach a height of 4 feet. The flowers are numerous, crowded, pale-green flushed with purple on the back. The hoods are squared-off at the end. Kansas.

A. LATIFOLIA has a cluster of mostly horizontal stems up to a foot long. The leaves have almost round blades, with or without short stalks. The flowers are greenish-yellow, the corolla-lobes up to $\frac{2}{5}$ inch long. The hoods are curved, and have two minute points at the tip. The pods stand on erect stalks.

April to June: in gravelly and clayey soil from southwestern Wyoming to western Colorado, Utah, and California. *Plate 164*. When this is placed in *Asclepias* its name is *Asclepias cryptoceras* (because there is a previously named *Asclepias latifolia*).

ASCLEPIODORA

Two species of *Asclepiodora* grow in our range.

A. ASPERULA (1–2 feet) is properly a species of *Asclepias*, as explained in the description of that genus. The difference is that the long hoods are extended on the spreading corolla, instead of standing erect around the stamens. Their tips curve up. The plants are roughish. The leaves are irregularly grouped, with narrow blades 4–8 inches long. The corolla is pale yellowish-green, with lobes up to $\frac{1}{2}$ inch long.

March to August: in deserts and on sandy and rocky hillsides from Kansas and Oklahoma to Utah. *Plate 164*. In our subspecies, as illustrated, the leaves are very narrow, and the hoods a dark crimson. *A. viridis* is similar; almost smooth. Leaves lanceolate or ovate. Corolla green, the corona purplish. On prairies and in fields and woods from Nebraska to Oklahoma. *Plate 164*.

ANGLE-PODS (MATELEA)

Our species of *Matelea* bear scattered long hairs mixed with minute, gland-like projections (visible through a magnifier). The leaf-blades are broad, mostly ovate, indented at the base. The stems twine about other stems. The corona is a small, thick cup with toothed or wavy edges. The pollen-masses extend horizontally, as in *Gonolobus*. The pods are angular.

Our species are southeastern, in our range found only in Oklahoma. They flower between April and June. *M. baldwyniana* has a white or yellowish corolla with lobes about $\frac{2}{5}$ inch long. The leaves are ovate, up to 6 inches long. *M. decipiens* has a red-brown corolla with narrow lobes about $\frac{1}{2}$ inch long. The leaves reach 5 inches in length.

GONOLOBUS

One species of *Gonolobus* is in Oklahoma. *G. gonocarpos* is a somewhat hairy vine with ovate leaves which may exceed 6 inches. The corolla is greenish, the lobes up to $\frac{1}{2}$ inch. The pollen-masses extend horizontally.

The corona is five-lobed, succulent. The stamens have winglike appendages. The pods also are winged. Flowering in June and July. This is close to *Matelea*, and many botanists now treat it in that genus.

SARCOSTEMMA

Our species of *Sarcostemma* are twining vines, with paired leaves and flowers in umbel-like clusters. The corolla is cleft into five spreading lobes mostly $\frac{1}{4}$–$\frac{1}{2}$ inch long. The corona is five almost spherical, sac-like bodies.

S. CYNANCHOIDES has two forms of leaves, making two subspecies: either with broad, lanceolate blades indented at the base, or with very narrow blades with basal lobes which may be pointed. The flowers are greenish-white or pinkish in the broad-leaved sub-species, tending to be pink or brownish-purple in the other.

May to September: along streams among bushes in Oklahoma and Utah. *Plate 165*.

S. hirtellum has narrowly lanceolate leaves not over $1\frac{1}{2}$ inches long. The flower-clusters contain not more than twelve flowers. The corolla is white, greenish, or pink. March to May: in washes in southern Nevada.

CYNANCHUM

Three species of the southern genus *Cynanchum* are within our range. They are twining climbers with paired leaves. The very small flowers are in clusters which simulate umbels or racemes. The corolla is mostly yellowish or greenish, and bell-shaped. The corona consists of five scales; or there may be none. The pollen-masses hang vertically.

C. UTAHENSE (8–20 inches) has very narrow leaves about an inch long. The short-stalked flower-cluster has up to ten flowers. The corolla is dull yellow. There is no corona.

April to June: in dry sandy places in southern Utah. *C. laeve* has white flowers in rather tight clusters. The leaves have broadly ovate blades, deeply indented at the base, on short stalks. The corona consists of scales each deeply cleft into two lobes. In Kansas. This has long been known to eastern botanists as *Ampelamus albidus*, and is so named in volumes 1 and 2 of this series. *Plate 164.*

C. nigrum is an European species which has escaped from cultivation in Kansas. It has dark purple flowers borne on stalks which rise from the axils of ovate leaves.

THE PHLOX FAMILY (POLEMONIACEAE)

The flowers of *Polemoniaceae* have a bell-shaped or funnel-shaped corolla with typically five lobes, or one composed of a slender tube with the lobes spreading at right angles (the "salver-form" of the botanist). The pistil generally has an ovary with three chambers and a style with three branches, these forming the stigma. The fruit is a capsule. The form of the plant varies from erect with broad leaves to mosslike cushions. The leaves may be divided or not, threadlike or prickly or broad and thin, borne singly or in pairs. The flowers are generally in a cyme at the summit of the stem, but in many species are borne singly.

Guide to Genera of Polemoniaceae

I.   *Plants not prickly or spiny.*

A. Plants with all or most leaves borne singly: *Polemonium* (leaves pinnately divided, the segments not threadlike; flowers bell-like or funnel-shaped); *Allophyllum* (leaves pinnately lobed or unlobed; flowers in small clusters, the corolla funnel-shaped); *Collomia* (whitish folds between adjacent calyx-teeth; corolla funnel-shaped; flowers without stalks, in dense clusters); *Gilia* (leaves generally pinnately divided or cleft; a basal rosette present in many species; corolla with a definite expansion, the throat, above the tube; compare *Ipomopsis*, under II).

B. Plants with at least the lower leaves paired: *Phlox* (leaves undivided, without lobes or teeth; flowers with definite corolla-tube); *Microsteris* (leaves undivided, without lobes or teeth; flowers mostly in pairs in axils, the corolla-tube yellowish); *Linanthus* (leaves mostly deeply cleft palmately; flowers in heads or cymes).

C. Plants with a circle of leaves just beneath the flower-cluster; otherwise none: *Gymnosteris*.

II. *Plants whose leaves or calyx-teeth are tipped with bristles, spines, or minute sharp, hard points.*

A. Plants with leaves or their segments or teeth definitely spine-tipped: *Leptodactylon* (leaves not cleft or divided, the lobes or teeth spine-tipped); *Langloisia* (leaves pinnately cleft, spiny; flowers small, clustered in the axils); *Navarretia* (plants small, very spiny; flowers in pincushion-like heads; leaves divided, cleft, or lobed); *Phlox* (cushion-plants with needle-like leaves; see under group I); *Gilia* (a few species have prickly leaves; see under I).

B. Plants whose leaves are not spiny: *Eriastrum* (plants cobwebby-woolly; calyx with awl-like teeth); *Ipomopsis* (leaves pinnately divided into narrow segments tipped with minute hard points; corolla flaring gradually, without a throat; much like *Gilia*).

POLEMONIUM

The corolla of *Polemonium* flares gradually, without division into a narrow tube and the expanded part called a "throat." The flowers are in cymes which may resemble heads or racemes. The leaves are pinnately divided.

P. FOLIOSISSIMUM (1–3 feet) has up to twenty-five rather narrow segments, those near the tip of each leaf running together (so that they are more accurately termed lobes). The corolla is white, cream, blue, or violet, about ½ inch long, the broad lobes about half of the length.

June to August: in moist soil along streams from Idaho and Wyoming to Nevada, Utah, and Colorado. *Plate 165.*

P. pectinatum (12–32 inches) is glandular-hairy in the inflorescence, elsewhere smooth. The leaf-segments, from eleven to seventeen, are very narrow, not close together, up to 2 inches long. The corolla is white or cream. In moist bottomlands in extreme eastern Washington.

P. OCCIDENTALE (8–40 inches) has a glandular-downy stem. The leaves have from nineteen to twenty-seven segments. The flowers are in several clusters which may simulate a branched raceme. The corolla is blue, about ½ inch long.

June to August: in wet places (such as swamps) from Washington to California and from Montana and Wyoming to Colorado. *Plate 165.*

P. PULCHERRIMUM (2–20 inches) has most of its leaves at the base of the stem, with from eleven to twenty-five segments; those higher on the stem have fewer. The inflorescence is compact, commonly somewhat glandular. The corolla is blue, generally with a yellow or white eye, ⅓–½ inch long.

May to August: in dry rocky places in mountains from Washington to Idaho and western Montana and southward to California, Nevada, Utah, and Colorado. *Plate 165.* Several varieties are known. At high altitudes the plants are rarely over 8 inches tall, and the leaf-segments are less than ½ inch long. At lower altitudes the plants are taller, and the leaf-segments ⅖–1⅖ inches. A third variety, in the Rocky Mountains, is intermediate; being geographically separated, it generally passes as a distinct species, *P. delicatum. Plate 165.*

P. VISCOSUM (2–20 inches) also has mostly basal leaves, with numerous segments less than ½ inch long, each cleft palmately into from three to five lobes. The inflorescence simulates a head or spike. In our range the corolla is blue or white, ⅘–1⅖ inches long. At high altitudes in mountains throughout our range, flowering from June to August. *Plate 165.*

P. MICRANTHUM (2–12 inches) is named for its small flowers, not more than ¼ inch long. They are borne singly, opposite the leaves. The corolla is white or bluish, no longer than the calyx. The leaf-segments, from nine to fifteen, are no more than ⅓ inch long.

March to May: in dry open places from Washington to California, western Montana, and Utah. *Plate 165.*

P. REPTANS (6–24 inches) is mostly smooth. The lower leaves have from eleven to seventeen mostly lanceolate, pointed segments, not close together. The flowers are in small clusters at the ends of long arching branches. The corolla is blue, averaging about ½ inch long.

April to June: in moist woods from North Dakota to Oklahoma. *Plate 165.*

PLATE 165

Johnson

Polemonium occidentale

Polemonium pulcherrimum *Johnson*

Polemonium reptans *Johnson*

Polemonium micranthum *George*

Jarrett

Polemonium foliosissimum

Sarcostemma cynanchoides *Koch*

Acerates viridiflora *Johnson*

Polemonium delicatum *Wilson*

Polemonium viscosum *Korling*

ALLOPHYLLUM

One species of *Allophyllum* crosses our western boundary.

A. VIOLACEUM (3–16 inches) has mostly forking stems. The lower leaves are pinnately lobed, or they may lack lobes; in the inflorescence the leaves are palmately lobed; all are borne singly; all are downy; the inflorescence is dense and glandular, with flowers two or three together. The funnel-shaped corolla is dark blue-violet, $\frac{1}{5}$–$\frac{1}{3}$ inch long.

May to July: in sandy and gravelly places from the Sierra Nevada to western Nevada.

COLLOMIA

Our species of *Collomia* have flowers in compact cymes, which may simulate heads, at the tips of the branches or, in one species, in the forks of the stems. The corolla is funnel- or trumpet-shaped with five short lobes. The teeth of the calyx are connected by whitish folds.

C. GRANDIFLORA (4–40 inches) has narrow leaves up to 2 inches long. The corolla ranges from salmon to yellow and white, $\frac{3}{5}$–$1\frac{1}{5}$ inches long.

April to August: in dry soil from Washington to California and eastward to western Montana and western Wyoming. *Plate 166.*

C. linearis (to 2 feet) is similar; more branched, with narrow ("linear") leaves up to 3 inches long. The corolla is from white to pink or purplish, $\frac{1}{3}$–$\frac{3}{5}$ inch long. From Washington to California and eastward to North and South Dakota, Nebraska, and Colorado. *Plate 166.*

C. macrocalyx (to 4 feet), in north-central Oregon, is distinguished by stiff, long-pointed, narrow calyx-lobes. The corolla is blue.

C. DEBILIS has sprawling stems (*debilis*, "weak"), which may form mats. The leaves tend to be crowded toward the tips; they may be variously cleft or without lobes. The corolla ranges from white to pink, lavender, and blue; or on some plants yellowish.

June to September: on rock slopes from Washington to California and eastward to Montana, western Wyoming, and central Utah. *Plate 166.*

C. TINCTORIA (2–6 inches) is sticky-glandular. The leaves are narrowly lanceolate. The flowers are in loose clusters of from two to five, commonly in the forks of the stems. The corolla is white, pink, or lavender, with a red-violet tube; $\frac{1}{3}$–$\frac{2}{5}$ inch long.

June and July: on dry open ground from central Washington to California and eastward to central Idaho, southeastern Oregon, and western Nevada. *Plate 166.*

C. tenella has flowers borne singly or in pairs in the forks or axils. The corolla is from white to pink and pale lavender, not more than $\frac{1}{4}$ inch long. From central Washington to Idaho, Nevada, and Utah.

GILIA

At one time or another most of the herbaceous *Polemoniaceae* have been placed in *Gilia*. Even after we subtract *Allophyllum*, *Linanthus*, *Ipomopsis*, and others, it remains a bewildering group of numerous heterogeneous species. The diagnostic characteristics are minor and technical; such obvious features as flower-color may vary greatly in plants that otherwise agree; and to make matters worse, many of the species interbreed in nature. It is not surprising, then, that some species have gone by many names, and that the species as we understand them today comprise arrays of subspecies.

The plants are small, the stems mostly branching. The leaves, borne singly on the stem and in many species in a basal rosette, are mostly pinnately cleft or divided, generally into narrow lobes or segments. The flowers are borne singly on long or short stalks, or in small clusters (generally from two to five together), or in dense heads. They are small, in only a few species an inch long, in most much smaller. The calyx consists of sharp, narrow teeth making a cup at the base and partly joined by a transparent membrane along their sides. The corolla consists of a narrow tube of joined petals which widens into a rather bell-shaped part called a throat; on the rim of the throat are the five lobes. The color varies greatly and is in many species attractive. The stamens are attached at the base of the spreading and partly joined lobes, or in the throat.

I.   *Species whose upper leaves are essentially like the lower, not markedly smaller.*

G. CAPILLARIS (1–12 inches) is finely glandular-downy. The leaves are very narrow, not lobed or

PLATE 166

Collomia tinctoria   *Spellenberg*

Collomia grandiflora   *Johnson*

Collomia linearis   *Paulson*

Gilia acerosa   *Todsen*

Collomia debilis   *Spurr*

Gilia subnuda   *Ure*

Gilia capitata   *P. R. Ferguson*

Gilia pinnatifida   *Oldemeyer*

cleft. The funnel-shaped corolla is pale violet, pink, or white, commonly purple-streaked or spotted, the tube on some plants yellow or white, $\frac{2}{5}$ inch long or less; the calyx half as long; the stamens shorter than the corolla-lobes.

June to September: on open or lightly wooded slopes in mountains from central Washington, northeastern Oregon, and western Idaho southward through the Sierra Nevada.

G. capitata (6–24 inches): Smooth or sparsely downy. Leaves once or twice pinnately divided, or undivided, up to 3 inches. Flowers in dense heads, pale violet or lilac. Mostly w of our boundary, but in n Ida. *Plate 166. G. campanulata* (1–6 inches): Leaves very narrow, with or without a few teeth. Flowers slender-stalked. Corolla funnel- or bell-shaped, $\frac{1}{5}$–$\frac{2}{5}$ inch, white with yellow throat. Stamens unequal. se Calif, s Nev. *G. inyoensis* (1–4 inches): Corolla $\frac{1}{8}$–$\frac{1}{4}$ inch, white with yellow throat, only the lobes emerging from the calyx. Stamens equal. Inyo Co., Calif.

G. RIGIDULA (3–10 inches) is finely glandular-downy.

The leaves are pinnately cleft into three or five narrow, sharp lobes $\frac{1}{6}$–$\frac{1}{3}$ inch long. The flowers are in a rather flat, open inflorescence. The corolla is about $\frac{2}{5}$ inch long, with spreading lobes, blue or purple. The stamens have bright yellow tips.

April to September: on plains and hills in southeastern Colorado, southwestern Kansas, and Oklahoma. Our plants form a variety which some have named as a separate species, *G. acerosa. Plate 166.*

II. *Species whose upper leaves are much smaller than the lower.*

A. Plants whose lower leaves are cobwebby-woolly.

G. SINUATA (2–12 inches) has a rosette of strap-shaped leaves at the base, from wavy-edged ("sinuate") to pinnately lobed, with a whitish central vein. The small upper leaves embrace the stem between basal lobes. The flowers are in small groups of from one to three, in an open inflorescence. The corolla is from pale violet to pink and white with a yellow throat, $\frac{1}{4}$–$\frac{1}{2}$ inch long.

April to June: on sandy plains from central Washington to southeastern California, southern Idaho, and western Colorado. The following two species have been merged in *G. sinuata* by at least one botanist who finds the distinctions among them not clear. *G. inconspicua* (4–12 inches): Leaves once or twice pinnately lobed. Corolla pink-violet with a yellow throat purple-spotted, the tube pale violet or pale yellow, $\frac{1}{5}$–$\frac{2}{5}$ inch. Stamens unequal. From c Wash to se Calif, s Ida, w Colo. *G. tweedyi* (2–8 inches): Leaves pinnately lobed. Corolla pale violet with yellow throat and white tube, $\frac{1}{6}$–$\frac{1}{4}$ inch. e Ore, c Ida, s Wyo, ne Nev.

G. brecciarum (3–14 inches): Leaves twice or thrice pinnately divided, the segments not very narrow. Calyx densely glandular. Corolla violet or white, the throat white with yellow spots, the tube dark purple in its lower half, $\frac{1}{4}$–$\frac{2}{5}$ inch. se Ore, se Calif, Nev.

The remaining species of this group have no purple in the corolla-throat (but the tube may be purple).

G. OPHTHALMOIDES (6–14 inches) has leaves once or twice pinnately lobed. The corolla-lobes are pink-violet or pink with the throat yellow or pale blue-violet near the opening, the tube light violet.

April to July: in sandy soil from southern Wyoming to eastern California, Nevada, Utah, and Colorado.

G. leptantha (2–8 inches): Leaves with crowded, sharp-pointed lobes. Corolla-lobes violet, throat and tube pale yellow, $\frac{1}{4}$–$\frac{2}{5}$ inch; style projecting above the stamens. ne Calif, nw Nev. *G. cana* (4–12 inches): Similar. Corolla pink-violet, $\frac{2}{5}$–$1\frac{1}{4}$ inches; tube purple, throat yellow. se Calif, s Nev. *G. transmontana* (4–14 inches): Leaves pinnately cleft, the lobes at least three times as long as the width of the midrib, perhaps with a few teeth. Corolla white or pale violet with yellow throat, $\frac{1}{6}$–$\frac{1}{3}$ inch. s Calif, w Nev.

B. Species (the upper leaves much smaller than the lower) with leaves not cobwebby-woolly. Plants of our southern regions, from southern California to Colorado.

G. SUBNUDA (8–20 inches) has leaf-blades widest between middle and tip, toothed or pinnately lobed. The corolla is rose or pink, $\frac{1}{2}$–1 inch long, funnel- or salver-form.

June and July: on plains and mesas in south-central Utah and western Colorado. *Plate 166.*

G. stenothyrsa (6–24 inches): Leaves 1–2 inches, except the lowest pinnately lobed, the basal in a rosette. Inflorescence narrow, the flowers in clusters at the tips of branches. Corolla $\frac{1}{2}$–$\frac{3}{4}$ inch long, from white to pale blue-violet. ne Utah. *G. sedifolia*: Leaves unlobed, about $\frac{2}{5}$ inch. Corolla violet. High altitudes, w Colo.

G. pinnatifida (6–24 inches): Leaves pinnately lobed, to $2\frac{1}{2}$ inches, the basal in a rosette. Inflorescence long, many-flowered. Corolla white or pale bluish, $\frac{1}{3}$–$\frac{1}{2}$ inch. sw Wyo, nw Colo, ne Utah. *Plate 166. G. pentstemonoides* (2–8 inches): Tufts of many stems. Leaves very narrow, to about 2 inches. Corolla $\frac{1}{4}$–$\frac{2}{5}$ inch, blue with yellow tube. Gunnison Co., Colo.

G. leptomeria (2–8 inches): Glandular-downy. Basal leaves pinnately cleft or coarsely toothed. Corolla mostly $\frac{1}{4}$ inch; the lobes commonly toothed. From Wash to Calif, Ida, Wyo, and Colo. *G. hutchinsifolia* (2–14 inches): Similar. Basal leaves twice pinnately cleft. Corolla $\frac{1}{3}$–$\frac{3}{5}$ inch; the lobes white, violet-streaked on the back. se Calif, sw Utah. *G. mcvickerae* (10–14 inches): Similar. Corolla sky-blue, $\frac{2}{5}$–$\frac{1}{2}$ inch. sc Utah. *G. stellata* (4–16 inches): Hairy near the ground, glandular above. Basal leaves several times pinnately cleft or divided. Corolla less than $\frac{1}{2}$ inch; the throat purple-spotted, the lobes from white to pale blue and lavender. Utah. *G. scopulorum* (4–12 inches): Hairy and glandular. Basal leaves with broad lobes, these lobed or toothed. Corolla about $\frac{1}{2}$ inch, the lobes pink-lavender, violet, or white. s Utah. *G. latifolia* (4–10 inches): Leaves shallowly lobed, prickle-toothed. Glandular, hairy, rank-smelling. Corolla $\frac{1}{4}$–$\frac{1}{2}$ inch, pink inside, pale or buff outside. Utah. *G. ripleyi* (4–12 inches):

Leaves holly-like, with broad prickly teeth, on a slender stalk, all crowded on the lower part of the stem. Glandular, hairy, rank-smelling. Corolla about $\frac{1}{4}$ inch, the lobes rose, the tube white. s Nev.

G. TENERRIMA (2–8 inches) is copiously glandular.

The leaves are almost all without teeth or lobes, narrow. The flowers are borne singly at tips of branches, the corolla $\frac{1}{16}$–$\frac{1}{8}$ inch, pale yellowish or faintly lavender.

June to August: on open or lightly wooded slopes from Oregon to southwestern Montana, Wyoming, and Utah.

PHLOX

Most flowers of the large genus *Phlox* are what the botanist calls salverform; by which he means a corolla with a definite tube of nearly equal width throughout, crowned by lobes which extend at right angles (strictly speaking, it is only these lobes which make the salver or tray; the tube has nothing to do with it). This contrasts with the funnel-shaped corolla of other genera (e.g. *Gilia*), in which the diameter of the tube is larger towards the end, and the lobes continue the line of the tube (and its "throat").

The flowers of *Phlox* are single or in cymes at the tips of stems. The prevailing colors range from red and violet to blue, pink, and white. The general stature of the plants varies from leafy stems several feet tall to mounds or cushions a few inches thick and covered with flowers.

Several species are ineptly named wild-sweet-William. Sweet-William is an Old-World species of *Dianthus*, in the pink family, with scant resemblance to *Phlox*.

I. *Plants with distinct leafy stems, erect or horizontal but not forming mats or cushions.*

The flowers are generally in an inflorescence of more than three. The stems of some are horizontal at the base, with erect leafy branches and tips.

A. The first six species are limited in our range to the plains and foothills from Montana and North Dakota to Colorado and Oklahoma, east of the continental divide in the Rocky Mountains.

Others occur both east and west of the divide; see under B.

P. DIVARICATA (8–20 inches) is erect or nearly so.

Runners are found at the base. The calyx and flower stalks are glandular.

April to June: in fields and woods from Nebraska to Oklahoma. *Plate 167*.

P. pilosa commonly has a downy stem. The leaves

are narrow, sharp-pointed. The flower is reddish. From North Dakota to Oklahoma. *Plate 167*.

P. oklahomensis (6–16 inches): Shrubby at the base. Glandular or glandular-hairy. Leaves lanceolate or very narrow, to $2\frac{1}{2}$ inches. Inflorescence of from three to nine flowers. Corolla white, pink, lavender, or lilac, $\frac{1}{3}$–$\frac{1}{2}$ inch. Kan and nc Okla. *P. bifida* (to 8 inches): Leaves narrow and stiff. Corolla-lobes deeply notched; color various, generally pale purple, with two reddish marks at the base of each lobe. From ec Neb to ne Okla.

The eastern *P. maculata* may be found in extreme northeastern Kansas. The stems are commonly red-spotted. Leaves narrow, tapering. Flowers in a cylindric inflorescence, purple or red-violet.

Besides these, the commonly cultivated *P. paniculata* may be found growing wild. Leaves ovate, lanceolate, or elliptic, bristly-edged. Inflorescence large. Stems 2–7 feet tall.

B. The remaining species of group I are widely distributed in our range.

Some are found on both sides of the continental divide.

P. SPECIOSA (6–16 inches) is somewhat woody at the base, glandular (and some plants hairy) above, rarely smooth. The leaves range from very narrow to broadly lanceolate, to $2\frac{3}{4}$ inches long. The inflorescence is loose, with some leaflike bracts. The corolla is pink or white, $\frac{2}{5}$–$\frac{3}{5}$ inch long.

April to June: with sagebrush and yellow pine from eastern Washington to north-central Oregon and northern Idaho; in west-central Montana. *Plate 167*. There are several varieties, in the two areas mentioned, and in California and Arizona.

P. LONGIFOLIA (4–16 inches) may be smooth, hairy, or glandular. The leaves are narrow, up to 3 inches long. The flowers are white, pink, or lilac; the corolla-tube $\frac{2}{5}$–$\frac{4}{5}$ inch long.

April to July: in dry, open, rocky places from Washington to California and eastward to western Montana, Wyoming, and Colorado. *Plate 167*. *P. stansburyi* (4–18 inches): Closely related. Flowers more numerous, up to twenty-one in an inflorescence. Corolla an inch long or longer, white, pink, or purple commonly with a paler eye. Utah. *Plate 167*. *P. viscida* (2–8 inches): Leaves narrowly lanceolate. Flowers malodorous. Corolla white, pink, or purple, about $\frac{1}{2}$ inch. From Wash, Ore, Ida to Nev, Utah. *Plate 169*. *P. cluteana* (to 8 inches): Erect branches from a rhizome. Leaves narrowly elliptic, to 2 inches; the upper hairy, fringed. Inflorescence compact, from six to twelve flowers; corolla purple. Utah. *P. idahonis* (20–40 inches): Stem solitary, partly hairy and glandular. Leaves lanceolate, up to 4 inches. Inflorescence open. Corolla pink. Clearwater Co., Ida.

P. COLUBRINA (6–20 inches) may be shrubby at the base. It is smooth, with very narrow leaves up to 3 inches long. The inflorescence is open. The corolla is pink, or less commonly white, the tube $\frac{1}{3}$–$\frac{1}{2}$ inch long, the lobes up to $\frac{4}{5}$ inch.

April to June: on dry slopes and cliffs in and near the Snake River cañon in Oregon (and barely in Washington) and Idaho.

II. *Species whose stems and leaves form mats or cushions.*

The flowers are generally single or in groups of not more than three at the tips of branches.

A few of these species may include some plants with evident leafy stems; e.g. *P. multiflora*, *P. caespitosa*, *P. alyssifolia*.

These "cushions" and mats are difficult to distinguish. The illustrations have been chosen as far as possible to show the differences in the leaves.

P. CAESPITOSA has loosely rising stems 2–6 inches long, somewhat woody. The plants are generally glandular-hairy. The leaves are narrow, stiff, and sharp, $\frac{1}{5}$–$\frac{3}{5}$ inch long. The flowers are mostly single at the ends of branches. Corolla whitish, pink, or lavender, the tube $\frac{1}{3}$–$\frac{3}{5}$ inch long.

May and June: most commonly with yellow pine from Washington and northeastern Oregon to northern Idaho and northwestern Montana. *Plate 167*. The name has been generally misapplied to the following species (if it is a species); it was so used in our volume 4. True *P. caespitosa* has been generally known as *P. douglasii.*

P. pulvinata forms more compact mats. The corolla is white or bluish. From Ore to sw Mont and southward to Nev, Utah, and Colo. *Plate 167*. Originally named as a subspecies, and certainly not always easy to distinguish.

P. condensata forms cushions of narrow, stiff leaves about $\frac{1}{2}$ inch long, with bristly margins. The calyx is glandular. Corolla white, about $\frac{1}{3}$ inch long, longer than the calyx. In Colorado. *Plate 168*.

P. hendersonii differs in its shorter ($\frac{1}{5}$–$\frac{2}{5}$ inch), more copiously glandular-hairy leaves, with thick margins. The flowers, single at the ends of stems, may have six petals, sepals, and stamens. The corolla is white, pink, or lavender, with a tube less than $\frac{1}{2}$ inch. e Wash and e Ore.

P. DIFFUSA (4–12 inches) has prostrate or curving stems, somewhat woody. The leaves are yellowish-green, very narrow, about $\frac{1}{2}$ inch long; those of many plants with long, fine marginal hairs near the base. Flowers mostly single. The corolla is white or pink or pale blue, the tube $\frac{1}{8}$–$\frac{3}{4}$ inch long.

May to August: in forests and on rocky slopes through the Cascade Mountains of Washington and Oregon to the Sierra Nevada and eastward to northwestern Montana. *Plate 168*.

P. HOODII forms cushions mostly 1–2 inches thick. The leaves are awl-like, cobwebby at the base, up to $\frac{1}{2}$ inch long. The flowers are borne singly; the corolla ranges from white to lavender.

April to June: on clayey soil from central Washington, eastern Oregon, and northeastern California to North Dakota, western Nebraska, and Colorado. *Plate 168*. *P. covillei*: Leaves hairy and fringed. Flowers single or in pairs. Corolla small, lavender or white. s Nev.

P. KELSEYI has stems up to 4 inches long mostly prostrate, some nearly erect, smooth or hairy. The leaves are mostly $\frac{1}{2}$–1 inch long, narrow, fringed near the base. The flowers are single at the tips of branches; the corolla white or light blue, the tube $\frac{1}{2}$ inch long or less.

May to July: in valleys, on foothills, from Idaho to western Montana, Nevada, and Colorado.

P. aculeata: Glandular-hairy. Stems numerous, crowded, less than 4 inches. Leaves very narrow, $\frac{2}{5}$–$1\frac{2}{5}$ inches. Flowers from one to three at stem-tips; corolla white or pink, the tube about $\frac{1}{2}$ inch. Ore, Ida. *P. gladiformis*: Similar: Leaves narrowly lanceolate, almost to 1 inch. Corolla-tube glandular. Corolla white with a bluish sheen, lavender, or lilac. sw Utah, adjacent Nev. *P. albomarginata*: Mats or cushions, not more than 2 inches tall. Leaves 1–2 inches. Flowers single at the tips; corolla white, pink, or purplish, the tube $\frac{1}{3}$–$\frac{1}{2}$ inch. Ida, sw Mont. *P. griseola*: Grayish-green. Leaves awl-shaped, fringed, $\frac{1}{4}$–$\frac{1}{2}$ inch. Flowers single; corolla white, pink, or purplish. Nev, Utah. *P. austromontana*: Leaves awl-like, up to 1 inch. Flowers from one to five at the tips of branches. Corolla from white to pink and lavender; calyx ridged. Colo. *Plate 168*. *P. jonesii*: Leaves very narrow, soft, $\frac{4}{5}$–$1\frac{1}{2}$

PLATE 167

Phlox caespitosa   *Kleinpeter*

Phlox stansburyi   *Roberts*

Phlox longifolia   *Korling*

Phlox pulvinata   *Huebner*

Phlox divaricata   *Rickett*

Phlox pilosa   *Rickett*

Phlox speciosa   *Spellenberg*

inches. Corolla bright pink, scarcely fragrant. Calyx ridged. s Utah. *P. mollis*: Densely hairy. Flowers pink or purple. se Wash, ne Ore, adjacent Ida. This may be considered a variety of *P. viscida* (group I).

P. ALYSSIFOLIA (to 4 inches) has many hairy stems, in
some places forming compact tufts. The flowers are single or two together at the tips of stems. The corolla is white, pink, or lilac, the tube about ½ inch long, the broad lobes ⅓–½ inch.

May to July: in dry open ground from southwestern Montana to western North and South Dakota and north-central Colorado. *Plate 168.*

P. MUSCOIDES forms tufts or cushions, generally cobwebby-woolly. The numerous leaves are ⅘–1⅖ inches long, narrow or triangular. The flowers are single at the tips of stems; the corolla is white, bluish,

or purplish, the tube less than ½ inch long.

May to July: on dry, open or sparsely wooded slopes from Oregon and Nevada to Montana, Nebraska, and Colorado. *Plate 168.*

P. MULTIFLORA (rarely 4 inches tall) forms mats. The
leaves are very narrow, ½–1¼ inches long. There are from one to three flowers at the end of a stem. The corolla is white or bluish, ⅖–⅗ inch long.

May to August: in open woods, generally rocky, in mountains from eastern Idaho and southwestern Montana to northeastern Utah and northwestern Colorado. *Plate 168. P. andicola* (to 5 inches): Erect, crowded shoots. Leaves very narrow, awl-like, sharp, smooth or hairy, to ⅘ inch long. Inflorescence with long kinky hairs. Corolla ⅖–⅗ inch long, white or more rarely yellowish or purplish, fragrant. From se Mont and sw ND to nw Kan, se Wyo, ne Colo. *Plate 168.*

MICROSTERIS

There is only one species of *Microsteris*.

M. GRACILIS (2–10 inches) may be glandular. The
leaves are narrowly elliptic, or lanceolate, or wider between middle and tip, ½–1 inch long, the lower paired, the upper borne singly. The flowers are

generally in pairs or single in the upper axils, the corolla with a yellowish tube ⅓–½ inch long, and white, rose, or lavender lobes.

March to August: in open woodland and grassland from Washington to California and eastward to Montana, western Nebraska, and Colorado. *Plate 169.*

LINANTHUS

The genus *Linanthus* contains many species of small plants with narrow leaves (or leaf-segments) and pretty flowers. The leaves are paired and practically without stalks, but in most species the blades are deeply cleft or divided palmately into a number of narrow parts which together create the appearance of a circle of narrow leaves. These pairs of leaves are in most species spaced widely along the stems. The flowers are either in dense heads or in cymes. The narrow teeth of the calyx are generally joined by a colorless membrane. The corolla may have a very long tube or almost none or anything between; with five lobes forming a sort of funnel or spreading out nearly flat as a "salver." The stamens are generally attached near the base of the lobes, only rarely within the tube.

I.   *Species whose flowers practically lack stalks and are in heads.*

Except in the first of these, the corolla-tube scarcely projects beyond the calyx-teeth.

L. CILIATUS (4–12 inches) has bristle-edged ("ciliate") leaf-segments, bracts, and calyx-teeth. The

corolla-tube is up to an inch long, the lobes only ⅙ inch long; from white to deep rose commonly with a darker spot at the base of each lobe and a white-edged yellow center.

April to July: in dry open places in eastern California and Nevada. *Plate 169.*

L. NUTTALLII (4–8 inches) has flowers scarcely in
heads, but with practically no stalks in "congested cymes." The flowers are about ½ inch long, the tube barely as long as the calyx; corolla white or cream. The plants are bushy and commonly bristly, with bunches of small leaves in the axils of the principal leaves.

May to August: in dry rocky and brushy places mostly at high altitudes from Washington to California and eastward to central Idaho, western Wyoming, and Colorado. *Plate 169.* It is sufficiently different from the other species to have been placed in a separate genus, *Linanthastrum*, intermediate between *Linanthus* and *Leptodactylon*.

L. melingii is closely similar; more compact, almost matted; in the mountains of our southwestern corner; by some botanists considered a form of *L. nuttallii*.

PLATE 168

Phlox diffusa   *Johnson*

Phlox condensata   *Rickett*

Phlox andicola   *Redfield*

Phlox alyssifolia   *Kravig*

Phlox hoodii   *Roberts*

Phlox muscoides   *Wilson*

Phlox austromontana   *Hesselberg*

Phlox multiflora   *Wilson*

II. *Species whose flowers are evidently in cymes.*

A typical cyme has a central flower, from whose stalk two other flowers grow, from *their* stalks two more arise, and so on. Such symmetrical cymes, however, are not common; in the species of *Linanthus* the branching is generally more irregular and tighter (approaching the inflorescence of *L. nuttallii*).

L. DEMISSUS (1–4 inches) has few flowers, almost without stalks. The corolla is bell-shaped with flaring lobes, about $\frac{1}{4}$ inch long, white with two dark lines at the base of each lobe.

March to May: on dry plains and washes from eastern California to southern Utah. *Plate 169.*

L. parryae may possibly be found in our southwestern corner. It forms a tuft of leafy branches, glandular and hairy. The flowers are few in compact cymes, only the corolla-lobes emerging from the leaves. Corolla white or less commonly cream or purplish. *Plate 169. L. aureus* (2–4 inches tall, widely spreading): Flowers bell-shaped or a short funnel, golden or pale yellow, commonly with purple spots at the base of the lobes. e Calif, s Nev. *L. arenicola* ($\frac{1}{2}$–4 inches): A plant of the southern California deserts, reported within our southwestern boundary. Flowers yellow, some with a purple center, opening in the evening.

L. HARKNESSII (2–10 inches) has relatively long-stalked flowers, in cymes. The corolla ranges from white to pale blue, up to $\frac{1}{8}$ inch long. The lobes of the leaves are very narrow.

June to August: in dry meadows and on open slopes and ridges from Washington to Idaho, California, and northeastern Nevada. *L. septentrionalis* is similar. Corolla longer than the calyx, white, light blue, or lavender. From Washington to California and eastward to Wyoming and Colorado. *Plate 169.*

L. PHARNACEOIDES (4–12 inches) is much branched, with leaves cleft into up to nine lobes. The flowers are long-stalked; the corolla much longer than the calyx, pale blue with a yellow center, funnel-shaped, $\frac{1}{4}$–$\frac{1}{2}$ inch long.

May to July: in dry open places in the lowlands from eastern Washington and adjacent northern Idaho to California. *Plate 169. L. bakeri* (2–12 inches): Corolla white, pink, or lilac, twice the calyx. Stamens very short-stalked. From e Wash to Calif.

Evening-snow, *L. dichotomus* (2–8 inches), may have undivided leaves; but most are divided into threadlike segments. Stem forked ("dichotomous"), with a single flower in each fork. Corolla about twice the calyx, funnel-shaped, the tube short, white (on some plants with a purple center); opening in the evening. Barely within our w boundary in Calif. *Plate 169. L. bigelovii:* Flowers similarly arranged, and evening-opening. Corolla barely emerging from the $\frac{1}{2}$-inch calyx, generally white tinged with purple outside, less commonly pale yellow. Leaves commonly undivided. s Nev, s Utah.

GYMNOSTERIS

The stems of *Gymnosteris* bear a circle of leaves, without teeth or lobes, just beneath the flower-cluster at the tip; and no others. The flowers are single or in a compact cluster; the corolla white, pink, or yellow, with a narrow tube crowned with spreading lobes. The plants are smooth.

G. NUDICAULIS (1–4 inches) has narrow leaves up to $\frac{3}{5}$ inch long. The corolla is white or yellow, the tube $\frac{1}{4}$–$\frac{2}{5}$ inch long, the lobes $\frac{1}{8}$–$\frac{1}{4}$ inch.

April and May: in dry open places, especially in sandy soil, on plains and foothills from eastern Oregon to western Idaho and Nevada.

G. PARVULA ($\frac{1}{3}$–2 inches) has lanceolate or ovate leaves up to $\frac{1}{2}$ inch long. The flowers may be single. The corolla-tube is $\frac{1}{10}$–$\frac{1}{5}$ inch long, scarcely emerging from the calyx; corolla white or pink.

May to July: in open, mostly dry meadows, on slopes, etc. at various altitudes from Oregon to Yellowstone National Park in Wyoming and southward to California and Colorado.

LEPTODACTYLON

Three species of *Leptodactylon* are in our range, characterized by flowers borne singly, without stalks, in the axils of leaves or at the tips of short branches. The leaves are divided palmately into narrow, spine-tipped segments.

L. CAESPITOSUM forms dense cushions less than 3 inches tall but up to a foot or more across, with crowded leaves cleft into lobes $\frac{1}{5}$–$\frac{1}{3}$ inch long. The flowers are single in the axils and at the tips; the corolla white or yellowish, $\frac{1}{2}$–$\frac{2}{3}$ inch long.

May to July: on dry hills and plains from Nebraska to Colorado, Wyoming, Nevada, and Utah. *Plate 170.*

PLATE 169

Phlox viscida   *George*

Linanthus demissus   *Jarrett*

Microsteris gracilis   *Roberts*

Spurr

Linanthus pharnaceoides

Linanthus ciliatus   *Myrick*

Linanthus nuttallii   *Korling*

Linanthus septentrionalis   *Twomey*

Linanthus parryae   *Stason*

Linanthus dichotomus   *Johnson*

L. PUNGENS (4–24 inches) is shrubby; the many
lobes of the leaves are not more than $\frac{1}{2}$ inch long.
The calyx has spine-tipped lobes. The corolla-tube is
slender, $\frac{1}{2}$–1 inch long, the spreading lobes white, yellowish, or salmon; opening mostly at night.

May to August: in dry rocky and sandy places

from Washington to California and eastward to Montana, western Nebraska and Colorado. *Plate 170.*

L. watsoni has all leaves paired. The corolla is
$\frac{3}{4}$–1 inch long, whitish or cream with purple in the
throat. On rocky cliffs and hills in Utah and western
Colorado.

LANGLOISIA

The plants of *Langloisia* are small, with bristly or
spiny, pinnately cleft, stiff leaves. The flowers are in
small clusters at the ends of branches, without stalks,
surrounded by bristly-toothed bracts. The corolla may
be slightly bilaterally symmetric, the three upper lobes
making an upper lip, the other two a lower lip.

L. SETOSISSIMA forms a low tuft 3–4 inches across.

The leaves are mostly wedge-shaped, with three
large teeth at the broad end. The corolla is pale violet,
about $\frac{1}{2}$ inch long.

May to July: in deserts, generally in sandy soil
from Oregon and Idaho southward to California and
Utah. *Plate 170.*

L. matthewsii (1–6 inches) may be found from
eastern California to southern Nevada. The corolla is
whitish or pinkish, the upper lip with red marks. In
sandy and gravelly places. *Plate 170. L. punctata* may
possibly be within our southwestern corner. The corolla is lilac, nearly an inch long. *Plate 170. L. schottii*
also is doubtfully in our area, with a white, pink, yellowish, or pale lavender corolla $\frac{1}{3}$–$\frac{1}{2}$ inch long.

NAVARRETIA

A number of small spiny plants with very small
flowers in pincushion-heads compose the genus *Navarretia*. The leaves are borne singly, and are divided
or lobed, the segments or lobes spine-tipped. The
corolla-tube is scarcely more than $\frac{1}{2}$ inch long, much
less in some species; the lobes of many are minute.
The bracts of the head are spiny; their lobing and division (see the drawings) are helpful in identification.

N. DIVARICATA (1–6 inches) has leaves either unlobed, or with side lobes much shorter than the
end lobe; all very narrow. The heads are sticky-downy.
The bracts are palmately cleft into narrow, tapering
lobes $\frac{1}{2}$–1 inch long. The corolla-tube is about $\frac{1}{8}$ inch
long, yellow, white, or blue; the lobes white, blue,
pink, or lavender.

June to August: on slopes from eastern Washington to California and eastward to central Idaho and
Montana. *Plate 170.*

N. breweri (1–5 inches) has yellow flowers about
$\frac{1}{4}$ inch long. The stamens project, the style does not.
The plant is downy. The leaves are pinnately divided,
the end segment the longest. Bracts are similar. From
Washington to California and central Idaho, western
Wyoming, Nevada, and Utah. *Plate 170.*

N. INTERTEXTA (2–10 inches) has white hairs at least
in the inflorescence; elsewhere it is downy. The
bracts may be divided twice pinnately. The flowers are
white, pale lavender, or blue, in one variety $\frac{1}{3}$–$\frac{1}{2}$ inch
long, in another $\frac{1}{6}$–$\frac{1}{3}$ inch and commonly shorter than
the calyx; the latter variety is rarely over 4 inches tall.

May to July: in spring pools and moist soil in
eastern Washington and Oregon and adjacent Idaho
and from California to Colorado.

N. MINIMA may be prostrate or nearly erect. The
leaves and bracts are relatively soft, commonly
pale green; leaves up to $1\frac{1}{2}$ inches long, with the side
segments few and small, or cleft into three; the end
segment is long and may have spiny teeth. The flowers
are white; a distinctive feature is the narrowness of the
corolla-lobes — their length (about $\frac{1}{25}$ inch) about
twice the width.

May to August: in moist soil from southern
Washington and Idaho to northern California and Nevada. *Plate 170.*

N. leucocephala is barely within our western limits
(in northeastern California). It may be prostrate. The
flowers are white, about $\frac{1}{3}$ inch long. April and May.
Plate 170.

ERIASTRUM

The flower-heads of *Eriastrum* are woolly (*eri-*).
The stems and leaves also may be woolly. The leaves
are borne singly, either threadlike and undivided, or

cleft or divided into threadlike lobes. The calyx consists of awl-like teeth joined by a transparent membrane. The corolla is white, blue, or violet.

PLATE 170

Leptodactylon caespitosum

Scribner

Navarretia minima

Myrick

Langloisia punctata

Reineking

Leptodactylon pungens

Nichols

Navarretia leucocephala

P. R. Ferguson

Langloisia setosissima

Olmsted

Navarretia breweri

Myrick

Navarretia divaricata

Spellenberg

Langloisia matthewsii

Myrick

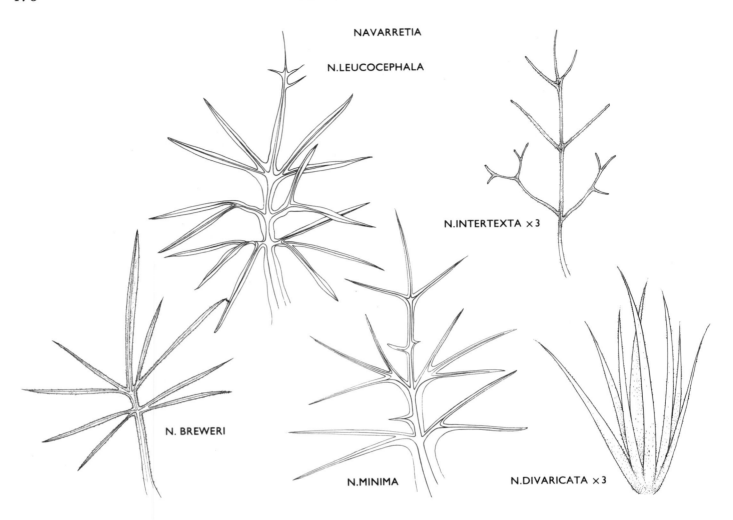

E. SPARSIFLORUM (4–16 inches) is generally woolly.

The leaves are narrow, undivided and unlobed or with a pair of short lobes at the base. The flowers are from two to five in a cluster, the corolla pale blue, whitish, or pink, about ⅓ inch long.

June and July: in dry open places, especially sandy, from central Oregon to southern Idaho, California, and western Nevada. *Plate 171.*

E. wilcoxii is similar and may perhaps be treated as a variety. The flowers are slightly longer, pale blue, not more than five together. The leaves have from one to three pairs of lobes. From eastern Washington to California and Idaho and Utah.

E. diffusum (1–6 inches) is doubtfully within our southwestern limits. The leaves are very narrow and undivided or divided into three or five narrow segments. The flowers are from three to twenty in a cluster, white or pale blue, ⅓ inch long. *Plate 171.*

IPOMOPSIS

The species here treated as genus *Ipomopsis* have been quite generally named *Gilia* (see the introduction to that genus). The distinction between the two genera is certainly not sharp; but, except perhaps for a few small species, and perhaps some hybrids, plants can be placed in one or the other, with help to identification. The flowers of *Ipomopsis* have a distinct tube and five flaring lobes but no "throat" — the rather abruptly expanded part, between tube and lobes, characteristic of *Gilia*. Each is accompanied by a single bract (this is difficult to see in group III). The leaves are borne singly, up to the flowers. They (or their lobes or segments) are tipped with minute sharp, hard points.

I.   *Species whose flowers are in small, short-stalked clusters, or single, in a narrow, raceme-like inflorescence.*

I. AGGREGATA (1–3 feet) may have hairy or woolly stems. The leaves are divided pinnately once or

PLATE 171

Korling

Ipomopsis aggregata

Ipomopsis polyantha   *Wilson*

Ipomopsis spicata   *Roberts*

Ipomopsis aggregata   *Korling*

Ipomopsis candida   *D. Richards*

Ipomopsis tenuituba   *Johnson*

Eriastrum sparsiflorum   *Myrick*

Ipomopsis multiflora   *Todsen*

Eriastrum diffusum   *Twomey*

twice into very narrow segments. The flowers are in small clusters. The corolla is a trumpet $1-1\frac{1}{2}$ inches long, bright red with yellowish mottling on the lobes, or white, or any shade between; some plants may have yellowish or purplish-rose flowers.

May to September: in open woods and rocky places and on roadsides from Washington to California and from Montana to Colorado. *Plate 171. I. candida* is closely related; the flowers are white. The sepals are joined nearly to their tip, making a cylindric calyx. In Colorado. *Plate 171. I. tenuituba,* with a pink corolla whose tube is very narrow and up to 2 inches long is otherwise like *I. aggregata,* and is by some treated as a subspecies. From California to Colorado. *Plate 171. I. multiflora* (4–12 inches): Downy. Leaves either threadlike or pinnately divided. Corolla violet, less than 1 inch. Stamens projecting. s Nev (and s Utah?). *Plate 171.*

I. SPICATA (4–14 inches) has a cobwebby stem. The leaves are crowded, over an inch long, threadlike and undivided or with irregular threadlike segments. The corolla is whitish, about $\frac{1}{2}$ inch long.

May to August: on dry hills and plains from Wyoming and South Dakota to Kansas, Colorado, and Utah. *Plate 171. I. polyantha* (1–2 feet): Leaves pinnately divided into $\frac{1}{2}$-inch segments. The corolla is white, dotted with purple, or violet in a variety, about $\frac{1}{2}$ inch long, with large lobes. s Colo. *Plate 171.*

I. rubra (2–6 feet), a southeastern species, in our range only in Oklahoma. Leaves with threadlike segments. Flowers clustered or single. Corolla 1 inch or less, red with yellow streaks or mottling. *Plate 172.*

II. *Species whose flowers are individually long-stalked, in a loose inflorescence.*

I. LONGIFLORA (1–2 feet) has most leaves divided into threadlike segments; the upper may be undivided. The corolla is white or pink, 1–2 inches long.

May to September: in dry soil from Utah to Nebraska and Colorado. *Plate 172. I. laxiflora* (4–16 inches) is similar. The corolla does not exceed an inch;

white or tinged with blue. Utah, southern Colorado.

I. MINUTIFLORA (4–24 inches) has most leaves narrow, undivided and unlobed; but some of the lower are commonly cleft into three; all nearly 2 inches long. The corolla is white or bluish, $\frac{1}{6}-\frac{1}{3}$ inch long.

June to August: on dry, sandy plains and in valleys, commonly with sagebrush, from central Washington and northern Oregon to Idaho.

III. *Species whose flowers are in heads at the ends of branches.*

I. CONGESTA (4–10 inches) is cobwebby-woolly. In many places the plants form mats or cushions. The leaves are pinnately or palmately cleft into short lobes, or unlobed. The corolla is white with a yellow tube $\frac{1}{4}$ inch long.

June to September: on dry slopes in mountains from Oregon to eastern California (Inyo County) and eastward to North Dakota and Utah. *Plate 172.*

I. POLYCLADON has spreading stems 2–6 inches long, tending to be glandular-hairy. The few leaves are mostly at the base, some crowded under the flower-clusters, all less than an inch long and pinnately cleft or lobed. The corolla is white, not more than $\frac{1}{4}$ inch long.

April to June: on sandy and rocky slopes from Oregon to California and eastward to Colorado. *I. depressa* is similar in manner of growth, but the leaves are elliptic and without lobes. In southern Utah and Nevada.

I. PUMILA has stems up to 8 inches long, with leaves cleft into a few very narrow lobes. The flowers are white, pink, or blue, about $\frac{1}{3}$ inch long.

May to August: on plains and hillsides from Wyoming to Utah and Colorado (and Oklahoma?). *I. gunnisoni* is similar and is perhaps a variety. Its leaves are mostly unlobed and threadlike. The white flowers do not exceed $\frac{1}{6}$ inch. In Utah and Colorado. *Plate 172.*

THE HEATH FAMILY (ERICACEAE)

The *Ericaceae* are all trees or shrubs and so excluded from our arbitrary definition of wild flowers. However, some – such as the heaths themselves – are so low, their woody stems so inconspicuous, that they are briefly described here.

These are characterized by mostly small bell-shaped or urn-shaped corollas, mostly white or pink. There are four or five petals, and about twice as many stamens. The stamens discharge their pollen through chinks or pores at their tips. The leaves are without division or lobes, and are evergreen. The fruits of some are succulent and may for our purposes be called berries (though

PLATE 172

Gaultheria ovatifolia   *On*

Ipomopsis congesta   *Scribner*

Gaultheria humifusa   *Werking*

Gaultheria hispidula   *Horne*

Stockert

Ipomopsis longiflora   *Oldemeyer*

Ipomopsis gunnisoni

Ipomopsis rubra   *McIntyre*

they may contain small nuts or even a capsule); those of others are capsules.

The reader may notice that some of the species do not have a continuous range in our area. The explanation is that they grow across Canada and extend southward in mountain ranges.

GAULTHERIA

The flowers of our species of *Gaultheria* are single in the axils. The corolla has four or five lobes; there are eight or ten stamens. Pollen is released through pores at or near their tips. The plants creep, mostly not rising more than 2 inches above the ground. The succulent outer layer of the fruit is formed from the calyx.

G. HUMIFUSA has trailing stems up to 4 inches long.

The leaves are ovate or oval, $\frac{1}{2}$–1 inch long, with or without fine teeth. The corolla is bell-shaped, pink. The berries are reddish.

July and August: in moist places at high altitudes from Washington to California and eastward to the Rocky Mountains. *Plate 172.*

G. ovatifolia has creeping stems up to 8 inches long with leaves $\frac{2}{5}$–1$\frac{3}{5}$ inches long. The flowers are white or pink. The berries are bright red. In pine forest and high bogs from Washington to California and eastward to Montana and Idaho. *Plate 172. G. hispidula* is also creeping, with leaves less than $\frac{1}{2}$ inch. The corolla is four-lobed. The berries are white. In northern Idaho. *Plate 172.*

ARCTOSTAPHYLOS

There are some forty-five species of *Arctostaphylos* in the West, all shrubs, some being known as manzanita. Only two are included here, both creeping plants with prostrate stems which form mats. The corolla has generally five lobes. The ten stamens release pollen through pores at their tips, where there are also two hornlike appendages.

BEARBERRY, A. UVA-URSI, has stems with tips turn-

ing upwards to 6 inches. The leaves are mostly broadest near their ends, short-stalked, leathery. The flowers are pink, about $\frac{1}{5}$ inch long, in short racemes. The berries are bright red.

April to June: across most of North America and southward in the mountains to Oregon. *Plate 173.*

A. nevadensis is similar. The leaves are more sharp-pointed. From eastern Washington and northeastern Oregon southward.

PHYLLODOCE

The flowers of *Phyllodoce* arise singly in the axils of leaves which are clustered at and near the stem-tips. The corolla is five-lobed. There are from seven to ten stamens; pollen is released by slits at their tips.

P. EMPETRIFORMIS (to 16 inches) is matted, with narrow leaves up to $\frac{2}{3}$ inch long. The flowers are deep rose, the corolla bell-shaped. The stamens do not

project from the corolla.

June to August: at high altitudes from Canada to California, Idaho, and Montana. *Plate 173. P. breweri* has a rose-purple corolla, from which the stamens project. At high altitudes in the Sierra Nevada and western Nevada. *Plate 173. P. glandulifera:* Similar. Corolla urn-shaped, dirty-yellowish or greenish-white, glandular. From Canada s to Ore and Wyo. *Plate 173.*

CASSIOPE

The flowers of *Cassiope* are borne singly in the axils or at the tips of branches. The corolla is generally five-lobed. The stamens, generally ten, have their pollen in almost spherical bodies which open through pores at the tip; each of these bears two long horns which point towards the base. The fruit is a capsule.

C. MERTENSIANA forms wide mats, up to a foot tall.

The leaves are paired, in four ranks, pressed against the stems, $\frac{1}{10}$–$\frac{1}{5}$ inch long, ovate or lanceolate. The flowers are bell-shaped, $\frac{1}{5}$–$\frac{1}{3}$ inch long, white.

July and August: in mountains from Washington to California, Montana, and Nevada. *Plate 173.*

PLATE 173

Vaccinium oxycoccos *Love*

Cassiope tetragona *Spurr*

Arctostaphylos uva-ursi *V. Richard*

Phyllodoce glandulifera *McRae*

Cassiope mertensiana *Jarrett*

Kalmia polifolia *Scribner*

Phyllodoce empetriformis *Jarrett*   Vaccinium scoparium *Guppy*   Phyllodoce breweri *Randall*

C. tetragona: Similar. Leaves grooved underneath, and downy. n Wash, Mont. *Plate 173. C. stel-* *leriana* (to 4 inches): Leaves borne singly, short-stalked. Flowers white or pink. High in the Cascades.

KALMIA

One species of *Kalmia* is sufficiently small and delicate to be treated as a wild flower.

SWAMP-LAUREL, K. POLIFOLIA (up to 3 feet), has narrow leaves, mostly paired. The flowers are clustered at the tip. The corolla is rose, bowl-shaped, five-lobed, with ten small pouches in which the heads of the stamens are caught, bending their stalks as the flower opens. At a touch, these are released and spring up, scattering pollen over an intruding creature.

June to September: in peat and bogs from Montana to Colorado and northern Utah. *Plate 173.*

VACCINIUM

The genus *Vaccinium* includes the blueberries, huckleberries, bilberries, and cranberries; all evidently shrubs. The corolla is urn-shaped, with four or five lobes, pink, white or greenish. The leaves are borne singly. The stamens release pollen through narrow tubes at their tips. The ovary is inferior. The following species are low and not so visibly woody.

CRANBERRY, V. OXYCOCCOS, has creeping stems, bearing ovate or lanceolate leaves up to $\frac{3}{5}$ inch long; grayish underneath, with edges rolled in. The flowers are on slender stalks, the corolla pink; four-lobed. From Canada southward in mountains to Oregon and Idaho, mostly in bogs. *Plate 173. V. scoparium* forms mats, up to 10 inches tall, with many angled, greenish or yellowish branches. Leaves lanceolate or ovate, less than an inch long, finely toothed. Corolla pink. Ida, ND, SD. *Plate 173. V. myrtillus* has thicker, more numerous branches; leaves ovate or elliptic, up to $1\frac{1}{5}$ inches long; berry from dark red to bluish. Wash; from Mont to Colo. *V. occidentale* (to 2 feet): Branches yellowish, not angled. Leaves widest between middle and tip, $\frac{2}{5}-1\frac{1}{5}$ inches long. Flowers from one to four in each axil, pink. Berry blue. From Wash to Calif and eastward to Mont and n Utah. *V. caespitosum* (to 20 inches): Matted. Twigs more or less angled. Leaves $\frac{2}{5}-2$ inches, widest and finely toothed between middle and tip. Flowers single in the axils, whitish or pink. Berry blue. From Wash to Calif and eastward to Ida and Colo.

THE ADOXA FAMILY (ADOXACEAE)

The family *Adoxaceae* has only the genus *Adoxa* with the single species *A. moschatellina;* it grows around the world, extending southward in the Rocky Mountains to Colorado. It is an insignificant plant 4 – 8 inches tall, with leaf-blades divided several times into three (the basal one long-stalked), and a small head of yellowish flowers. These have from two to four calyx-teeth and four or five petals joined into a tube (the numbers of parts vary even in one head). In each notch between adjacent corolla lobes stands a pair of stamens. The ovary is partly inferior. In moist places, especially with moss, at high altitudes.

GROUP XI

SEPALS five. Petals five, joined and radially symmetric. Stamens as many as the petals. Leaves mostly borne singly on the stem, generally lobed, toothed, and divided except in the forget-me-not family and some species of other families.
Exceptions: *Echium* in the forget-me-not family has a bilaterally symmetric corolla. Some species of the waterleaf and potato families have some or all their leaves paired; in others the leaves may be all at the ground level.

I. *Plants with flowers in false racemes, generally coiled at first.*

  A. Plants with leaves mostly lobed, cleft, or divided; style cleft into two branches, or two styles on one ovary: waterleaf family.

  B. Plants with leaves not lobed, cleft, or divided; ovary four-lobed, with one style: forget-me-not family.

II. *Plants with flowers in the axils of leaves.*

  A. Plants with trailing, creeping, or climbing stems: morning-glory family.

  B. Erect plants with a superior ovary: several species of the potato family.

  C. Erect or creeping plants with an inferior ovary: bluebell family.

III. *Flowers in loose, stalked clusters, or borne singly in the forks of stems: potato family.*

THE WATERLEAF FAMILY (HYDROPHYLLACEAE)

The waterleaf family (see under *Hydrophyllum* for the name) contains many small and some larger herbaceous plants (as well as some shrubs), most of them native in western North America. The leaves of most genera are borne singly or in a rosette at ground level: those of many species are pinnately lobed, cleft, or divided. The flowers are prevailingly blue, lavender, or purple, but white flowers are common and a few species have yellowish flowers.

The inflorescences are various types of cymes. There are five stamens, attached to the corolla. The five petals make a funnel, bell, or bowl, or a narrow tube with spreading lobes. The pistil has a generally one-chambered ovary with a style cleft into two branches, or two styles.

Guide to Genera of Hydrophyllaceae

I. *Genera with stamens of equal length.*

  A. Plants whose stamens project beyond the corolla: *Hydrophyllum* (leaves pinnately or palmately cleft or divided; cyme compact, erect, symmetric); *Phacelia* (some species; cymes generally narrow, coiled; leaves with or without lobes or segments; see under B).

B. Plants whose stamens do not project beyond the corolla: *Hydrolea* (leaves unlobed, undivided; two styles); *Phacelia* (mostly bristly and glandular; leaves mostly lobed, cleft, or divided; flowers mostly in narrow coiled cymes); *Emmenanthe* (glandular-sticky; flowers yellowish, pendent); *Pholistoma* (prostrate or climbing, succulent; stems with prickly angles); *Eucrypta* leaves pinnately cleft or divided; sticky, bristly; flowers on thread-like stalks, yellowish-white or bluish; style scarcely cleft); *Ellisia* (leaves pinnately cleft; flowers single in the axils; corolla white, scarcely longer than the calyx); *Romanzoffia* (leaf-blades roundish, long-stalked; flowers white, in loose clusters).

II. *Genera with stamens of unequal length, which do not project beyond the corolla.*

A. Plants with leaves undivided and unlobed: *Nama* (stems commonly prostrate; two styles in most species; flowers single in the axils, grouped at the tip); *Hesperochiron* (all leaves at ground level, in a rosette, stalked; flowers single in the axils; style cleft only near the tip); *Tricardia* (leaves mostly at ground level, in a rosette; the few flowers in short false racemes; calyx enlarging and enclosing the fruit as it develops).

B. Plants with leaves lobed, cleft, or divided: *Nemophila.*

HYDROPHYLLUM

We have eastern species of *Hydrophyllum* up to 3 feet tall, and western species scarcely 2 feet, all but one with pinnately cleft or divided, rather large leaves. The cymes are compact, some almost headlike. The flowers are white or pale violet, with conspicuous stamens. The style is cleft only near the tip.

The name means waterleaf, and the plants are so named in many books. The species first named was *H. virginianum*, which does not seem particularly watery-leaved, but it does grow by water! Another, equally improbable explanation refers to the pale marks on leaves of some species (including *H. virginianum*) as "watermarks."

H. VIRGINIANUM (8–28 inches) has leaves pinnately cleft or divided, the lobes or segments (generally five) sharply toothed and tapering to sharp points. The flowers are in long-stalked clusters well above the leaves.

May to August: in moist woods, especially along stamens, from North Dakota to Kansas. *Plate 174. H. appendiculatum* has leaves palmately five-lobed. The inflorescence is looser, the stamens less conspicuous. In eastern Kansas.

H. OCCIDENTALE (6–20 inches) has leaves up to 8 inches long, pinnately divided, the segments from seven to fifteen. The cymes are like heads, the stalks of individual flowers being very short. The corolla is white or blue-violet.

April to July: in woods and thickets and in moist open ground from Oregon to central California and eastward to Idaho and Utah. *Plate 174.*

H. CAPITATUM (4–16 inches) has long-stalked leaves with blades up to 4 inches long, pinnately deeply cleft or divided, the lobes or segments lobed at the end. The headlike ("capitate") cymes are generally on stalks shorter than the leaves (except in a variety near the Oregon–Washington boundary). The flowers are white or more generally blue-violet or lavender.

March to July: on moist open slopes and in woods and thickets from Washington to California and eastward to Idaho and Colorado. *Plate 174.*

H. FENDLERI (8–32 inches) has bristly-hairy stems. The leaves have blades up to a foot long, pinnately lobed or divided, the lobes and segments variously lobed and toothed, in one variety softly white-haired underneath. In this variety also the stalks of the cymes are generally shorter than the leaves; in the other, longer. The flowers range from white to purplish.

May to August: in moist open places and thickets from the Cascade Mountains in Washington and Oregon to central Idaho and southwestward to Utah and Colorado. *Plate 174.*

HYDROLEA

One species of *Hydrolea* is in our area.

H. UNIFLORA has undivided and unlobed leaves, the blades elliptic or lanceolate, 3–4 inches long, on very short stalks. The stem tends to be prostrate and rather spiny. The flowers are clustered in the axils and at the tip; the corolla is blue, deeply cleft. The stalks of the stamens are flat.

June to September: in swampy woods and shallow pools (*hydro-*, "water") in Oklahoma.

PLATE 174

Phacelia crenulata   *Tatum*

Hydrophyllum fendleri   *Uttal*

Phacelia corrugata   *Korling*

Hydrophyllum occidentale   *Johnson*

Phacelia neomexicana   *Green*

Phacelia splendens   *Ure*

Hydrophyllum virginianum   *Johnson*

Hydrophyllum capitatum   *Korling*

PHACELIA

The genus *Phacelia* is one of those (notably prominent in the West) that has so many species distinguished by such small and technical differences as to be largely inaccessible to the amateur – and to many a professional (cf. *Eriogonum, Astragalus*). *Phacelia* has about two hundred species, all American and mostly western; sixty-two are briefly described here. (More have been named, but may be considered forms or varieties. As usual, we have tried to include all species actually found in the region; if any are missing – there are still enough.)

The leaves are borne singly except the lower ones of some species. Many species are glandular and sticky. The flowers are borne in what we have called a false raceme (technically a cincinnus), all in two rows on one side of a stem; in *Phacelia* the stem is coiled, straightening as the fruits mature. The corolla is generally some shade of blue, violet, or purple; or white; or, in one group, yellow. The ovary has two chambers and a style cleft into two branches in various degrees.

This vague and perplexing tangle of plants is classified by botanists into groups characterized by different markings on the seeds, by chromosomes, and by other minute details. I have kept the species in these "natural" groups, which do have certain outward aspects by which to recognize them. However, in attempting to use the easily seen characteristics of leaves and flowers, the reader will find some species which do not conform to the group label. I have tried to avoid too much frustration by providing cross-references. The reader must be prepared to search several groups in identifying a single plant. Even so, identification will sometimes be impossible; but the correct group may be determined.

The groups, with makeshift English names added to the botanical names, are as follows: I. Pinnately-cleft-, divided-, or scalloped-leaved (*Crenulatae*). II. Oblong- or roundish-, pinnately-cleft-leaved (*Euglypta*). III. Broad-leaved with teeth (*Pulchellae*). IV. Tansy-leaved (*Tanacetifoliae*). V. Different-leaved (*Magellanicae*). VI. Pinnately-lobed- or cleft-leaved, silky or sticky (*Eutoca*). VII. The humble ones (*Humiles*). VIII. Yellow-flowered (*Miltitzia*). IX. Pinnately-cleft-basal-leaved; eastern (*Cosmanthus*).

I.   *A group of mostly erect plants, little branched from the base, with rather narrow, pinnately cleft or divided leaves, the lobes or segments small; or the leaves may be merely scalloped or wavy-edged.*

Species in other groups may have pinnately divided, cleft, or lobed leaves.

The stamens project from the corolla except as noted. The corolla is mostly bell-shaped.

These are found chiefly in the southern half of our range.

P. CRENULATA (6–16 inches) branches from the base. It bears stiff white hairs which may be glandular. The leaf-blades (1½–5 inches long) may be merely scalloped ("crenate") and, if cleft, the lobes generally are. The corolla is blue or violet, bell-shaped, about ¼ inch long.

April and May: In deserts in Nevada and southern Utah. *Plate 174. P. splendens* (May and June): Generally not glandular. Corolla blue. se Utah, sw Colo. *Plate 174. P. corrugata* (6–36 inches): Glandular-downy. Leaf-blades ovate or oblong, pinnately lobed or wavy-edged. Corolla deep blue or violet, bell-shaped, ⅓–½ inch. Utah, w Colo. *Plate 174. P. utahensis:* Sticky-hairy, glandular. Leaves coarsely toothed. Corolla blue or violet, ⅕ inch wide. c Utah. *P. formosula:* Densely bristly, commonly glandular. Grayish. Leaf-segments commonly again pinnately divided. Corolla blue or violet, about ¼ inch. nc Colo. *P. palmeri:* Grayish-glandular, bristly. Corolla tubular, white or very pale blue, about ¼ inch. s Nev, s Utah. *P. anelsonii* (8–16 inches): Leaves 1–4 inches, pinnately cleft with scalloped margins. Corolla bell-shaped with spreading lobes, blue or violet, ¼ inch long. Stamens not projecting. se Nev.

P. GLANDULOSA (4–12 inches) is very glandular and sticky, and commonly white-hairy. The leaf-segments are roundish. The corolla is bell-shaped, purple, about ¼ inch long.

June to August: on loose rocky slopes from central Idaho, and southwestern Montana to eastern Utah and western Colorado. *Plate 175.*

P. NEOMEXICANA (6–16 inches) is sticky-hairy, commonly beset with stalked glands. The leaf-blades are ovate or lanceolate, once or twice pinnately cleft, 1½–4 inches long. The corolla is bell-shaped, white, blue, or violet, with toothed or fringed lobes, about ⅕ inch long.

June to August: mostly in sandy soil, on flats and mountainsides from southeastern Wyoming to Colorado and southern Utah. *Plate 174.*

P. denticulata (8–16 inches): Usually unbranched, densely beset with stalked glands. Leaves 1½–3 inches long, the segments irregularly pinnately cleft. Corolla tubular, white or pale blue or violet, ⅕ inch long. Stamens not projecting. e Wyo, c Colo. *P. integrifolia* (6–24 inches): Branches none or at the base. Leaf-blades cleft or scalloped, 1–6 inches. Glandular and bristly. Corolla tubular, white or pale blue, about ¼ inch long. sc Kan, Okla, s Utah.

II. *A group of plants with leaves pinnately cleft or lobed (less commonly divided), roundish or oblong in outline.*

The corolla bears a pair of small scales at the base of each stamen.

A. Species whose corolla does not exceed $\frac{1}{4}$ inch in length.

P. GLANDULIFERA ($1\frac{1}{2}$–12 inches) is prominently glandular. The leaf-blades are 1–2 inches long, lanceolate, pinnately cleft, on stalks up to 1 inch. The raceme barely overtops the leaves. The corolla is somewhat funnel-shaped, the tube yellowish, the lobes lavender.

June: in loose and sandy soils from Washington to eastern California, western Wyoming, and central Nevada.

P. thermalis: Stems commonly prostrate or bending up, 4–12 inches long, glandular-hairy. Leaves $\frac{2}{5}$–$3\frac{1}{2}$ inches, pinnately cleft, the lobes few-toothed, or pinnately lobed. Corolla $\frac{1}{8}$–$\frac{1}{6}$ inch, lavender or whitish. ne Calif, se Ore, sw Ida. *P. ivesiana*: Similar, 2–10 inches. Leaves pinnately divided or lobed. Corolla $\frac{1}{10}$–$\frac{1}{6}$ inch, the tube yellowish, the lobes white. From s Wyo to w Colo and s Nev.

P. affinis (2–12 inches): Stems erect or spreading. Leaves mostly on the lower half of the stems. Inflorescence well above the foliage. Leaf-blades of the basal rosette to $1\frac{3}{4}$ inches, pinnately divided, some segments lobed. Corolla pale lavender or white with a pale yellow tube. ne Nev, nw Utah.

B. Species whose corolla is at least $\frac{1}{4}$ inch long.

P. GYMNOCLADA (2–8 inches) has branches rising from the base. There is a basal rosette of leaves with oval blades $\frac{1}{2}$–1 inch long on slender stalks as long or longer, shallowly pinnately lobed. Stem-leaves may be in pairs, lobed or unlobed. The cymes have few flowers. The corolla is funnel-shaped or bell-shaped, the tube yellowish, the lobes violet, over-all $\frac{1}{4}$–$\frac{1}{3}$ inch.

May and June: on dry slopes from southeastern Oregon to northern Nevada and southeastern California. *P. crassifolia*: Very similar. Stem-leaves mostly paired. Corolla pale violet with yellowish tube, $\frac{1}{4}$ inch. se Ore, nw Nev. *P. bicolor* (2–14 inches): Stems leafy and glandular. Leaf-blades ovate, pinnately cleft or divided, up to 2 inches, on stalks as long. Cymes not overtopping the foliage. Corolla bluish-lavender or reddish-violet, the tube yellow, narrow or funnel-shaped, $\frac{2}{5}$–$\frac{2}{3}$ inch. s Ore, w Nev, se Calif. *P. fremontii* (2–12 inches): Leaves mostly near the base, in a rosette and scattered upwards. Blades oblong, $\frac{4}{5}$–$2\frac{1}{2}$ inches, pinnately cleft, the lobes lobed or not. Flowers well above the foliage. Corolla bright blue or nearly white, the tube yellow, funnel- or bell-shaped. s Nev, sw Utah. *Plate 175.*

III. *A group of plants with relatively broad leaf-blades, which may be toothed (less generally lobed).*

Mostly found from California westward.

P. PULCHELLA (2–8 inches) is leafy, hairy, and glandular. The leaf-blades may be roundish, $\frac{1}{5}$–1 inch long, on stalks about as long, with or without teeth. The corolla is rather funnel-shaped, $\frac{1}{3}$–$\frac{2}{5}$ inch long, the lobes purple or violet, the tube yellow.

April to July: on slopes and flats from southeastern California to southwestern Utah. *P. indecora*: Closely related. Corolla about $\frac{1}{8}$ inch long. Stamens without hairs. se Utah.

P. rotundifolia ($1\frac{1}{2}$–12 inches): Leafy, hairy, glandular. Blades roundish, $\frac{1}{5}$–$\frac{4}{5}$ inch across, toothed or lobed; stalks to $1\frac{1}{2}$ inches. Corolla tubular, about $\frac{1}{4}$ inch, white or pale mauve, yellow below. From se Calif to sw Utah. *Plate 175. P. piersoniana*: Leaves $\frac{3}{5}$–$1\frac{2}{5}$ inches across, scalloped or toothed. Corolla white or mauve, tubular-bell-shaped, about $\frac{1}{5}$ inch. se Calif, s Nev. *P. saxicola* (2–6 inches): Glandular-bristly. Leaf-blades widest at the end, about $\frac{1}{3}$ inch long, tapering to the stalk. Corolla bluish, the tube white, about $\frac{1}{8}$ inch. se Calif, s Nev. *P. mustelina*: Similar. Corolla violet, $\frac{1}{4}$–$\frac{1}{3}$ inch. w Nev. *P. parishii* (2–6 inches): Glandular-downy. Leaf-blades $\frac{2}{5}$–$1\frac{1}{2}$ inches. Corolla lavender, the tube yellowish, about $\frac{1}{4}$ inch. se Calif, Nev. *P. lemmonii* (4–8 inches): Glandular-downy. Leaf-blades oblong or nearly round, $\frac{2}{5}$–1 inch long. Corolla white or pale violet, about $\frac{1}{4}$ inch long. se Calif, w Nev.

P. demissa ($1\frac{1}{2}$–8 inches): Leaves near the ends of the stems. Glandular-downy. Blades roundish, to 1 inch long. Corolla lavender or purplish with a pale yellow tube, $\frac{1}{4}$–$\frac{1}{3}$ inch long. From sw Wyo to Utah and w Colo. *Plate 175. P. cephalotes*: Similar. Stems tending to be prostrate. Leaves oblong or elliptic. Corolla lavender, the tube pale yellowish, about $\frac{1}{6}$ inch. s Utah.

P. INCANA (2–6 inches) is glandular and hairy. The leaf-blades are ovate or elliptic, $\frac{1}{5}$–$\frac{3}{5}$ inch long, without lobes or teeth. The corolla is white, or tinged with lavender, the tube pale yellowish, $\frac{1}{8}$–$\frac{1}{6}$ inch long.

May to July: on rocky slopes from Idaho and Wyoming to eastern Nevada and western Utah. *P. nevadensis*: Closely related, with slightly larger flowers. ne Nev.

IV. *The tansy-leaved group.*

These species are characterized by pinnately divided leaves with rather large gaps between the segments; the segments may be themselves divided or variously lobed. The general effect is somewhat like the leaves of tansy, *Tanacetum*, in the Compositae.

　　Most of them are plants of our southern limits; others are Californian and may enter our area from the west.

P. RAMOSISSIMA (2–4 feet) is generally hairy or bristly and may have sticky glands in the inflorescence. The leaves are 2–4 inches long, divided into rather blunt segments which may be toothed, lobed, or cleft. The small, dense flower-clusters are at the ends of generally numerous branches (*ramosissima*, "much branched"). The corolla is whitish or bluish.

　　May to August: in rocky places and on dry slopes from Washington to California and eastward to southwestern Idaho and western Nevada. *Plate 175*.

　　P. rattanii (to 2 feet): Leaves scarcely lobed, rather broad, bristly. Flowers tiny, white or bluish. ne Ore, Ida. With a different aspect from the others in the group; included for technical reasons.

　　P. distans: Stems commonly prostrate, up to 4 feet long. Plants rough with small bristles. Leaves 2–5 inches long, the segments long, well separated, variously toothed, lobed, or cleft. Flower-clusters scattered. Corolla cream, pale blue, or purplish-blue. From Calif to Utah. *Plate 176*.

　　Two other species may possibly be found in southern Nevada. *P. tanacetifolia* (1–4 feet): Leaves up to 8 inches long, the segments narrow and finely cleft; all resulting in a delicate, almost fernlike aspect. Corolla bluish-purple. *P. cryptantha* (4–16 inches): Stems weak, bristly-hairy. Leaf-lobes or segments jaggedly toothed. Corolla less than $\frac{1}{3}$ inch; stamens projecting.

V.　*The "heterophylla" or different-leaved group.*
　　These species are distinguished by their leaves, some undivided, but generally divided into a large end segment and several smaller on the sides; their margins are smooth, and the veins are generally conspicuous, nearly parallel from the midvein to the tip.
　　All the species have at times been lumped under the name *P. magellanica*.

A. Species with generally undivided basal leaves.

P. HASTATA (8–20 inches) has leaf-blades with white- or silvery-hairy upper surfaces. Stems and leaf-stalks are white-woolly. The corolla is white or lavender, about $\frac{1}{4}$ inch long.
　　May to August: in open sandy and rocky soils from Washington to California and westward to North and South Dakota and Colorado. *Plate 175*. Some varieties are difficult to distinguish from *P. heterophylla*. See also *P. mutabilis. P. frigida* (to 10 inches): Leaves hairy on the upper surface, the leaf-stalks bristly.

Corolla lavender or white, about $\frac{1}{4}$ inch. se Ore, ne Calif.

B. Species whose basal leaves are generally cleft or lobed.

P. HETEROPHYLLA (8–48 inches) has densely hairy stems and leaf-stalks. The basal leaves generally have from one to four pairs of lobes. The inflorescence is tall and narrow. The corolla is white or cream, about $\frac{1}{4}$ inch long.
　　May to July: in open and rocky places from the Cascade Mountains to the Rockies. *Plate 175. P. leptosepala* (6–20 inches): Similar; bristly and hairy. Larger leaves generally with a pair of lobes. Corolla tubular-bell-shaped, about $\frac{1}{4}$ inch, from dull whitish to purplish. Wash, ne Ore, n Ida, nw Mont. By some treated as a variety of *P. heterophylla. P. mutabilis* (8–24 inches): Stems and leaf-stalks more or less bristly. Corolla white, cream, or deep lavender, about $\frac{1}{4}$ inch. n Calif, se Ore. *Plate 176*. Not sharply distinct from *P. hastata*.

VI.　*A group of mostly erect plants with leaves pinnately lobed, cleft, or divided (or some merely toothed), and silky or sticky.*

P. SERICEA (up to 2 feet) is silvery-silky. The leaves have blades 1–2 inches long, pinnately cleft; the lobes may or may not be lobed or toothed. The small dense flower-clusters form a cylindric inflorescence. The corolla is blue or purple, about $\frac{1}{4}$ inch long.
　　June to August: on rocky slopes, open or wooded, from Washington to northeastern California and Nevada and through the Rockies to Colorado. *Plate 176*.
　　P. idahoensis (8–32 inches): Less hairy. Corolla lavender or bluish, $\frac{1}{6}$–$\frac{1}{4}$ inch. c Ida. *P. lyallii* (2–10 inches): Generally glandular, with short stiff hairs lying flat. Leaves coarsely toothed or pinnately lobed. Corolla blue-purple, $\frac{1}{5}$–$\frac{2}{5}$ inch. w Mont. *P. lenta* (4–6 inches): Found only once, in sc Wash. Glandular. Leaves pinnately cleft, the lobes lobed. Corolla white, $\frac{1}{4}$–$\frac{1}{3}$ inch. *P. franklinii* (4–28 inches): Hairy and rather sticky. Leaves pinnately cleft or divided, the lobes or segments coarsely toothed or not. Corolla violet, lavender, or white, smooth inside, $\frac{2}{5}$–$\frac{3}{5}$ inch. Stamen-stalks hairy. c Ida, w Mont, n Wyo.

VII.　*The humble ones; their principal leaves generally at or near ground level, mostly undivided and without teeth.*

P. HUMILIS (2–12 inches) is hairy. The leaves are on the stem, unlobed, undivided, without teeth; short-stalked, with lanceolate or ovate blades $\frac{1}{4}$–$\frac{4}{5}$ inch long. The flowers are in a small compact inflorescence;

PLATE 175

Phacelia rotundifolia   *Buckalew*

Phacelia hastata   *Korling*

Phacelia ramosissima   *Hesselberg*

Phacelia demissa   *Kelly*

Phacelia heterophylla   *Oldemeyer*

Phacelia hastata   *Dilley*

Phacelia fremontii   *UCLA*

Phacelia glandulosa   *Love*

the corolla lavender or blue-violet, bell-shaped, about $\frac{1}{4}$ inch long. The stalks of the stamens are hairy.

May to July: in moist and also in dryish soil from central Washington to eastern California and western Nevada. *Plate 176*.

P. austromontana: Plants glandular-hairy. Leaves perhaps with a few teeth or lobes. Corolla lavender or pale blue, $\frac{1}{8}$-$\frac{1}{5}$ inch. Stamens smooth. sw Utah. *P. inconspicua*: Plants not glandular. Leaves elliptic, up to $1\frac{1}{2}$ inches. Corolla tubular-bell-shaped, $\frac{1}{8}$ inch long, whitish or blue-tinged. nw Nev.

P. curvipes (1-6 inches): Widely branched. Lowest leaves paired, all with blades $\frac{1}{5}$-2 inches long, with or without a few teeth. Corolla from white to purplish-blue, bell-shaped, $\frac{1}{6}$-$\frac{2}{5}$ inch long. Stamens with sparse hairs. c Calif, Nev, sw Utah. *Plate 176*. *P. linearis* (4-20 inches): Stem finely downy. Leaves narrow, $\frac{3}{5}$-5 inches long, with or without a pair of lobes near the base. Corolla blue-lavender, bell-shaped, about $\frac{1}{4}$ inch. Stamens sparsely hairy. From Wash to Calif, Utah, Wyo. *Plate 176*. *P. minutissima* (to 4 inches): Glandular and short-hairy. Leaf-blades about $\frac{2}{5}$ inch long, widest between middle and tip. Corolla lavender, narrow, $\frac{1}{10}$-$\frac{1}{6}$ inch long. From ne Ore and Ida to ne Nev.

VIII. *Yellow-flowered species*.
      The corolla may be tinged lavender. It remains attached as the fruit develops.

P. LUTEA (1-3 inches) may be glandular. The leaves are generally not lobed, with or without coarse teeth. The corolla is $\frac{1}{5}$-$\frac{1}{3}$ inch long.

May to July: in alkaline soil from central Oregon to California, southwestern Montana, and western Colorado. *Plate 176*.

P. inundata (4-16 inches): Similar. Corolla about $\frac{1}{5}$ inch long, with lobes about as long. s Ore, ne Calif,

w Nev. *P. glaberrima* ($1\frac{1}{2}$-8 inches): Similar. Smooth or nearly. Corolla light yellow, deeply lobed. nc Nev.

P. ADENOPHORA (4-12 inches) has horizontal or upward-bending stems, glandular-downy. Leaf-blades oblong or ovate, to $1\frac{1}{2}$ inches long, pinnately lobed or divided, on stalks about as long. Corolla $\frac{1}{8}$-$\frac{1}{4}$ inch long, tubular or bell-shaped. Stamens with hairy stalks.

May to July: in alkaline soil in southeastern Oregon, northeastern California, and western Nevada. *P. tetramera* (1-4 inches): Similar in growth. Corolla generally with four lobes, whitish, about $\frac{1}{10}$ inch long. e Ore, e Calif, w and c Nev.

IX. *Delicate plants mostly with pinnately divided, cleft, or lobed basal leaves, the segments or lobes oblong or roundish (those of stem-leaves narrow)*.
      The corolla-scales seen in some other groups are lacking. Eastern and southern species.

P. GILIOIDES (4-16 inches) is usually branched. The inflorescence is hoary. The basal leaves are up to 2 inches long, with from two to five pairs of segments, with or without teeth. The corolla is bell-shaped or has spreading lobes, $\frac{1}{3}$-$\frac{3}{5}$ inch across, deep lavender, the lobes fringed or toothed.

May and June: in woods and on barrens from eastern Kansas and eastern Oklahoma eastward.

P. hirsuta (4-20 inches): Stems densely hairy. Basal leaves much as in *P. gilioides*. Calyx-lobes spreading or bent down. Corolla light bluish-lavender with whitish center and two purple spots near the base of each lobe. se Kan, Okla. *P. glabra* (2-16 inches): Similar but smoothish. se Okla. *P. strictiflora* (2-6 inches): Similar. Basal leaves toothed or pinnately lobed. Flowers short-stalked. Corolla purplish. se Okla.

EMMENANTHE

There is only one species of *Emmenanthe*.

WHISPERING-BELLS, E. PENDULIFLORA (up to 2 feet), has a branching, hairy stem. The leaves are narrow, the upper pinnately lobed or cleft. The flowers are clustered at the ends of branches, soon hanging

(*penduli-*) on $\frac{1}{2}$-inch stalks. The corolla is bell-shaped, five-lobed, yellow, $\frac{1}{3}$-$\frac{1}{2}$ inch long.

April to July: in dry soil from the Sierra Nevada through Nevada to southern Utah. *Plate 177*. The corolla dries without falling and rustles ("whispers") in a breeze.

PHOLISTOMA

One species of *Pholistoma* is in southeastern California and probably in southern Nevada. *P. membranaceum* has weak stems 8-20 inches long. The leaves are pinnately divided, the segments from five to eleven,

narrow or ovate. The flowers are in cymes or in the axils; the corolla white, commonly with a narrow purple mark on each lobe, deeply lobed, less than $\frac{1}{2}$ inch across. In shady places in foothills, from March to May.

PLATE 176

Phacelia mutabilis *Spellenberg*

Phacelia lutea *Scribner*

Phacelia humilis *Spurr*

Phacelia linearis *George* Phacelia sericea *Korling*

Hesperochiron pumilus *Hood*

Phacelia curvipes *Cruden*

Phacelia distans *Johnson*

EUCRYPTA

The lower leaves of *Eucrypta* are paired, the upper borne singly, all pinnately cleft or divided. The yellowish-white or bluish, bell-shaped flowers are in loose clusters on threadlike stems. The plants grow in shady places, flowering from February to June. *E. micrantha* has weak, glandular stems up to 10 inches long. The lower leaves have seven or nine segments, which may be toothed. The stalks of the upper leaves have basal lobes which embrace the stem. The flowers are bluish, ⅕ inch across. From southern California to southern Utah. *Plate 177*. *E. chrysanthemifolia* has a variety in eastern California and western Nevada. It is rather hairy and glandular, with yellowish flowers, about ¼ inch across. The lobes of the leaves are themselves pinnately lobed or cleft (like "chrysanthemum leaves"). *Plate 177*.

ELLISIA

There is only one species of *Ellisia*.

E. NYCTELEA is a little weed, not much more than a foot tall, with leaves pinnately cleft into from seven to thirteen narrow lobes, which may be toothed. The flowers hang singly on stalks from the leaf-axils, each a white bell not more than ⅓ inch long. The calyx enlarges as the seed-pod forms within it, with ovate lobes nearly ½ inch long.

April to July: in woods, along streams, and on lawns from Montana and North Dakota to Colorado and Kansas, and eastward. *Plate 177*.

ROMANZOFFIA

One species of *Romanzoffia* is in our area.

R. SITCHENSIS (4–8 inches) has leaf-stalks with broad bases which overlap, forming a bulblike body at the base of the plant. The leaf-blades are roundish, with deeply scalloped or lobed margins, up to an inch across. The flowers are in loose clusters. The corolla is white with a yellow center, funnel-shaped, about ⅓ inch long.

June to September: on wet rocks from Washington to northwestern Montana and northern Oregon, and far northward. *Plate 177*.

NAMA

The leaves of *Nama* are not divided nor deeply cleft, but may be toothed; they are borne singly. The flowers are in the axils or in compact cymes at the tips of the stems, nearly without stalks. The corolla is generally funnel-shaped. The stamens are unequal in length and do not project from the corolla. The style is cleft into two branches, or there may be two styles.

N. ROTHROCKII (6–12 inches) is bristly. The leaves are generally lanceolate, coarsely toothed or scalloped, glandular, up to 2 inches long. The numerous flowers are in compact clusters at the tips. The corolla is lavender, not more than ⅓ inch across.

July and August: in dry sandy places from the Sierra Nevada to western Nevada. *Plate 178*.

N. ARETIOIDES has prostrate, hairy stems with narrow leaves. The flowers are borne singly, the corolla rose-purple with a yellow eye and tube.

May and June: in sandy and rocky places from Washington and Idaho to California. *Plate 177*. N. *densum* is similar. The corolla is white or lavender, ⅛ inch long. From Washington to California and eastward to Idaho and western Nevada; also in southern Wyoming and east-central Utah.

N. DEMISSUM has prostrate, hairy stems up to 6 inches long, the leaves mostly at their ends. The flowers are borne singly in the axils, but form a cluster with the leaves. The corolla is purplish-red, about ½ inch long.

April and May: in sandy deserts from southern California to Utah. *Plate 177*.

N. HISPIDUM is prostrate or nearly erect, and bristly ("hispid"). The leaves are narrow and rather succulent. The flowers are in clusters at the tips. The corolla is purplish-red, about ½ inch long.

February to June: in sandy soil from southern California to Oklahoma. *Plate 178*. N. *stevensii* is grayish, with narrow, bunched leaves and tubular flowers. In Oklahoma.

PLATE 177

Ellisia nyctelea *Stockert*

Eucrypta micrantha *Todsen*

Nama aretioides *Tatum*

Romanzoffia sitchensis *Twomey*

Nama demissum *Reineking*

Emmenanthe penduliflora *Johnson*

Eucrypta chrysanthemifolia *Myrick*

HESPEROCHIRON

The two species of *Hesperochiron* have all their leaves in a rosette at ground level; they are stalked, the blades without teeth or lobes. The rather funnel-shaped, white or bluish flowers are borne singly in the axils on long slender stalks. The stamens do not project. The style is cleft only near the tip. These are plants of rather alkaline, moist soils.

H. PUMILUS has the more open corolla, about $\frac{1}{4}$–$\frac{1}{2}$ inch long, with spreading lobes; it is densely hairy inside. The leaves are rather wider between middle and tip.

April to July: at high altitudes from Washington to California and eastward to western Montana and Colorado. *Plate 176.*

H. californicus has a funnel-shaped corolla up to an inch long, nearly smooth inside. The leaf-blades are oval, fringed with hairs. Much the same range as *H. pumilus*, but not in Colorado. *Plate 178.*

TRICARDIA

There is only one species of *Tricardia*.

T. WATSONII (up to a foot) has most leaves in a rosette at ground level; the blades undivided and unlobed. The few flowers are in false racemes. The corolla is bell-shaped, purplish with white lobes veined with purple, about $\frac{1}{4}$ inch across. The stamens do not project. The style is cleft into two branches. After the petals fall, the calyx enlarges greatly, enclosing the fruit; it may be an inch long.

April to June: on dry slopes from the southern Sierra Nevada to Utah.

NEMOPHILA

The stems of *Nemophila* are generally weak. The leaves are mostly paired, the blades variously toothed, lobed, or pinnately divided. The pretty flowers are borne singly in the axils of paired leaves, or opposite to leaves borne singly. The corolla is white or blue, more or less bell-like. The style is cleft into two. These usually weak-stemmed plants generally grow in moist, shady places.

I.   *Species with at least the lowest leaves paired.*

N. PEDUNCULATA commonly has prostrate stems up to a foot long. The leaf-blade is deeply cleft into broad lobes; it tapers to the stalk. The corolla is white or pale blue generally with dark spots or veins or a purple blotch on each lobe; less than $\frac{1}{2}$ inch across.

April to August: from Washington to California and eastward to Idaho and Nevada. *N. spatulata:* Similar, with fewer lobes in the leaves, and the blades not so deeply cleft. From the Sierra Nevada to western Nevada. *N. parviflora:* Densely hairy. Leaf-blades roundish or ovate with five or seven lobes. Corolla bowl-shaped, not more than $\frac{1}{5}$ inch across. From Washington to California and eastward to Idaho and northern Utah.

N. kirtleyi (4–12 inches): Erect or nearly so. Hairy. Leaves commonly with two pairs of side lobes; these possibly with one or two teeth. Many flowers in forks of branches; corolla blue-lavender with the center nearly white, $\frac{1}{3}$–$\frac{3}{5}$ inch across. Near the junction of Washington, Oregon, and Idaho.

II.   *Species with all leaves borne singly.*

N. BREVIFLORA (4–12 inches) has weak stems, almost prostrate or more or less erect. The leaves are thinly hairy, with a fringe of hairs especially on the stalk; the blades are commonly deeply cleft into two pairs of narrow, sharp lobes. The corolla is lavender, about $\frac{1}{10}$ inch long, not so long as the calyx.

April to July: in woods and thickets from Washington to northern California and eastward to Montana and Colorado.

BABY-BLUE-EYES, N. PHACELIOIDES (2–24 inches), is branched from the base. The leaves are 2–4 inches long, hairy, pinnately divided into nine or eleven segments which are commonly sharply cleft or lobed. The flowers are borne singly, opposite the leaves; or also in clusters at the tips.

April and May: on prairies in Oklahoma. *Plate 178.*

PLATE 178

Nama rothrockii
Hood

Nemophila phacelioides
Merkle

Coldenia canescens
Hesselberg

Nama hispidum
Twomey

Hesperochiron californicus
Dye

Coldenia hispidissima
Stockert

Echium vulgare
Horne

Pectocarya setosa
Myrick

THE FORGET-ME-NOT-FAMILY (BORAGINACEAE)

The many species of our *Boraginaceae* range from small bristly plants with minute white flowers to plants 3 feet tall with showy yellow and orange flowers. The characteristic inflorescence is the type of cyme called in this book a false raceme or false spike: a branch, generally coiled at first, with flowers in two rows on one side (the upper or outer as it is coiled); bracts, if any, are opposite the corresponding flowers. (These are miscalled racemes even in some technical treatises; but in a raceme flowers are in the axils of bracts, if present.) In a few of our species the flow-ers are borne in the axils of foliage leaves, either singly or, more commonly, in clusters. The five petals form a funnel, or a tube with lobes spreading at right angles (called by botanists a salver). Scales are generally present at the base of the lobes, in some species almost closing the throat; the stamens being within the tube. The ovary is generally four-lobed, forming from one to four small, one-seeded nuts, which may be prickly (but see *Heliotropium*). (Compare the *Hydrophyllaceae*, many of which have similar inflorescences and flowers, but different fruits.)

Guide to Genera of Boraginaceae

I.   *A genus with style deeply cleft, each branch bearing a stigma: Coldenia.*

II. *Genera whose style is not cleft and bears one or two stigmas at the tip.*

   A. A genus with bilaterally symmetric flowers: *Echium.*

   B. Genera with radially symmetric flowers.

1.   Genera whose corolla-tube is less than $\frac{1}{2}$ inch: *Asperugo* (flowers blue, $\frac{1}{8}$ inch long; calyx much enlarged in fruit); *Pectocarya* (flowers white; style very short; nuts bristly on the edges); *Cynoglossum* (flowers reddish, blue, or white; nuts bristly all over; leaves near the ground much larger than those above); *Cryptantha* (flowers white or partly or wholly yellow, generally minute; calyx cleft nearly to the base; leaves narrow; mostly hairy or bristly); *Plagiobothrys* (flowers white, less than $\frac{1}{4}$ inch across; plants hairy; lower leaves paired or crowded); *Eritrichium* (flowers blue, commonly with a yellow eye; calyx cleft to the base; plant a small tuft; cymes at first compact); *Heliotropium* (flowers white or purplish, in some species in the axils of foliage leaves; ovary and stigma not lobed);

Lappula (flowers white, minute; nuts edged with barbed prickles; leaves narrow); *Hackelia* (flowers white or blue; flower-stalks bending down in fruit; nuts with barbed prickles; leaves narrow); *Dasynotus* (flowers few, white, up to 1 inch across; only in nc Ida); *Myosotis* (flowers blue, pink, or white; inflorescence commonly with two branches; nuts smooth and shiny; mostly in wet places); *Amsinckia* (flowers yellow or orange; stigma two-lobed); *Lithospermum* (a few species have small flowers; see under 2).

2.   Genera whose corolla-tube is at least $\frac{1}{2}$ inch long: *Onosmodium* (flowers white, greenish, or yellowish; corolla tubular; styles projecting; leaves with prominent veins); *Lithospermum* (flowers yellow, orange, or white; cymes compact, with leaflike bracts; style with two stigmas; calyx cleft nearly to the base); *Mertensia* (flowers pink turning blue, pendent, in compact cymes; tube expanded into a definite throat; plants smooth or nearly so); *Symphytum* (flowers white or dull red, yellow, or blue; corolla-lobes tending to be pointed; plants harsh); *Anchusa* (flowers blue, $\frac{1}{2}$–$\frac{4}{5}$ inch across; plants bristly-hairy); *Borago* (flowers blue; corolla deeply cleft; flower-stalks bending down; plants bristly); *Amsinckia* (some species may have a corolla $\frac{1}{2}$ inch long; see under 1).

COLDENIA

The leaves of *Coldenia* are undivided, unlobed, veiny. The small flowers are in their axils, single or clustered, without stalks. The corolla is funnel-shaped with five spreading lobes, white, pink, or lavender. The stamens do not project. The style is cleft into two branches. These are plants of deserts.

C. NUTTALLII is prostrate, forming branching rosettes up to a foot or more across. The leaves have bristly and downy, ovate or elliptic blades $\frac{1}{8}$–$\frac{1}{3}$ inch long, markedly furrowed along the veins on the upper side. The flowers are in tightly coiled clusters in the forks of the stems and at their tips. The corolla is pink or whitish, not more than $\frac{1}{10}$ inch across. The fruits are smooth.

May to August: in sandy places from Washington to California and eastward to Wyoming and Utah.

C. hispidissima is very bristly. The leaves are lanceolate or narrower. The flowers are single in the axils, pink. In Nevada and Utah. *Plate 178.*

C. canescens may be matted. The leaves are white-woolly ("canescent"), less than $\frac{1}{2}$ inch long, ovate or oblong; the veins not conspicuous. Barely within our limits in southern Nevada. *Plate 178.* In the same territory *C. plicata* may be found. The leaves are densely hoary or silvery. The corolla is blue or lavender, up to $\frac{1}{4}$ inch long.

ECHIUM

One species of *Echium* is found in our range.

VIPER'S BUGLOSS, BLUE-WEED, or BLUE-DEVIL, E. VULGARE (1–3 feet), differs from all our other *Boraginaceae* in having flowers markedly bilaterally symmetric. They are in many short false racemes along the stem, making a cylindric inflorescence. The corolla is bright blue, the stamens red. The leaves are narrowly lanceolate, without stalks. The plant is bristly. A common and troublesome weed in the East, introduced from Europe, and now established in various places in our range; especially in waste ground about Spokane. *Plate 178.*

The one species of *Asperugo*, *A. procumbens*, from the old World, has become a weed over much of the northern United States, and is well established east of the Cascade Mountains. The leaves are bristly, and the weak stems prickly on the angles. The flowers are on curved stalks at or near the axils. The corolla is blue, about $\frac{1}{8}$ inch across. The prickly calyx enlarges as the fruits develop.

PECTOCARYA

The stems of *Pectocarya* are spreading and may be prostrate or erect. The leaves are narrow, about an inch long or less. Most of the plant is inflorescence, composed of coiled false racemes with interspersed bracts. The corolla is small, white, with scales inside. The style is very short.

P. SETOSA may be erect, the stem forking, up to 4 inches tall. The leaves are $\frac{1}{5}$–1 inch long, widest at the end, bearing long stiff bristles (*setae*). The corolla is not more than $\frac{1}{25}$ inch across.

April and May: in dry ground from Washington and Idaho to California, Nevada, and Utah. *Plate 178.*

P. platycarpa is distinguished chiefly by the irregularly toothed margin of the nuts. From the Californian deserts to Utah. *P. heterocarpa* also differs in its nuts, which have hooked bristles along the edges. In Utah. *P. penicillata* has hooked bristles only at the tips of the nuts. Idaho, southwestern Wyoming, and Nevada. The nuts of *P. recurvata*, which may possibly be in our southwestern corner, are curved or even coiled. These plants which differ only in such minute respects, may perhaps be better treated as varieties of *P. linearis* of southern California.

P. PUSILLA (2–8 inches) may be erect or nearly so. The lower leaves are paired and slightly over $\frac{1}{2}$ inch long. The calyx-lobes have hooked bristles near their tips, and the nuts have them all around their edges. From Washington to California.

HOUND'S-TONGUES (CYNOGLOSSUM)

The "hound's tongue" is any of the broad-bladed, long-stalked, basal leaves of *Cynoglossum* (*cyno-*, "dog"; *glossa*, "tongue"). The flowers are in small cymes near the tip of the stem. The corolla has a short tube, the throat almost closed by five scales; the stamens do not project.

C. OCCIDENTALE (8–24 inches) is hairy. The lower leaves are up to 6 inches long, widest between middle and tip, tapering to the stalk. The upper may have basal lobes extending around the stem. The corolla is dull red tinged with brown or blue, about $\frac{1}{4}$ inch long.

May to July: in woods from Oregon to the Sierra Nevada. *Plate 179.*

Two (or perhaps three) eastern species are within our eastern boundaries. *C. virginianum* is bristly-hairy. The leaves have basal lobes on either side of the stem. The flowers are pale blue, violet, or white, less than $\frac{1}{2}$ inch across. In Kansas and Oklahoma. *Plate 179.* *C. boreale*, a group of far northern plants, is found in northern North Dakota. It might be treated as a variety of *C. virginianum*, which has larger flowers.

C. officinale (2–3 feet or more) is European, now well established in North America and found throughout our range. The lower leaves are stalked, the upper have lanceolate blades with no stalks, mostly softly hairy. The flowers are dull reddish-purple, about $\frac{1}{3}$ inch across. The plant has a "mousy" or "doggy" odor (according to various authors). *Plate 179.*

CRYPTANTHA

The numerous species of *Cryptantha* are properly identified by characteristics of the generally minute flowers and the small nuts into which the ovary develops. It is therefore not surprising that they have by some botanists been lumped with *Eritrichium*, while others have split the genus into several with such names as *Oreocarya, Allocarya.* The distinctions between these latter genera are even more difficult than those between species, and the entire group of mostly very small plants includes many species which the amateur can hardly distinguish. Some, however, are large; a few have yellow flowers instead of the prevailing white; the form of the inflorescence is often diagnostic, as is the presence or absence of bracts; and close attention should be given to the geographical range. By combining these factors the reader may at least come close to naming a plant in the genus.

The plants are mostly bristly or coarsely hairy. The leaves, which may be clustered at the base or also scattered on the branches, are narrow with parallel sides or narrowly lanceolate, or widest towards the tip. The flowers are in the false racemes characteristic of the family, mostly tightly coiled at first, straightening as fruits are developed. The corolla is white in most species, often scarcely emerging from the calyx; the calyx is deeply cleft; the stamens do not project from the corolla.

I. *Species whose leaves are mostly in a dense basal cluster and tend to be widest near the tip.*
    The corolla is generally $\frac{1}{5}$ inch across or wider.

A. Plants with yellow corolla.
    See also *C. barnebyi* and *C. flavoculata*, which may have pale yellow flowers.

C. FLAVA (4–12 inches) has flower-clusters in cylindric inflorescences. The corolla is less than $\frac{1}{2}$ inch long, but longer than the calyx. The numerous leaves are pale, with short bristles lying flat.
    May and June: in sandy ground from Wyoming to Utah and Colorado. *Plate 179. C. confertiflora* (5–20 inches): White-hairy at the base. Leaves to 4 inches. Inflorescence to 2 inches across. Corolla pale yellow, up to $\frac{2}{5}$ inch across. From e Calif to w Utah. *C. ochroleuca* (1–7 inches): Stems with bristles lying flat and some longer hairs. Leaves narrow. Corolla pale yellow, about $\frac{1}{5}$ inch across. se Utah.

B. Plants of group I with white corolla (generally yellow in the center).

1. Species with a corolla-tube distinctly longer than the calyx.

C. FLAVOCULATA (4–16 inches) may have a pale yellow corolla, but it is generally white with a yellow eye (which is the meaning of the name). The leaves are narrow. The nuts have conspicuous ridges.
    April to July: on rocky slopes from eastern California to southwestern Wyoming and western Colorado. *Plate 179.*
    The following five have smooth shining nuts. *C. leucophaea* (6–16 inches): Inflorescence with conspicuous white bristles. Corolla-tube about $\frac{2}{5}$ inch long, lobes about $\frac{2}{5}$ inch across. sc Wash. *C. capitata* (6–12 inches): Inflorescence headlike. Corolla $\frac{1}{4}$–$\frac{1}{3}$ inch across. sc Utah. *C. semiglabra* (6–12 inches): Stems with short stiff hairs pointing down and some spreading weak bristles. Corolla $\frac{1}{3}$–$\frac{2}{5}$ inch across. sc Utah. *C. barnebyi* (6–14 inches): Corolla-tube about $\frac{1}{4}$ inch, the lobed part bell-shaped, $\frac{1}{3}$–$\frac{2}{5}$ inch wide. ne Utah. *C. johnstonii* (4–10 inches): Corolla-tube $\frac{1}{2}$–$\frac{3}{5}$ inch; lobes $\frac{1}{2}$–$\frac{3}{4}$ inch across. ec Utah.
    The remaining species of group 1 have roughish nuts. All are found only in eastern Utah and western Colorado.
    C. longiflora (3–20 inches): Hairy and longbristly. Leaves widest at and near the end. Inflorescence broad, open. Corolla-tube $\frac{1}{2}$–$\frac{3}{5}$ inch long; lobes about $\frac{2}{5}$ inch across. Nuts with tubercles and low ridges. *Plate 179. C. paradoxa* (2–6 inches): Stems slender, the bristles weak. Leaves generally folded. Corolla-tube generally yellow, $\frac{1}{2}$ inch long, the lobes white, $\frac{1}{2}$–$\frac{3}{5}$ inch across. *C. bakeri* (4–12 inches): Stems spreading, bristly-hairy. Leaves blunt, widest in the outer half. Corolla-tube about $\frac{1}{4}$ inch, the lobes $\frac{1}{4}$–$\frac{1}{3}$ inch across. *C. tenuis* (5–10 inches): Stems slender, with short hairs lying flat and weak bristles. Leaves narrow, widest at the end, blunt. Corolla-tube about $\frac{1}{4}$ inch, the lobes $\frac{1}{4}$–$\frac{1}{3}$ inch across. se Utah. *C. wetherillii* (4–14 inches): Stems branched at the base, the branches slender. Leaves widest in the outer half or at the end, blunt or roundish at the tip. Corolla-tube $\frac{1}{4}$–$\frac{2}{5}$ inch, the lobes $\frac{1}{4}$–$\frac{1}{2}$ inch across. ec Utah. *C. rollinsii* (4–14 inches): Stems with long bristles. Leaves much as in the preceding but also bearing small pustules (blister-like projections) on the surfaces. Corolla-tube about $\frac{1}{3}$ inch, the lobes about $\frac{1}{3}$ inch across. ne Utah. *C. fulvocanescens* (3–12 inches): Dense tufts. Leaves as in the preceding. Inflorescence with white or yellowish bristles. Corolla-tube $\frac{1}{4}$–$\frac{2}{5}$ inch, the lobes $\frac{1}{3}$ inch across. *Plate 179. C. jonesiana* (2–6 inches): Leaves

PLATE 179

Cryptantha fulvocanescens *W. Weber*

Cryptantha virgata *Korling*

Cryptantha celosioides *Korling*

Cryptantha flavoculata *Korling*

Cryptantha longiflora *Ure*

Cryptantha flava *Roberts*

D. Richards

Cynoglossum virginianum *Johnson*

Cynoglossum officinale

Cynoglossum occidentale *Wilson*

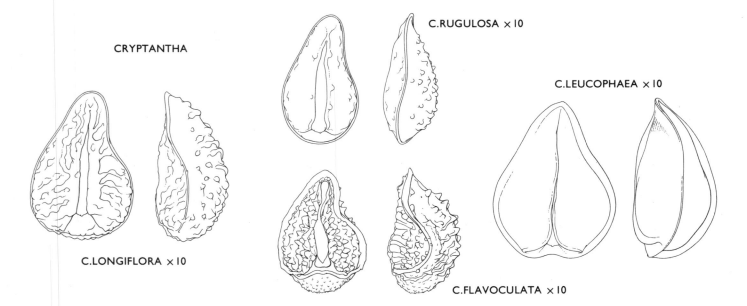

CRYPTANTHA

C.RUGULOSA × 10

C.LEUCOPHAEA × 10

C.LONGIFLORA × 10

C.FLAVOCULATA × 10

with bristles lying flat. Corolla-tube $\frac{2}{5}$–$\frac{3}{5}$ inch, the lobes $\frac{2}{5}$–$\frac{1}{2}$ inch across. ec Utah.

2. Species with a corolla-tube scarcely if at all longer than the calyx.

This large group is here divided geographically (except the first three species which are widespread). At the meeting-places of two groups, both should be searched for a satisfactory identification (since the plants know nothing of political boundaries).

a. Three widespread species. The nuts are rough in the first two.

C. HUMILIS (2–12 inches) has many stems, with bristles lying flat or spreading and longer. The leaves may be slightly woolly; they bear pustules (blister-like spots) on their surfaces. The corolla-tube is up to $\frac{1}{5}$ inch long, the lobes $\frac{1}{3}$–$\frac{2}{5}$ inch across.

April to August: from southeastern Oregon to eastern California and eastward to southwestern Montana and Utah.

C. CELOSIOIDES (4–24 inches) has one or several stems, with short bristles lying flat, or rising from blister-like spots, and slightly woolly. The corolla-tube is $\frac{1}{8}$–$\frac{1}{3}$ inch long, the lobes $\frac{1}{3}$–$\frac{1}{2}$ inch across.

May to August: from Washington and Oregon to Montana, Wyoming, and North Dakota, and thence southward to northeastern Colorado. *Plate 179.*

C. JAMESII (4–24 inches) has one or more stems which may be smooth or hairy. The leaves have blister-like spots. The inflorescence is open. The corolla-tube is $\frac{1}{8}$ inch long, the lobes $\frac{1}{5}$–$\frac{1}{3}$ inch across with conspicuous crests. The nuts are smooth and glossy.

April to September: from southeastern California to Nevada, Utah, and Wyoming, western North and South Dakota, and western Nebraska, Kansas, and Oklahoma. *Plate 180.*

b. Species of southwestern Utah and southern Nevada.

C. *setosissima* (12–40 inches): From one to three stems. Corolla-tube to $\frac{1}{5}$ inch, the lobes $\frac{1}{3}$ inch across. Nuts with a winged margin. *Plate 180. C. virginensis* (6–24 inches): One or several stems. Corolla-tube $\frac{1}{6}$ inch, the lobes $\frac{1}{3}$ inch across. Nuts rough, distinctly ridged. *C. hoffmannii:* Very similar. Calyx-lobes on mature fruit not more than $\frac{1}{3}$ inch. Barely in sw Nev. *C. abata* (2–9 inches): Stems many, with short hairs lying flat and weak bristles. Leaf-stalks fringed with hairs. Corolla-tube $\frac{1}{6}$ inch, the lobes $\frac{1}{3}$ inch across.

c. Species of central and western Utah, Nevada (except nw corner), and e Calif.

C. *nubigena* (3–10 inches): Stems several. Leaves limp, with blister-like spots. Corolla-tube about $\frac{1}{10}$ inch long, the lobes up to $\frac{1}{5}$ inch across. Nuts nearly smooth. e Ore, c Ida, ec Calif at high altitudes. *Plate 180. C. rugulosa* (6–12 inches): Stems one or more. Leaves with pustules (blister-like spots) and conspicuously long-bristly. Corolla-tube $\frac{1}{6}$ inch long, the lobes $\frac{1}{5}$–$\frac{1}{3}$ inch across. Nuts with ridges. c Utah, ne Nev. *C. interrupta* (7–24 inches): Stems few or several, with slender white hairs. Corolla-tube about $\frac{1}{10}$ inch, the lobes $\frac{1}{4}$ inch. Nuts nearly smooth or with tubercles. ne Nev. *Plate 180. C. compacta* (1–4 inches): Stems many. Leaves with long bristles lying flat. Corolla-tube about $\frac{1}{10}$ inch, the lobes $\frac{1}{5}$ inch across. w Utah.

d. Species of Wyoming, southeastern Idaho, eastern Utah, Colorado, North and South Dakota, and Nebraska.

C. cana (2–8 inches): Stems many, weakly bristly. Leaves dense at the ends of basal stems, all silky-hairy. Corolla-tube to $\frac{1}{6}$ inch, the lobes $\frac{1}{4}$–$\frac{2}{5}$ inch across. Nuts with tubercles or projections. w Neb, ne Colo, se Wyo. *C. thyrsiflora* (7–16 inches): Stems stout, one or several. Leaves with conspicuous bristles and pustules (blister-like spots). Corolla-tube to $\frac{1}{6}$ inch, the lobes $\frac{1}{5}$–$\frac{1}{3}$ inch across. Nuts wrinkled and with tubercles. se Wyo, sw SD, w Neb, e Colo, w Okla. *C. virgata* (10–40 inches): Stems one or few. Leaves rough-hairy, with pustules. Inflorescence cylindric with conspicuous narrow leaflike bracts. Corolla-tube $\frac{1}{6}$ inch, the lobes $\frac{1}{3}$–$\frac{1}{2}$ inch across. From se Wyo to c Colo. *Plate 179. C. stricta* (4–15 inches): Stems one or several, bristly-hairy. Leaves bristly. Inflorescence narrow, the clusters at intervals. Corolla-tube $\frac{1}{6}$ inch, the lobes $\frac{1}{3}$–$\frac{2}{5}$ inch across. Nuts with crosswise ridges. sw Wyo, nw Colo, ne Utah. *C. caespitosa* (2–6 inches): Dense tufts. From one to many stems, weakly bristly. Leaves with bristles lying flat. Corolla-tube $\frac{1}{6}$ inch long, the lobes $\frac{1}{6}$–$\frac{1}{4}$ inch across. se Ida, sw Wyo; probably adjacent Utah and Colo. *C. sericea* (6–18 inches): Stems one or several, with spreading bristles. Leaves silky on the upper surface. Corolla-tube to $\frac{1}{8}$ inch, the lobes $\frac{1}{3}$ inch across. Nuts with low tubercles. sw Wyo, ne Utah, nw Colo. *Plate 180. C. breviflora* (6–12 inches): Stems several, slender, densely white-bristly at the base. Leaves densely silky. Corolla-tube about $\frac{1}{6}$ inch, the lobes $\frac{1}{3}$–$\frac{1}{2}$ inch across. ne Utah. *C. grahamii* (6–8 inches): Stems several, weakly bristly. Leaves conspicuously bristly from blister-spots. Corolla-tube to $\frac{1}{5}$ inch, the lobes $\frac{2}{5}$–$\frac{3}{5}$ inch across. Nuts nearly smooth. ne Utah. *C. mensana* (4–6 inches): One or more stems, bristly. Leaves bristly. Corolla-tube $\frac{1}{6}$ inch, the lobes $\frac{1}{5}$–$\frac{1}{3}$ inch across. c and ec Utah. *C. elata* (12–20 inches): From one to six stems, weakly bristly. Leaves with pustules and short hairs lying flat. Corolla-tube to $\frac{1}{5}$ inch, the lobes $\frac{1}{4}$–$\frac{1}{3}$ inch across. ec Utah, wc Colo. *C. aperta* (5–8 inches): Stems slender, several, conspicuously white-bristly. Leaves with pustules and bristles. Corolla-tube $\frac{1}{8}$ inch, the lobes to $\frac{1}{4}$ inch across. Grand Junction, Colo. *C. weberi* (4–7 inches): Many stems, weakly bristly. Leaves densely hairy, with pustules. Corolla-tube $\frac{1}{8}$ inch. c Colo. *C. osterhouti* (3–6 inches): Many slender stems, with hairs lying flat and spreading. Leaves with pustules. Corolla-tube $\frac{1}{8}$ inch, the lobes $\frac{1}{4}$ inch across. e Utah, wc Colo.

e. Species of Washington, Oregon, Idaho, western Montana, northeastern California, northwestern Nevada.

C. thompsonii (6–12 inches): Stems several, bristly-hairy. Leaves yellowish-woolly with scattered bristles. Corolla-tube $\frac{1}{6}$ inch, the lobes $\frac{1}{4}$–$\frac{1}{3}$ inch across. Wenatchee Mts, c Wash. *C. sobolifera* (4–9 inches): Stems one or several, some prostrate and without flowers and ending in shoots. Leaves bristly-hairy. Corolla-tube $\frac{1}{6}$ inch, the lobes $\frac{1}{4}$–$\frac{1}{3}$ inch across. Glacier National Park, Mont. (By some identified with *C. nubigena*.) *C. spiculifera* (6–12 inches): Stems one or several, with long spreading bristles and short ones lying flat. Leaves not broader than $\frac{1}{4}$ inch, bristly with pustules (blister-like spots), the stalks fringed with hairs. Corolla-tube $\frac{1}{6}$ inch, the lobes $\frac{1}{5}$–$\frac{2}{5}$ inch across. se Wash, ne Ore, s Ida. *C. propria* (4–10 inches): Stems several, finely bristly. Leaves finely bristly with bristles lying on the surface. Inflorescence resembling a raceme. Corolla-tube $\frac{1}{6}$ inch, the lobes $\frac{1}{4}$–$\frac{1}{3}$ inch across. Nuts densely minutely wrinkled. ec Ore, adjacent Ida. *C. subretusa* (4–8 inches): Stems several, bristly. Leaves blunt or slightly notched at the tip; crowded at the base of the stem, woolly, with weak bristles; pustules conspicuous. Inflorescence compact, nearly cylindric. Corolla-tube $\frac{1}{6}$ inch, the lobes up to $\frac{1}{4}$ inch across. Nuts with sharp edges, some with narrow wings. From e Ore to ne Calif and nw Nev. *C. hypsophila* (4–8 inches): Stems several, rough-bristly. Leaves with bristles both lying flat and spreading; pustules present. Corolla-tube $\frac{1}{6}$ inch. Nuts with tubercles. c Ida. *C. salmonensis* (6–14 inches): Stems with mostly short hairs lying flat. Leaves with pustules, spreading long bristles, and shorter bristles lying flat. Corolla-tube $\frac{1}{6}$ inch, the lobes $\frac{1}{4}$–$\frac{2}{5}$ inch across. Nuts smooth, glossy. ec Ida.

II. *Species whose leaves are narrow with parallel sides or wider between base and middle.*
    The corolla is generally less than $\frac{1}{5}$ inch across; this perhaps disqualifies them as wild flowers; certainly identification is almost impossible, and most of the descriptions below are extremely brief, to save space.

C. CIRCUMCISSA consists of numerous branches forming a mound up to 4 inches thick; the narrow leaves are scarcely more than $\frac{1}{2}$ inch long. The small flower-clusters are at the ends of the branches; they are provided with numerous bracts on the side of the short stem away from the flowers. The corolla is minute, only about $\frac{1}{12}$ inch across.
    April to July: mostly in sandy places from Washington to California and eastward to Idaho and Utah. *C. micrantha* (up to 6 inches) is more slender, with fewer bracts. Leaves $\frac{1}{8}$–$\frac{1}{3}$ inch long. Corolla even smaller. From Ore to Calif and Utah.

C. INTERMEDIA (2–20 inches) is covered with stiff hairs. The narrow leaves are $\frac{2}{5}$–2 inches long, borne singly. The flower-clusters lack bracts; they are on longish stalks, two or three together. The corolla has a yellow eye.

May to September: in open, dry ground from Washington and Idaho to California. *Plate 180.*

C. PTEROCARYA (4–16 inches) has a branched or unbranched stem. The inflorescences are without bracts and tend to be in pairs. The corolla is up to $\frac{1}{10}$ inch wide. There are three nuts with broad wings and one wingless.

April to June: in dry, open ground from Washington to eastern Oregon, southwestern Idaho, Colorado, and California. *C. utahensis:* Similar. Corolla $\frac{1}{10}$–$\frac{1}{8}$ inch. Generally only one nut, with a wing or sharp angle. s Utah. *C. oxygona:* Similar. Corolla up to $\frac{1}{4}$ inch across. se Calif.

The remaining species* are here placed in alphabetical order with brief notes.

C. affinis: Spikes in two ranks, the flowers at wide intervals. Corolla $\frac{1}{20}$ inch. Nuts shining. From Wash and w Mont to Calif, s Wyo, n Nev. *C. ambigua:* Spikes generally single. Corolla $\frac{1}{20}$ inch. Nuts granular or tubercled. From s Wash to ne Calif, sw Mont, w Nev, n Colo. *C. angustifolia:* Spikes 2 inches long or less. Corolla $\frac{1}{10}$ inch or less. Nuts of different shapes, with projections. s Utah. *C. barbigera:* Erect, branched, very bristly. Corolla $\frac{1}{20}$–$\frac{1}{10}$ inch. Nuts warty. From s Calif to s Utah. *C. crassisepala:* Stems many. Corolla $\frac{1}{20}$ inch. One nut, with fine grains and projections. s Utah, sw Colo. *C. dumetorum:* Stems commonly scrambling in bushes. Mature calyx asymmetric. s Calif, w Nev. *C. echinella:* Low, loosely branched. Corolla $\frac{1}{20}$ inch. Nuts with conspicuous small projections. e Calif, s Nev. *C. fendleri:* One central stem. Corolla $\frac{1}{20}$ inch. Nuts smooth, shining. e Wash, w Nev, e Neb. *C. flaccida:* Spikes without bracts, stiffish. Corolla to $\frac{1}{6}$ inch. Only one nut, smooth. From Wash

and Ida to Calif. *C. glomeriflora:* Only to 4 inches. Flowers in axils, commonly clustered at the ends of short branches. Corolla $\frac{1}{20}$ inch. Rare, central Sierra Nevada. *C. gracilis* (to 8 inches): Corolla $\frac{1}{20}$ inch. Calyx-lobes densely tawny-bristly. One nut, smooth, shining. From s Ida to se Calif and e Colo. *C. inaequata:* Four nuts of different shapes, dark with pale tubercles. Panamint Mts, e Calif. *C. kelseyana:* Corolla $\frac{1}{20}$ inch. Four nuts of different shapes, with tubercles. From Mont to Utah and n Colo. *C. maritima:* Stems commonly reddish. Spikes crowded, commonly with small spherical clusters, leafy-bracted. Corolla $\frac{1}{20}$ inch. Four or fewer nuts, of different shapes, one smooth. s Nev. *C. minima* (to 8 inches): Generally many stems. Inflorescence with bracts like the upper leaves. Spikes generally single. Four nuts of different shapes. Kan, Colo, Okla. *C. nevadensis:* One or several stems. Corolla $\frac{1}{20}$ inch. Nuts warty. Nev, Utah. *C. pattersonii:* Stems several. Corolla $\frac{1}{20}$ inch. Nuts of different forms. Wyo, Colo. *C. recurvata:* Stems slender, branched. Leaves at wide intervals. Corolla $\frac{1}{20}$ inch. One nut. From e Ore to se Calif and Utah. *C. rostellata* (up to 8 inches): Little branched. Stems commonly reddish. Leaves few, paired. Corolla $\frac{1}{20}$ inch across. Calyx beset with hooked or curved hairs. One nut matured, smooth. From s Wash southward through e Ore to e Calif. *C. scoparia:* Erect. Spikes stiff. Corolla $\frac{1}{20}$ inch. Nuts with small spines. e Wash, sw Wyo, s Ida. *C. simulans:* Erect, pale, with few branches. Corolla up to $\frac{1}{10}$ inch. Nuts grainy. From s Wash, s Ore to s Calif, n Ida. *C. torreyana:* Spikes long and loose or dense. Corolla $\frac{1}{20}$ inch. Nuts smooth. From Wash to Calif, w Wyo, and n Utah. *C. watsonii:* One stem. Corolla $\frac{1}{20}$ inch. Nuts smooth with angular edges. From e Wash to w Mont and southward to Nev and n Colo.

PLAGIOBOTHRYS

The genus *Plagiobothrys* comprises small, delicate plants which are hairy rather than bristly, with leaves largely near the ground. The flowers are in slender false racemes at the tips of the stems, with a white corolla which in many species scarcely emerges from the calyx. Many have a purple dye in their roots, stems, and leaves.

The species of *Plagiobothrys*, like those of *Cryptantha*, are properly identified mainly by characteristics of their small nuts. They also have been placed in *Eritrichium*, *Allocarya*, and other genera, often in association with species now in *Cryptantha*.

I. *Species with the lower leaves on the stem, or some of them, paired, the upper borne singly.*

* One botanist has written that even a botanist has only a 50 per cent chance of identifying a plant in this group

P. SCOULERI commonly has several stems, up to 8 inches long, varying from prostrate to nearly erect. The leaves are up to $2\frac{1}{2}$ inches long, $\frac{1}{5}$ inch wide. The inflorescence is tall and loose, commonly with leaflike bracts. The corolla is $\frac{1}{20}$–$\frac{1}{6}$ inch across.

May to August: in moist ground from Washington to California and eastward to Montana and Colorado. *Plate 181.*

P. leptocladus has prostrate stems, to 10 inches. The calyx-lobes elongate as the fruit develops, all tending to be directed to one side. From e Ore and s Ida to Calif and Utah. *P. mollis* has hairy stems which trail and arch, rooting at the joints. Leaves up to 3 inches long and $\frac{1}{3}$ inch wide. Corolla $\frac{1}{5}$–$\frac{2}{5}$ inch across. se Ore, n Calif, w Nev.

II. *Species all of whose leaves are paired.*

PLATE 180

Plagiobothrys hispidus *Spurr*

Cryptantha jamesii *Johnson*

Cryptantha setosissima *Johnson*

Cryptantha sericea *Ure*

Plagiobothrys nothofulvus *Myrick*

Cryptantha intermedia *Wilson*

Spurr

Cryptantha interrupta

Cryptantha nubigena *Johnson*

POPCORN-FLOWER, P. NOTHOFULVUS (6–20 inches) is erect, hairy, with leaves mostly at the ground, widest between middle and tip, up to 4 inches long. The inflorescence generally lacks bracts. The corolla is $\frac{1}{4}$–$\frac{1}{3}$ inch across.

March to July: common in grassy fields and on hillsides and roadsides in southeastern Washington and northeastern Oregon, and in California. *Plate 180.* *P. kingii:* Leaves not more than 2$\frac{1}{2}$ inches, roughly hairy. Corolla $\frac{1}{6}$–$\frac{1}{3}$ inch across. From Ore and the e slope of the Sierra Nevada to Utah. *P. harknessii* (to 10 inches): Coarsely hairy all over. Leaves up to 2$\frac{1}{2}$ inches long, $\frac{2}{5}$ inch wide between middle and tip. Inflorescence compact, few-flowered. se Ore, e Calif, w Nev.

P. TENELLUS (2–10 inches) is erect or nearly so, roughly hairy. The leaves at the base form a tuft, up to 1$\frac{1}{2}$ inches long and $\frac{1}{3}$ inch wide. There are commonly two branches in the inflorescence, becoming very long. The corolla is $\frac{1}{10}$–$\frac{1}{6}$ inch across.

April to June: in dry open ground from Washington to California and eastward to western Idaho, Nevada (and Utah?).

P. hispidus (2–8 inches): Bushy, hairy. Leaves well spaced along the stem, to 1$\frac{1}{2}$ inches long. Inflorescences many, small, compact, few-flowered. e Ore, e Calif, w Nev. *Plate 180.* *P. jonesii:* Inflorescence with leaflike bracts. se Calif (barely in our range). *P. arizonicus:* Leaves lanceolate, to 2 inches. Inflorescence without bracts. se Calif (possibly in our range).

ERITRICHIUM

The leaves of *Eritrichium* form tufts or cushions at ground level, as well as being borne singly on the short, erect flowering branches. The flowers are at the tips in compact clusters which may elongate later. The calyx is cleft almost to the base. The corolla is a short tube crowned with five spreading lobes ("salverform"), blue, commonly with a yellow center (less commonly white). The stamens do not project.

E. ELONGATUM forms a small cushion or tuft with flowering shoots not over 4 inches tall. The leaves are narrow, scarcely $\frac{1}{2}$ inch long, loosely clad with long hairs. The corolla is $\frac{1}{6}$–$\frac{1}{3}$ inch across.

June to August: in open rocky places at high altitudes from eastern Oregon (the Wallowa Mountains) to the Rocky Mountains from Montana to Colorado. Also in Europe and Asia. *Plate 182.*

This has been by some authors included, as a variety, in *E. nanum*, a wide-ranging Old-World species; our plants mostly differ in being more densely hairy, but plants in the Wallowa Mountains are said to be indistinguishable from the European species. Plants in the southern Rockies have nuts with toothed edges, and have been treated by some as a separate species, *E. argenteum*, or as a subspecies or variety of *E. nanum*.

E. howardii is similar, the leaf surface generally hidden by coarse straight hairs, giving it a silvery appearance. In dry open places in western Montana and northern Wyoming. *Plate 182.*

HELIOTROPES (HELIOTROPIUM)

The cultivated heliotropes, grown for their fragrance, are derived from *H. peruvianum* and *H. corymbosum*. The genus has many species in the warmer countries. They are distinguished from other genera by the position of the style at the tip of the unlobed ovary instead of arising from the base of four lobes. The round stigma generally has a conical projection. In some of our species, the flowers are in the cymes characteristic of the family: coiled false racemes, straightening as the fruit develops. In others, they may be borne singly in the axils of leaves.

H. CONVOLVULACEUM (up to a foot) is distinguished from all our other heliotropes by its large, fragrant flowers. The white corolla may be nearly an inch across. The flowers may grow singly in the axils, or just outside the axils, or on the stem between two leaves (compare the *Solanaceae*). The leaf-blades are ovate, mostly $\frac{1}{2}$–1 inch long, on short stalks.

March to October: in sandy soil from Nebraska to Utah and Oklahoma. *Plate 181.*

H. tenellum (6–12 inches) has flowers singly in the axils: no coiled cymes. They are tiny, white. In dry open woodland and on prairies in southeastern Kansas and Oklahoma.

H. CURASSAVICUM, from South America, may be recognized by its rather thick and succulent smooth leaves; they are mostly $\frac{1}{2}$–1$\frac{1}{2}$ inches long, tending to be widest between middle and tip. The cymes are single or in pairs; the corolla is up to $\frac{1}{4}$ inch across, white with a yellow eye.

June to September: mostly in salty (alkaline) soil at low altitudes from southern California to Utah, North Dakota, southeastern Kansas, and Oklahoma. *Plate 181.* Smooth plants with smaller flowers in bractless cymes are *H. spathulatum*; treated by some authors as a variety of *H. curassavicum*.

PLATE 181

Heliotropium curassavicum *Davisson*

Heliotropium convolvulaceum *Henze*

Plagiobothrys scouleri *Rickabaugh*

Heliotropium indicum *McDowell*

Lappula redowskii *Rickett*

Hackelia jessicae *Phelps*

Hackelia californica *Scribner*

Hackelia floribunda *Korling*

Turnsole, *H. indicum*, is an Asian species, widely naturalized around the world. It is 2 feet tall or taller. The leaves have ovate blades on long stalks. The minute blue or violet flowers are in unbranched cymes, which may uncoil to a length of 6 inches. In southeastern Kansas and Oklahoma. *Plate 181.*

STICKSEEDS (LAPPULA)

The plants of *Lappula* are small, rough. The flowers are blue or white in tall, branching false racemes. The "stickseeds" are really "stickfruits," being formed from the ovary; four from each ovary, each with one seed. They are edged with barbed bristles which "stick" to clothing. The stamens do not project from the corolla, which is "salver-form," i.e. a slender tube with five spreading lobes.

L. REDOWSKII (30 inches) is finely bristly. The leaves are lanceolate or narrower. The pale blue corolla is about $\frac{1}{8}$ inch long, only about $\frac{1}{16}$ inch wide.

March to September: a weed in waste ground and on roadsides throughout the West. *Plate 181. L. echinata* (6–20 inches) has a slightly wider corolla ($\frac{1}{8}$ inch) and longer leaves (1–2 inches). The nuts are edged with two rows of prickles.

STICKSEEDS (HACKELIA)

The stickseeds of *Hackelia* resemble those of *Lappula*. They are slender plants with small blue or white flowers in false racemes. The nuts are edged with barbed prickles. They are distinguished by the curving of the short flower-stalks so that the fruit points down. Another feature is that the style is short, overtopped by the nuts.

In the first two species the prickles on the edges of the nuts are not much longer than those on the faces. In the remaining species the nuts have relatively large marginal prickles, smaller or none on the faces.

H. CALIFORNICA (16–40 inches) has several finely hairy stems. The leaves are up to 6 inches long, $1\frac{1}{2}$ inches wide, widest between middle and tip. The corolla is white.

June and July: near the Cascade Mountains from Oregon to northern California. *Plate 181.*

H. virginiana (1–4 feet) is much branched. The basal leaves have roundish blades on slender stalks; those above have ovate or lanceolate blades tapering at both ends. The flowers are about $\frac{1}{12}$ inch long. In Kansas and Oklahoma. *Plate 182.*

H. JESSICAE (12–40 inches) has several or many stems.

The lower leaves are stalked, up to 14 inches long, widest near the tip. There are many flowers. The corolla is blue with a yellowish or whitish eye, the lobes $\frac{1}{5}$–$\frac{1}{2}$ inch across.

June to August: in meadows and forest openings from Washington to California and eastward to Montana, western Wyoming, and Utah. *Plate 181. H.*

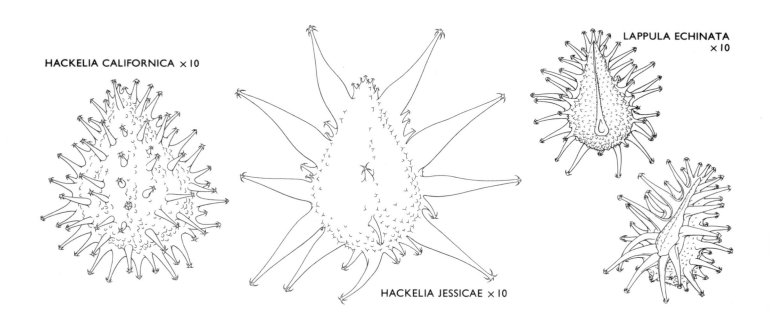

HACKELIA CALIFORNICA × 10

HACKELIA JESSICAE × 10

LAPPULA ECHINATA × 10

PLATE 182

Eritrichium howardii   *On*

Myosotis scorpioides   *Williamson*

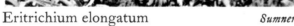

Eritrichium elongatum   *Sumner*

Hackelia venusta   *Thompson*

Myosotis sylvatica   *Spurr*

Hackelia virginiana   *D. Richards*

Hackelia ciliata   *Spurr*

floribunda: Similar. Stems one or several. Corolla $\frac{1}{6}$–$\frac{1}{3}$ inch across. From Wash to Calif and eastward to ND, Wyo, and Colo. *Plate 181. H. deflexa:* Corolla blue, $\frac{1}{10}$–$\frac{1}{6}$ inch across. Marginal prickles joined half-way; no others. From Wash and Ida to Utah, Colo, Neb. By some named *H. americana, H. deflexa* being a similar European species.

H. PATENS (8–32 inches) is more or less bristly and fringed. The basal leaves are stalked, to 12 inches long. The stem-leaves are without stalks. The corolla is $\frac{1}{4}$–$\frac{1}{2}$ inch across, white with a yellow center, commonly with ten blue marks.

June to August: in dry open ground, commonly with sagebrush, from Idaho to southwestern Montana, western Wyoming, central Utah, and northeastern Nevada.

H. CILIATA (1–3 feet) may be coarsely hairy. The basal leaves are up to 6 inches long, stalked; they may be softly hairy. The stem-leaves are narrow. The corolla is light blue, probably with a yellow eye, the lobes $\frac{1}{5}$–$\frac{1}{2}$ inch across.

May and June: on dry slopes and flat ground in

Washington. *Plate 182. H. davisii* (8–12 inches): Stems curved. Corolla $\frac{2}{5}$–$\frac{1}{2}$ inch across, blue with a yellow eye. c Ida. *H. cusickii* (8–16 inches): Like *H. ciliata.* With juniper, e Ore, ne Calif. *Plate 182. H. gracilenta* (10–36 inches): Stems bristly. Corolla $\frac{1}{4}$–$\frac{1}{3}$ inch across, blue or whitish. sw Colo.

H. CINEREA (8–32 inches) has bristly stems and roughly hairy leaves. The basal leaves are stalked, up to 8 inches long. The stem-leaves have narrower blades. The corolla is white with a yellow eye, $\frac{1}{5}$–$\frac{1}{2}$ inch across. The marginal prickles of the nuts are joined one-third of their length.

May to July: in open or lightly forested places, especially rocky, from Washington to northwestern Montana. *H. arida:* Very similar. Marginal prickles not joined or slightly. Leaves less than $\frac{2}{5}$ inch wide. c Wash. *H. diffusa:* Similar. Leaves $\frac{1}{3}$–1 inch wide. Corolla white, rarely blue. Columbia R valley in Wash and Ore. *H. hispida:* Like *H. cinerea,* greener. Corolla pale yellowish or greenish, about $\frac{1}{5}$ inch across. Ore, Ida near Snake R, and se Wash. *H. venusta:* Similar. Herbage bristly-hairy. Corolla $\frac{1}{5}$–$\frac{4}{5}$ inch across. c Wash. *Plate 182.*

DASYNOTUS

There is only one species of *Dasynotus.*

D. DAUBENMIREI (1–2 feet) has many leaves up to 7 inches long, coarsely bristly, the bristles mostly lying flat. The white corolla is $\frac{4}{5}$–1 inch across. In forest openings in north-central Idaho.

FORGET-ME-NOTS (MYOSOTIS)

The forget-me-nots are small plants, mostly growing in wet places, commonly creeping or bending down. The stem generally ends in a forked inflorescence (two false racemes), each branch coiled at first and uncoiling at the base as fruits ripen. The corolla is blue or white, five-lobed, in some species with a yellow eye; the short tube bears at its throat five scales; these may be cleft and seem to be ten.

There is an old German tale of a knight who, drowning in a river, caught a sprig of *Myosotis* (which grows in wet places) and tossed it to his lover on the bank, crying (in old German, of course), "Forget me not." The story was introduced to England by Coleridge in a poem published in 1802 (though the name had previously been used for a different plant), and forget-me-not is now the accepted name for all the species of this genus. It was the symbol of love, and is still known in some parts of England as love-me.

M. SCORPIOIDES has angular stems up to 2 feet long, partly creeping. The flowers are blue, up to $\frac{1}{3}$ inch across, with a yellow center.

May to October: from the Old World, now common in wet places (as along small streams) through most of the country. *Plates 182, 183.*

M. laxa is similar. The flowers do not exceed $\frac{1}{4}$ inch in width. There are commonly leaves in the inflorescence. The corolla-tube is no longer than the calyx. In shallow water and wet ground along the eastern base of the Cascade Mountains.

M. sylvatica has a blue, pink, or white corolla. The calyx has some hairs standing straight out, others lying flat. In central Idaho, northern Wyoming, and the Black Hills of South Dakota. *Plate 182.*

M. micrantha is named for the smallness of its blue corolla, about $\frac{1}{10}$ inch wide. The inflorescence is leafy. The plants may be 8 inches tall, with leaves less than an inch long. A native of the Old World now well established in North America. Scattered through our area.

M. verna (up to 16 inches) has white flowers, about $\frac{1}{8}$ inch across. Two calyx-lobes are longer than the others. In Kansas, Oklahoma, Washington, Oregon, and Idaho. *Plate 183.*

PLATE 183

Myosotis scorpioides *Rickett*

Lithospermum incisum *Johnson*

Lithospermum canescens *Johnson*

Finne

Amsinckia vernicosa

Amsinckia intermedia *Reineking*

Lithospermum caroliniense *Johnson*

Myosotis verna *Johnson*

Amsinckia tesselata *Weisser*

FIDDLE-NECKS (AMSINCKIA)

The English name refers to the coiled cymes (false spikes) in which the flowers are borne. The corolla is small, yellow or orange. The plants are generally bristly. Our six species stand up to 2 feet tall unless another height is indicated below. They flower mostly from April to June or July.

In the first two species two of the calyx-lobes are partly joined. In the rest, all the lobes are separate and alike.

A. TESSELATA has more or less bristly leaves varying greatly in width. The flowers are orange, commonly with red marks in the throat, $\frac{1}{3}$–$\frac{1}{2}$ inch long, the corolla up to $\frac{1}{5}$ inch across.

In dry mostly sandy and gravelly soils and on roadsides from Washington to California and eastward to Idaho and Utah. *Plate 183. A. vernicosa* has been collected once in southeastern Oregon; and may possibly be in our southwestern corner. It is smooth or nearly so, the leaves lanceolate or ovate, commonly with basal lobes embracing the stem. Corolla bright yellow. *Plate 183.*

A. INTERMEDIA (8–32 inches) has bristly stems, a few soft hairs mingled with the bristles only in the upper part. The leaves are lanceolate or narrower, up to 6 inches long, rather sparsely hairy. The cymes have leaflike bracts at the base. The corolla is pale orange, with red marks in the throat, less than $\frac{1}{2}$ inch long, up to $\frac{1}{4}$ inch across.

April and May: common in grassy places and waste ground and on roadsides from Washington to California and eastward to Idaho. *Plate 183. A. menziesii* is similar. Leaves hairy, the blades up to 6 inches long, the lower long-stalked. Corolla pale yellow, less than $\frac{1}{3}$ inch long, up to $\frac{1}{8}$ inch across. From Washington to Montana, Nevada, and Utah. *A. retrorsa*, of much the same territory, differs in having shorter, softer, down-pointing hairs among the bristles.

A. LYCOPSOIDES (4–24 inches) has bristly hairs on leaves and stem mixed with shorter, softer hairs. The leaves are very narrow. The corolla is yellow or orange, with red marks in the throat, mostly about $\frac{1}{3}$ inch long, and with five hairy lumps almost closing the tube.

On dry open ground from Washington to California and eastward to Montana and Nevada.

PUCCOONS AND GROMWELLS (LITHOSPERMUM)

The name puccoon refers to plants from which the Indians used to obtain dyes. A purple dye is present in the roots of several species of *Lithospermum*. Gromwell is a name of doubtful significance, from the old French *gremil;* possibly referring to the hard, glistening nuts which formed the fruits of European species and were used in medieval medicine (*litho-*, "stone"; *sperma*, "seed"). Most species of *Lithospermum* are downy or hairy, some of them bristly and rough. The leaves are borne singly. The flowers are in long or short cymes, or more rarely single in the axils. The corollas of most species are yellow or orange, with a tube, which may be long, crowned by five spreading lobes (i.e. "salver-form"). There may be a fold or appendage in the throat opposite each lobe.

YELLOW PUCCOON or INDIAN PAINT, L. CANESCENS (4–18 inches), has a fine, soft, white down. The flowers are orange-yellow, about $\frac{1}{2}$ inch across, close together.

April to June: in sandy soil from North Dakota to Oklahoma (and Colorado?). *Plate 183. L. croceum* differs only in minute features of the petals and the bristly hairs. In Oklahoma.

L. caroliniense (8–40 inches) is similar but with longer and harsher hairs. The flowers are up to an inch across. In Kansas, Colorado, and Oklahoma. *Plate 183.*

L. INCISUM (4–20 inches) is rough. The flowers are distinctive, the golden-yellow corolla with lobes ruffled and toothed at the edges. The tube is twice as long as the calyx.

April to July: on prairies and open ground generally from Montana and North Dakota to Utah, Colorado, and Oklahoma. *Plate 183.*

L. MULTIFLORUM (9–18 inches) has narrow, blunt leaves, clad with short bristles lying flat. The corolla is yellow, rather funnel-shaped, $\frac{1}{2}$ inch long or longer, the lobes spreading to $\frac{1}{2}$ inch.

May to September: mostly with pine and juniper from Wyoming to Utah and Colorado. *Plate 184.*

L. RUDERALE (8–20 inches) has a clump of hairy stems, either soft or rough. The leaves are lanceolate or narrower, 1–4 inches long. The flowers are in small clusters in the upper axils. The corolla is pale yellow or greenish-yellow, about $\frac{1}{3}$ inch long.

April to June: in open places such as dry hillsides from the Cascade Mountains and the Sierra Nevada to Montana and Colorado. *Plate 184.*

CORN GROMWELL or BASTARD ALKANET, L. ARVENSE (8–30 inches), is slender, hoary, with many narrow leaves up to $2\frac{1}{2}$ inches long. The white

PLATE 184

Beesley

Lithospermum latifolium

Lithospermum ruderale   *Ure*

Mertensia bella   *Mansfield*

Mertensia paniculata   *Jarrett*

McDowell

Lithospermum arvense

Mertensia ciliata   *Korling*

Johnson

Onosmodium hispidissimum

Lithospermum multiflorum   *Korling*

Mertensia lanceolata   *Roberts*

flowers are single in the axils, about $\frac{1}{8}$ inch across.

April to July: an European plant now naturalized in sandy fields and on roadsides and railroad embankments as a weed practically throughout North America. *Plate 184.* Because of certain differences in the small nuts and in the pollen, this has by some authors been placed in the genus *Buglossoides*.

L. latifolium, in eastern Kansas, has broader leaves and greenish-white or pale yellow flowers in the axils; the corolla nearly $\frac{1}{4}$ inch across. *Plate 184.*

FALSE GROMWELLS (ONOSMODIUM)

Two species of *Onosmodium* are found in our area. The genus is characterized by mostly rough-hairy leaves with prominent veins. The cymes are short, curved, the flowers pointing sideways or downward. The flowers are small, the whitish or greenish corolla almost tubular, the lobes not spreading. The calyx-lobes are narrow. The style projects noticeably.

O. OCCIDENTALE (20–40 inches) is very densely hairy, the hairs spreading. The white or greenish flowers are about $\frac{1}{2}$ inch long or longer.

May to July: on dry prairies and in open woodland from Montana and North Dakota to Colorado, Utah, and Oklahoma. *O. hispidissimum* is found in Kansas and Oklahoma. It is clothed with stiff hairs, and some characteristics of the nuts differ. *Plate 184.*

Both these species (and several others) have been recently treated as varieties of *O. molle* (this, in its original, narrower sense, is clad with soft grayish hairs). The supposed species are said to "intergrade."

MERTENSIA

With *Mertensia* we find *Boraginaceae* of decidedly attractive aspect. The flowers may be at first tightly clustered at the tips of the stems, but the clusters generally lengthen into typical false racemes, the flowers hanging. The corolla is at first pink and turns blue. The petals of most species form a tube which expands abruptly into a bell, the throat, its margin scarcely lobed.

These are generally known as lungworts, from an European species whose spotted leaves indicate the plant (by the doctrine of signatures) as divinely "signed" as a remedy for lung diseases. The plants are also known as bluebells, though not related to English or Scottish bluebells.

I. *A species whose corolla is bell-shaped, without division into tube and lobes.*

M. BELLA (4–28 inches) has long-stalked lower leaves with ovate blades $\frac{3}{5}$–3 inches long. The flowers are clustered at the tip of the stem, or at the tips of branches from the upper axils. The corolla is $\frac{1}{4}$–$\frac{2}{5}$ inch long.

May to July: in moist places in mountains in southwestern Oregon and northwestern Idaho. *Plate 184.*

II. *Species whose corolla is clearly divided into tube and expanded lobes.*

A. Plants whose leaves have veins branching from the midvein.

M. PANICULATA (1–5 feet) generally has a clump of stems. The lower leaves are long-stalked, the blades $\frac{3}{5}$–6 inches long. The flowers are at the tips of short arching stems which arise in the upper axils. The corolla is $\frac{2}{5}$–$\frac{2}{3}$ inch long.

May to August: on stream-banks and in meadows and damp thickets from Canada southward to central Oregon, central Idaho, and western Montana. *Plate 184.*

M. virginica (8–28 inches) is very smooth with a bloom. There are basal shoots with long-stalked leaves which have ovate or elliptic blades up to 8 inches long. The corolla is about $\frac{1}{2}$ inch long. In woods and moist bottom-lands in Kansas.

M. campanulata (12–40 inches) has stalked basal leaves with lanceolate or elliptic blades, tapering downwards. The calyx-teeth blunt, much shorter than the joined part. Corolla $\frac{3}{5}$–$\frac{4}{5}$ inch long. In central Idaho.

M. CILIATA (4–40 inches) has long-stalked leaves with lanceolate or ovate blades up to 5 inches long. The flowers are on stems which arise in the upper axils. The corolla is $\frac{2}{5}$–$\frac{4}{5}$ inch long.

June to August: in wet places and foothills and at high altitudes from Oregon and Idaho to Montana to California and Colorado. *Plate 184. M. franciscana* is similar, with elliptic leaf-blades up to 4 inches long. The inflorescence is at the tip of the stem. In wooded moist places in Nevada, Utah, and Colorado.

M. ARIZONICA (12–32 inches) has one or more stems. The basal leaf has a narrowly ovate blade up to 6

PLATE 185

Mertensia viridis   *Rickett*   Mertensia fusiformis   *W. Weber*

Mertensia longiflora   *Dye*

Borago officinalis   *Cole*   Mertensia arizonica   *Frost*

Mertensia bakeri   *Uttal*

Mertensia oblongifolia   *Lingenfelter*   Mertensia alpina   *Roberts*

inches long on a stalk as long. The upper stem-leaves lack stalks. The flowers are in a branched inflorescence. The calyx is cleft half-way or more to the base. The corolla is $\frac{1}{2}$–$\frac{4}{5}$ inch long.

May to August: from southwestern Wyoming to eastern Nevada, southwestern Utah, and western Colorado. *Plate 185. M. toyabensis:* Stems few, 12–20 inches. Leaves densely hairy. Corolla-tube $\frac{1}{5}$–$\frac{1}{3}$ inch, the lobes $\frac{1}{4}$–$\frac{1}{3}$ inch across. c Ida.

   B. Plants whose leaves have no veins branching
       from the midvein.

LANGUID-LADIES, M. LANCEOLATA (to 18 inches),
   has basal leaf-blades to 5 inches long, the veins parallel to the midvein. The upper leaves are smaller.

Early spring: on dry slopes and foothills from Montana to Nebraska and Colorado. *Plate 184.*

M. ALPINA (usually less than 1 foot) has several stems
   in a clump. Leaves narrow, with one vein, to 3 inches long. Flowers tightly clustered; corolla $\frac{1}{4}$–$\frac{1}{2}$ inch long.

July and August: in high mountain meadows from Idaho and Montana to Colorado. *Plate 185. M. brevistyla:* Similar. Calyx-lobes and stems downy. Flowers not so tight. se Ida, s Wyo, wc Utah. *M. humilis:* Similar. Less than 8 inches. Leaves smooth. se Wyo, adjacent Colo. *M. fusiformis:* Similar. Calyx downy. Leaves smooth or densely hairy with short hairs lying flat. Wyo, c Utah, Colo. *Plate 185.*

M. VIRIDIS (to 16 inches) is smooth or nearly so. The
   basal leaves have elliptic or ovate blades up to 4 inches long, on a stalk. The stem-leaves are without stalks. The corolla is $\frac{2}{5}$–$\frac{3}{4}$ inch long. The stamens project.

June to August: at moderate and high altitudes from Idaho and Montana to Utah and Colorado. *Plate 185. M. perplexa:* Similar. Stamen-stalks very short. From sw Mont to Colo. Plants with white-downy leaves and densely downy calyx have been named *M. bakeri.* Utah, Colo. *Plate 185.*

M. OBLONGIFOLIA (4–16 inches) is smooth or nearly
   so. The basal leaves have elliptic or ovate blades up to 6 inches long, 2$\frac{1}{2}$ inches wide, well stalked. The stem-leaves are mostly without stalks. The corolla is $\frac{2}{5}$–$\frac{4}{5}$ inch long.

April to July: on open slopes and drier meadows from Washington to northern California and western Montana, Wyoming, and Utah. *Plate 185. M. oreophila:* Similar. Leaves smooth, their length commonly less than three times their width, rather leathery. Big Horn Mts, Wyo.

M. LONGIFLORA (to 10 inches) is smooth or nearly
   so. The basal leaves are rarely present, and stem-leaves are few. The inflorescence is compact, the flowers crowded. The corolla is $\frac{2}{5}$–1 inch long.

April to June: in open or lightly wooded areas on plains and foothills from Washington to northeastern California and eastward to Montana. *Plate 185.*

COMFREY (SYMPHYTUM)

Two species of the Old-World genus *Symphytum* are probably to be found in our range. They are coarse plants with large, harsh leaves and small whitish, dull blue, reddish, or yellowish flowers hanging in short false racemes from the tips of branches.

S. OFFICINALE (1–4 feet) has stalked leaves at the
   base, the blades ovate or lanceolate up to a foot long. The leaves on the stem are smaller, the upper without stalks, all with edges continuous with flanges or wings on the stem; the leaves are said to "run

down" (to be "decurrent") on the stem. The flowers run the gamut of colors from yellowish to dull blue. The corolla is about $\frac{3}{5}$ inch long.

May to August: established on roadsides and other disturbed ground through much of the United States; reported in Washington and Montana. *Plate 186. S. asperum* (20–40 inches) is similar. The leaves are not decurrent or only slightly so. The corolla is pink, turning blue as it opens. This has escaped from cultivation in many places and may be found in our range.

ALKANET (ANCHUSA)

ALKANET, ANCHUSA OFFICINALIS (1–3 feet), is
   roughly hairy. The lower leaves are stalked, up to 8 inches long, the blades widest (up to 1 inch) between middle and tip. The corolla is blue, $\frac{1}{4}$–$\frac{1}{2}$ inch across.

From the Mediterranean, found on roadsides and other disturbed sites east of the Cascade Mountains. Other species of *Anchusa* may be found but probably do not maintain themselves out of cultivation.

The cultivated herb *Borago officinalis* may be found growing wild in scattered places. It is 2 feet tall, bristly, with elliptic leaf-blades 1–4 inches long, the lower on long stalks. The flowers are in a branched inflorescence, their stalks curving down. The corolla is blue; its lobes are joined only at the base. *Plate 185.*

THE POTATO FAMILY (SOLANACEAE)

Many species of *Solanaceae* produce poisonous alkaloids, used for medicinal and other purposes: atropine (belladonna), hyoscyamine, scopolamine, nicotine, strychnine, and others. Several genera are familiar in ornamental and vegetable gardens: petunia, ornamental *Nicotiana, Salpiglossis, Nierembergia, Schizanthus*, potatoes, tomatoes, green and red peppers, and egg-plant. Some of these may be found growing wild in the southern regions of our area.

The family is characterized by flowers with parts in fives and by an ovary generally with two chambers containing many ovules. The fruit is a berry or capsule. The position of the flowering branches is peculiar in many species (see under *Solanum*).

Guide to Genera of Solanaceae

I. *Genera that form berries.*

   A. A genus whose berry is not partially or wholly enclosed by an enlarged calyx: *Solanum* (flowers white or purple, in clusters on short sidebranches; pollen shed through pores in the tips of the stamens; see also under B).

   B. Genera whose berry is partially or wholly enclosed by an enlarged, generally bladder-like or prickly calyx: *Physalis* (corolla funnel-shaped or bell-like, yellowish, greenish, or white); *Nicandra* (like *Physalis* but corolla blue); *Chamaesaracha* (corolla white, scarcely lobed; enlarged calyx only at the base of the fruit, like a saucer);

Solanum (berry enclosed by a prickly calyx in two species and by a smooth calyx in one).

II. *Genera that form capsules.*

   A. A genus with prickly capsules; flowers large, trumpet-shaped: *Datura.*

   B. Genera with smooth capsules: *Nicotiana* (flowers in a raceme-like inflorescence; corolla greenish or white); *Oryctes* (flowers clustered in axils of leaves, minute, white); *Hyoscyamus* (clammy, malodorous; corolla dull greenish-yellow with a network of purple veins; capsule enclosed by the enlarged calyx).

NIGHTSHADES, HORSE-NETTLES, AND OTHERS (SOLANUM)

There are perhaps two thousand species of *Solanum*, most of them tropical. A number are native or introduced in the West. The best known cultivated species are the potato, *S. tuberosum*; and egg-plant, *S. melongena*. The shrubby, so-called Jerusalem-cherry is *S. pseudo-capsicum* (not a cherry and not from Palestine). These may occasionally be found growing in waste ground and on compost heaps, but probably never maintain themselves in our area.

The flowers are in short cymes which in many of our species arise from the stem midway between the attachments of leaves; a very unusual condition. In other species each cyme is opposite a leaf. The petals are joined in their lower halves, or less. The stamens generally form a cone around the style. The pollen escapes through pores or slits in their ends. The fruit is a berry (apparently a capsule in some species) with many seeds in two chambers.

I. *Prickly plants.*

   A. Species whose berries are enclosed by the enlarged, prickly calyx.

BUFFALO-BUR, S. ROSTRATUM (about 2 feet), is invested with star-shaped hairs and yellowish prickles. The leaves are cleft or divided pinnately. The corolla is bright yellow. The lowest stamen is longer than the other four. The "bur" is the prickly calyx around the berry.

June to October: on prairies and in disturbed soil in the plains from Montana and North Dakota to

Oklahoma and in scattered places elsewhere through our range. *Plate 186.* This is believed to be the plant that first harbored the Colorado potato beetle. It is a pest in range land.

S. heterodoxum also has yellowish prickles and its leaves are similarly cleft. The corolla is violet. The one larger stamen is tinged violet. The sepals form a bur. In eastern Colorado.

B. Species whose berries are not enclosed by the calyx.

TROMPILLO, S. ELAEAGNIFOLIUM (about 3 feet), has a covering of silvery hairs mixed with prickles. The leaves lack lobes and division; the edges may be wavy. The corolla is violet-purple, $\frac{3}{4}$–1 inch across, not deeply lobed. The berry is yellow turning black.

May and June (and in some places later): on roadsides and waste ground in Colorado, Kansas, and Oklahoma, and eastward and southward. *Plate 186.* A troublesome weed. The Indians use the berries in making cheese. Some plants lack prickles.

S. dimidiatum (1–3 feet) is not so prickly; some plants not at all. The leaf-blades are ovate, up to 6 inches long, lobed or with wavy edges. The corolla is violet-purple, 1–1$\frac{1}{4}$ inches across, only shallowly lobed. The yellow berry averages about $\frac{1}{2}$ inch through. In Kansas and Oklahoma. *Plate 186.* Horse-nettle, *S. carolinense*, has a white or pale lavender corolla. The prickles are mostly on the under side of the leaves, and on stems and leaf-stalks. The leaves are pinnately cleft. The yellow berry is about $\frac{1}{2}$ inch through. A common weed, most abundant in our eastern states. *Plate 186.*

II. *Species without prickles.*
    See also *S. elaeagnifolium* and *S. dimidiatum*, some plants of which may lack prickles.
    Except the first, all these have white flowers.

S. DULCAMARA, a straggling vine, is distinguished by its purple corolla. At least some of the leaves will have a pair of small lobes near the base of the blade. The berries are red. This is the bittersweet of the Old World, found throughout our area, generally in moist soil. *Plate 186.*

BLACK NIGHTSHADE, S. AMERICANUM (to 3 feet), has undivided and unlobed leaves. The flowers, in small clusters, may be tinged with purple. The berries are black.

June to November: in dry woods and thickets and waste and cultivated land from North Dakota to Oklahoma. *Plate 186.* This has been generally confused with the European *S. nigrum*, which is rare in North America. Both have been called deadly nightshade, and in my boyhood I was adjured to avoid the berries. These do indeed contain enough solanine to kill small animals; but this disappears from the berries as they ripen, and they are generally eaten, cooked or raw, without ill effects. However, some persons are apparently susceptible to small amounts, so that it is well to be cautious. The name deadly nightshade is given in England also to a much more dangerous plant, *Atropa belladonna*, which is not found wild in this country.

S. jamesii may be downy. The leaves are pinnately divided, the segments commonly small. The corolla is about $\frac{1}{2}$ inch across. In Utah.

S. sarachoides, a native of Brazil, is found as a weed throughout the West. The stems are hairy, the leaves wavy-edged and on some plants toothed; they are also sticky, with short hairs. The corolla is only about $\frac{1}{4}$ inch across. The small greenish or yellowish berry is loosely enclosed by the enlarged calyx.

S. TRIFLORUM has sprawling stems up to 16 inches long. The leaf-blades are cleft pinnately, somewhat downy. The corolla is about $\frac{1}{3}$ inch across. The berries are green.

May to September: on roadsides and in streambeds throughout the Rocky Mountains. *Plate 186.*

GROUND-CHERRIES (PHYSALIS)

The ground-cherries are small plants, mostly about 2 feet tall, with branched stems and flowers borne singly. Although the lower leaves on the stem are single, the upper ones, where flowers are borne, are commonly paired. Flower-stalks may arise between two opposite leaf-stalks. Sometimes a branch arises at the same level, in the axil of one of the leaves. Or the flower may grow in a fork of the stem. The petals (yellow in our species) form a hanging bell, the edge of which is scarcely divided into lobes. The calyx is at first small but enlarges greatly so as to completely enclose the berry (the "ground-cherry"); it forms a sort of pointed bladder (whence the name of the genus, which is Greek for "bladder") with five angles, often indented at the top.

The berries are edible though rather tasteless. They have been much used by country people for making preserves.

The species have been confused. By limiting our distinguishing characteristics to such minutiae as the color of the stamen-heads and the presence or absence of dark spots on the corolla it has been possible to reduce a number of variable and indistinct species to a smaller number of more clearly distinct species.

PLATE 186

Solanum americanum   *Murray*

D. Richards

Symphytum officinale

Solanum dimidiatum   *Johnson*

Solanum triflorum   *Korling*

Physalis pubescens   *Kirtley-Perkins*

Solanum dulcamara   *Johnson*

Solanum rostratum   *Rickett*

Solanum carolinense   *Gottscho*

Solanum elaeagnifolium   *Rickett*

But these species are still extremely variable, and the following organization must be used with caution.

All our species are 2–3 feet tall, growing in disturbed soil besides the habitats mentioned below.

I. *Species with dark blotches inside the corolla. The hairs, if any are present, are rarely branched.*
    See also *P. hederaefolia.*

P. VIRGINIANA (6–24 inches) usually has hairs on the stem pointing down. The leaves are downy and sticky, the blades ovate, lanceolate, or narrower, with irregularly toothed margins. The berry is red.

April to October: in open woods and along fencerows from North Dakota to Oklahoma. *Plate 187. P. subglabrata* (1–5 feet) may best be considered a variety. It has smoother leaves with no teeth. *P. longifolia:* Not so tall. Leaves thick, narrowly lanceolate, short-stalked. Berry yellow. From Wyo and Mont to Utah, Colo, and Okla.

P. heterophylla: Leaf-blades ovate. Plants covered with short, sticky, glandular hairs, commonly mixed with longer, non-glandular hairs. From ND to Utah and Okla. *Plate 187. P. pubescens:* Beset with long hairs, sticky or not. Leaf-blades ovate, with or without teeth. Stamens with short blue heads. Kan, Okla. *Plate 186. P. pumila:* Hairs standing out, appearing bristly. Stamens with yellow heads $\frac{1}{10}$–$\frac{1}{8}$ inch long. From Kan to Colo and Okla. *P. ixocarpa:* Much branched, nearly smooth. Leaf-blades ovate, with or without teeth, up to 2$\frac{1}{2}$ inches long. Corolla about $\frac{1}{2}$ inch across. Berry purple. Chiefly an escape from cultivation, recorded from ND to Okla. *Plate 187.*

II. *Species without dark blotches on the corolla. At least some hairs, if any are present, are generally branched. The stamen-tips are yellow.*

P. HEDERAFOLIA is covered with short, sticky hairs. The first species differs in having only unbranched hairs. The leaf-blades are roundish, toothed, to 1$\frac{1}{2}$ inches across. The corolla is about $\frac{1}{2}$ inch across.

May to July: on hills and plains from Utah to Kansas and Oklahoma. *Plate 187. P. fendleri* may be included; it differs chiefly in having branched hairs. *P. viscosa* has leaves ranging from very narrow to ovate, stalked or not, toothed or not. The flowers are greenish with a darker center. In south-central Kansas. *P. neomexicana* (1–2 feet) is downy. The stems are angular. The leaves are ovate or roundish, up to 3 inches long. The corolla is yellowish with dark center. On plains in Colorado and westward.

III. *Species without dark blotches on the corolla and without branched hairs. The stamens have bluish tips.*
    See also *P. hederaefolia.*

P. MISSOURIENSIS is hairy and may be somewhat sticky. The leaf-blades are ovate, mostly toothed or wavy-edged, on long stalks. The stamen-tips are minute.

June to October: in rocky woods and barrens in Kansas and Oklahoma. *P. angulata* may be found along our eastern limits. It is smooth. The leaves have ovate or lanceolate blades, generally coarsely and irregularly toothed, on stalks which may be more than an inch long. The corolla is pale.

QUINCULA

The southern *Q. lobata* crosses our southern boundaries in Nevada, and reaches Kansas. It resembles *Physalis* (where it is placed by some botanists) except in the color of the corolla, which is bright blue-purple, and in the stigma, which is not lobed. The berry is enclosed by the bladdery calyx. *Plate 187.*

NICANDRA

The one species of *Nicandra* is a native of Peru, now established in scattered places in North America. Apple-of-Peru, *N. physalodes,* is much like *Physalis* but with a pale blue-violet corolla. The stem grows up to 5 feet tall. The leaves are stalked, the blades coarsely and irregularly toothed. Established in Kansas and probably elsewhere in the eastern states of our range. *Plate 187.*

CHAMAESARACHA

The berries of *Chamaesaracha* are not enclosed by an inflated, bladdery calyx; this forms a sort of saucer at the base. The flowers have a spreading – not bell-shaped – corolla. In most respects the plants resemble *Physalis.* Small downy pads alternate with the stamens.

PLATE 187

Chamaesaracha nana *Myrick*

Quincula lobata *Morris*

Nicandra physalodes *Beesley*

Physalis hederaefolia *Koch*

Chamaesaracha sordida *Twomey*

Chamaesaracha coronopus *Johnson*

Physalis ixocarpa *Myrick*

Physalis virginiana *Johnson*

Physalis heterophylla *Johnson*

C. CORONOPUS (2–10 inches) is much branched. The many leaves are lanceolate or narrower, commonly cleft pinnately, short-stalked, with a minute scaly down. The corolla is greenish-white.

April to September: on dry plains from Kansas to Oklahoma and Utah. *Plate 187.*

C. sordida is rather glandular-downy and sticky, some plants having longer hairs also. The leaves have oblong, lanceolate, or ovate blades on short stalks; they may be pinnately cleft or merely toothed. The corolla is yellow or whitish with a darker center. The berries are eaten by the Indians. In Kansas and Colorado. *Plate 187.* *C. nana* (4–10 inches) has few or no branches. It bears a minute scaly down. The leaf-blades are ovate, 1–2 inches long, on stalks about half as long. The corolla is white, with a green spot at the base of each lobe. The berry is dull white or yellowish. From Oregon to California and Nevada. *Plate 187.*

DATURA

The thorn-apples and jimsonweeds, genus *Datura*, are rank, poisonous plants with large, ovate leaf-blades. The flowers are in the forks of the stem. The corolla is funnel- or trumpet-shaped, with five very sharply pointed lobes. The capsule is generally prickly, with two cavities containing many flat seeds.

JIMSONWEED or THORN-APPLE, D. STRAMONIUM (up to 5 feet), is a smooth plant with coarsely toothed leaves. The corolla is up to 4 inches long, the lower half enclosed in a tubular, angled calyx.

June to October: in waste ground and fields from North Dakota to Oklahoma and in scattered places westward. *Plate 188.* The stem may be green or purple, the flowers white or pale violet. The plant contains several dangerously poisonous alkaloids; the preparation known as stramonium, containing several of these, has been used medicinally.

An old negro couple, too poor to buy coffee, brewed the seeds of Jimsonweed from their back yard, as a substitute. They were found a day or two later, quite dead.

The name Jimsonweed is a corruption of Jamestown-weed, the plant having appeared around the dwellings of that early settlement.

INDIAN APPLE or TOLGUACHA, D. WRIGHTII (up to 4 feet) has leaf-blades covered with a fine gray down; they are 4–10 inches long. The corolla is white.

June to October: a weed in waste ground from Colorado to California. *Plate 188.* The plants are sometimes used by Indians to produce visions. They may also cause skin inflammations like those due to poison-ivy. *D. quercifolia*, a Mexican species, is naturalized. It has a violet-tinged corolla, and pinnately lobed leaves. In Kansas and Oklahoma.

NICOTIANA

The genus *Nicotiana* comprises a number of rank, heavy-smelling, mostly sticky herbaceous and shrubby species. The narcotic properties of the plants are well known. The tobacco of commerce is obtained from a hybrid group; but several of the wild species contain nicotine and are or were smoked by Indians (chiefly in ceremonies). The genus was named for J. Nicot, ambassador of France to Portugal, who introduced tobacco into France in the sixteenth century.

The leaves are without teeth or lobes but may have wavy edges. The flowers are borne at the top of the stem in an inflorescence which may resemble a raceme but is in fact a cyme. The corolla is tubular or funnel-shaped, or may spread its lobes flat. The fruit is a capsule which has numerous small seeds in two chambers, freed by the lengthwise splitting of the wall into two or four "valves."

N. acuminata: Corolla $\frac{1}{2}$ inch broad or broader. Calyx with five dark stripes, and long narrow lobes of different lengths. Primarily Californian, but was once collected in the Columbia River Gorge and may still be just within our boundary. Native of South America. *Plate 188.*

N. ATTENUATA (1–4 feet) may lack branches. It may be glandular-downy or smooth. The leaves have ovate blades 2–6 inches long, tapering into short stalks. The corolla is white, about $\frac{1}{2}$ inch across, up to nearly 2 inches long.

June to September: in sandy soil and other dry open places from Washington and Idaho to California and Nevada. *Plate 188.*

N. trigonophylla (up to 3 feet) is sticky-downy. Branches are few. The leaf-blades are lanceolate or ovate, 1–3 inches long, the lowest stalked. The corolla is greenish-white, $\frac{1}{3}$–$\frac{2}{5}$ inch across. This may be in our southwestern corner. *N. palmeri*, by some treated as a variety of the preceding species, is doubtfully in our range. The corolla is $\frac{2}{5}$–$\frac{3}{5}$ inch across.

PLATE 188

Convolvulus arvensis   *Johnson*

Hyoscyamus niger   *Johnson*

Nicotiana attenuata   *Mackintosh*

Convolvulus sepium   *Green*

Nicotiana acuminata   *Korling*

Datura wrightii   *Roberts*

Datura stramonium   *D. Richards*

ORYCTES

The only species of *Oryctes* is in our range.

O. NEVADENSIS (2–8 inches) has a leafy stem, the leaves scarcely more than an inch long, tapering into short stalks. The flowers are in small clusters in the axils. The corolla is tubular, yellowish perhaps tinged with purple, ¼ inch long. The calyx enlarges about the developing capsule.

May: in sandy soil in eastern California and western Nevada and northward to Idaho.

HYOSCYAMUS

One species of *Hyoscyamus* is in our range.

HENBANE, H. NIGER (to 40 inches) is rank-smelling and sticky-hairy. The leaves are without stalks, pinnately lobed, 2–8 inches long. The calyx enlarges and encloses the fruit, a capsule. The corolla has a network of purple veins on a pale ground, commonly dull greenish-yellow.

May to August: a weed from Europe naturalized on roadsides and in waste ground over much of the United States. *Plate 188*. As the name indicates, reputedly poisonous.

THE MORNING-GLORY FAMILY (CONVOLVULACEAE)

In temperate countries the *Convolvulaceae* are mostly twining or trailing plants (there are erect woody species in the tropics). The petals, except in one genus, are joined to form a funnel which may flare at the end into a disk; there may be five lobes or teeth, or none. The corolla of most species is twisted or rolled up in the bud – and may twist again as it withers. The sepals are almost separate; some species have bracts just below the calyx, which may be mistaken for the calyx. The ovary has two or three chambers, in each of which two seeds are formed.

Guide to Genera of Convolvulaceae

I. *Genera with a single, undivided style.*

    A. Plants with two stigmas: *Convolvulus* (flowers white or pink; leaves undivided, unlobed or with basal lobes; stigmas narrow).

    B. Plants with one, undivided stigma (it may be lobed): *Ipomoea* (flowers white, purple, or red; leaves undivided and unlobed or palmately divided or lobed); *Quamoclit* (flowers bright red, the corolla-tube narrow, with five small lobes; leaves undivided or pinnately divided).

II. *Genera with a style cleft into two branches or two styles.*

    A. Plants with green leaves: *Stylisma* (flowers white; one style, branched near the tip; leaves very narrow); *Evolvulus* (flowers white or lavender; two styles, each cleft; downy or hairy); *Cressa* (flowers white, very small; two styles; leaves silky).

    B. Plants with no green leaves, twining on other plants: *Cuscuta* (flowers small, many in dense clusters; stems yellow or orange).

BINDWEEDS (CONVOLVULUS)

The bindweeds are common twining or trailing weeds with handsome pink and white funnel-shaped flowers. Except in one of our species, the margin of the corolla is only very shallowly lobed or notched, with five small points at the tips of the five petals. There are two bracts below the calyx. The leaves are more or less arrow-shaped or heart-shaped, with pointed or blunt lobes extending down from the base of the blade. The single style is tipped with two stigmas.

I. *Species whose calyx is enclosed, partly or wholly, by two bracts.*

This group has by many authors been treated as a separate genus, *Calystegia*.

HEDGE BINDWEED, C. SEPIUM, has a corolla 2–3 inches long, white or pink. The two broad bracts may be mistaken for sepals; but the calyx is inside.

May to September: in moist soil practically throughout our range. *Plate 188*. This is a variable species: some forms are native in North America, others introduced from Europe. In England this weed has acquired many names, being variously attributed to the devil (devil's-garter, devil's-gut), to father (daddy's-white-shirt), and to grandmother (granny's-nightcap). And in Somerset it was called morning-glory before our American *Ipomoea* took over that name. It is well-named hedge bindweed, for it often clambers over the English hedges, as it does over American thickets.

C. pellitus is an Asian species found along our eastern boundary in Kansas. It is softly downy, with narrow leaf-blades like arrowheads, on short stalks. The corolla is pink or less commonly white, $1\frac{1}{2}$–2 inches long. In waste ground.

C. spithamaeus has been recorded in Oklahoma. It is generally erect, up to 20 inches tall, with variously shaped leaf-blades 1–3 inches long, on short stalks. There are from one to four flowers together in the lower axils. The corolla is white, $1\frac{1}{2}$–3 inches long. In sandy and rocky open soils.

II. *Species whose calyx is not enclosed by the two bracts, these being some distance below.*

FIELD BINDWEED, C. ARVENSIS, has triangular leaf-blades, rather blunt, on short stalks. The stems twine or trail, commonly forming tangled mats. The corolla is white (or pink-tinged), less than an inch long. The two bracts are narrow and may be $\frac{1}{2}$ inch below the calyx.

May to September: a native of Europe established in fields and waste ground throughout the United States. *Plate 188*. Extremely difficult to eradicate; one of our worst weeds.

C. INCANUS is downy, with slender, mostly prostrate stems up to 3 feet long. The leaf-blades may be ovate or lanceolate or palmately cleft into narrow lobes. There are one or two flowers on a stalk, which also bears minute bracts. The corolla is white or rose-tinged, about $\frac{1}{2}$ inch long.

May to October: on prairies, mesas, and hills from Nebraska to Oklahoma. *Plate 189*.

C. polymorphus may be found along our western boundary in Oregon and possibly northern Nevada. It has lanceolate bracts, and sepals round or notched at the tip. The leaves have spreading lobes at the base of the blade. *C. longipes* is doubtfully present in our southwestern corner. It is somewhat woody and bushy, with very narrow-bladed leaves. The corolla is white or cream, perhaps with lavender veins, an inch long or longer.

MORNING-GLORIES (IPOMOEA)

Many species of *Ipomoea* grow in warm and tropical countries the world around. Of the tropical and Mexican species a number are shrubs or even small trees; but our species are herbaceous – erect, creeping, or twining. The most popular cultivated morning-glories are descended from a Mexican species. Sweet-potato is *I. batatas*. It is sometimes found growing wild, the stem trailing on the ground, bearing leaves with heart-shaped or angular blades up to 4 inches long. Other species are troublesome weeds. The corolla of a morning-glory flares into a more or less flat disk at the end of the trumpet. The style bears only one stigma, but this may have two or three lobes. The leaf-blades are heart-shaped or lobed, cleft, or palmately divided. Most of our species are twining vines.

The English name refers to the habit of certain species which open rather precisely in the morning. Others, however, are just as precise in opening in the evening. Linnaeus devised a "floral clock" by assembling flowering plants thus exact in their ways.

I. *Species whose corolla does not exceed 2 inches in length.*

I. HEDERACEA has broad leaf-blades, deeply indented at the base, and deeply three-lobed (or sometimes five-lobed), the lobes tapering to points. The sepals are distinctive, being shaggy with white or rust-colored hairs and tapering suddenly to long tail-like tips. The flowers open sky-blue and turn rose-purple as they age. The corolla is 1–2 inches long.

July to October: a weed in cultivated and coarse ground from North Dakota to Oklahoma. *Plate 189*.

I. lacunosa has unlobed leaf-blades (they may be angular), ovate and deeply indented at the base. The sepals taper to long points and are fringed with hairs. The corolla is generally white, lobed. In Kansas and Oklahoma. *Plate 189*. *I. trichocarpa* may be found in Oklahoma. The leaves may be unlobed or with three taper-pointed lobes. The sepals are fringed with hairs. The corolla is pink or purple.

II. *Species whose corolla is at least 2 inches long.*

I. PURPUREA has blue, purple, red, white, or varie-
gated flowers, generally two or more on each long
stalk from an axil. The corolla ranges from about $1\frac{1}{2}$ to
3 inches long. The stigma has three lobes; the ovary
three chambers.

On roadsides and in waste land and cultivated
fields in many parts of the United States. *Plate 189.*
This is a tropical species, originally brought into cultivation in this country and now established as a troublesome weed.

I. shumardiana, in Kansas and Oklahoma, has undivided and unlobed leaves, the blades lanceolate or
ovate, to 4 inches long. The corolla is 2–3 inches long.

MAN-OF-THE-EARTH, I. PANDURATA, is chiefly remarkable for its extraordinary tuberous root;
this may be several feet long and 20 pounds in weight,
and is edible. Such a root would be treasure trove to a
hungry Indian family. The rest of the plant resembles
common morning-glory, but may be recognized by
the large white flowers (up to 3 inches long; they may
have a purple center) and the two-lobed stigma. The
leaves may be either heart-shaped or fiddle-shaped.

June to September: in dry woods in Kansas and
Oklahoma. *Plate 189.*

I. leptophylla is bushy with narrow, unlobed
leaves 2–4 inches long. The flowers are borne singly
or two together, the corolla pink, about 3 inches long.
On dry plains from Montana to Oklahoma. *Plate 189.*

QUAMOCLIT

The cypress-vine and its sister species are by
some botanists included in *Ipomoea*. They differ in
their scarlet corolla, and may conveniently be separated from our species of that overloaded genus. The
name is not Latin but Mexican. Our species are tropical plants introduced in cultivation and escaping into
waste places and thickets. They flower from July to
October.

SCARLET-MORNING-GLORY, Q. COCCINEA, has ovate
leaf-blades indented at the base, some with angles,
and some lobed or cleft. The corolla is a flaring tube
about an inch long bearing a five-lobed disk.

In Kansas and Oklahoma. Cypress-vine, *Q. pennata*, is found in the same country. The leaves are divided into hairlike segments. The corolla-tube is more
than an inch long, with five pointed lobes. *Plate 189.*

STYLISMA

One species of *Stylisma*, *S. pickeringii*, is found in
the eastern half of Kansas and in Oklahoma. It has
trailing stems, with narrow leaves up to 3 inches long,
pointed at both ends. There is one style, branched

near the tip. June to September: in sandy soil.
In volume 1 of this series this was labeled *Breweria
pickeringii*, which has been recently shown to be an
incorrect name.

EVOLVULUS

One species of *Evolvulus* is known in the eastern
states of our range, and a second is to be expected.

E. NUTTALLIANUS has low or creeping stems bearing
lanceolate leaves, all densely downy. The flowers
are in the axils, almost without stalks. The corolla is
lavender, funnel-shaped. The ovary bears two styles,

each cleft and each branch bearing a stigma, four in
all.

March to October: in sandy and rocky soils from
North Dakota to Colorado and Oklahoma. *Plate 190.*

E. alsinoides, a world-wide weed, should be found
in Kansas and Oklahoma. It is hairy. Flowers in a
small cluster on a long threadlike stalk.

CRESSA

One species of *Cressa* is in our range.

C. TRUXILLENSIS (up to 8 inches) is a low, much
branched plant, with small leaves, and small flowers singly in the axils. The leaves are silky, not more

than $\frac{1}{3}$ inch long. The flowers are white, about $\frac{1}{4}$ inch
long. There are two styles.

May to October: in salt soil in northeastern California, southeastern Oregon, and western Nevada.
Plate 189.

PLATE 189

Ipomoea pandurata   *Uttal*

Convolvulus incanus   *Emery*

Ipomoea leptophylla   *Roberts*

Quamoclit pennata   *Weiss*

Ipomoea lacunosa   *Elbert*

Ipomoea hederacea   *Johnson*

Cressa truxillensis   *Myrick*

Ipomoea purpurea   *Johnson*

DODDER (CUSCUTA)

Some twenty-one species of unlovely parasitic vines in the genus *Cuscuta* have been reported in our range;* of which seven grow throughout the area and six are found only in the Intermountain Region; the rest being in the Rocky Mountains (four) and the plains (four). These are all leafless plants with yellow or orange stems which twine or trail over other (green) plants, sending suckers into the stems of those plants and absorbing food from them. This is a truly parasitic way of life, relatively rare among flowering plants. Their flowers are small, mostly white or pink, in clusters.

The calyx generally has five teeth, and the corolla also; but in some species both are four- or even three-parted. There may be two styles on the ovary, or one style cleft into two branches. Some species have bracts beneath the calyx.

The differences between the numerous species are minute and technical. Few amateurs will care to tackle the task of identification. Those that wish to must use the technical books. All that we can do here is to supply a brief summary, with a few illustrations which show how the species differ.

The genus is divided into three groups (sub-genera). One is characterized by stigmas which are generally round lumps or disks – not taller than they are broad. This is mainly a North American group and includes nineteen of our species. Another group has stigmas longer than broad, in many species erect and somewhat tapering. These are all natives of the Old World.

To distinguish these twenty-one species by their botanical (technical) characteristics would be impossible here (it would involve careful dissection of the small flowers, and some additional terminology). However, to arrange them geographically will narrow the field for identification; and within each group the brief notes may perhaps enable the reader to give his specimen a name. Of course the first group must be used in conjunction with any one of the other four.

The "lobes" mentioned are the corolla-lobes.

I. *Species found throughout our range.*

A. Species with generally five lobes. *C. gronovii:*

Lobes blunt, spreading. *Plate 190. C. cuspidata:* Lobes pointed, spreading. *C. indecora:* Lobes triangular, the tips bent in. *C. campestris:* Lobes triangular, spreading; flowers to $\frac{1}{8}$ inch long. *C. pentagona:* Lobes sharp, narrow, spreading, the tips bent in.

B. Species with generally three or four lobes. *C. coryli:* Lobes triangular, erect, the tips bent in. *C. cephalanthi:* Lobes very short, blunt.

II. *Species found in our range only in INT.*

All have five corolla-lobes except as noted. *C. californica:* Lobes long, narrow, sharp, bent down; corolla $\frac{1}{8}$–$\frac{1}{5}$ inch long. *C. occidentalis:* Lobes lanceolate, narrow, spreading; corolla round, up to $\frac{1}{8}$ inch. *C. suksdorfi:* Lobes long, narrow, sharp, erect; four or five; corolla about $\frac{1}{8}$ inch. *C. salina:* Lobes short, ovate, pointed, generally erect; corolla $\frac{1}{12}$–$\frac{1}{8}$ inch. *Plate 190. C. denticulata:* Lobes very short, roundish, spreading. *C. epithymum*, from Europe: Lobes triangular, sharp, spreading; see also *C. approximata.*

III. *Species found in R.*

Two are found also in adjacent regions. All have five corolla-lobes. *C. plattensis:* Lobes triangular, sharp, spreading or bent down, the tips bent upward or inward. *C. curta:* Lobes triangular, rather blunt, spreading or erect. *C. umbellata:* Lobes lanceolate, sharp, bent down. *C. approximata:* Lobes triangular-ovate, rather blunt, spreading; corolla round, $\frac{1}{8}$–$\frac{1}{6}$ inch. Introduced from Europe; in INT as well as R.

IV. *Species found in PL.*

C. polygonorum: Flowers in dense clusters. Corolla $\frac{1}{10}$ inch. Lobes four, triangular, sharp, erect. *C. obtusiflora:* Flowers about $\frac{1}{12}$ inch. Lobes five, triangular-ovate, mostly sharp, spreading or bent down. *C. compacta:* Flowers $\frac{1}{6}$–$\frac{1}{5}$ inch. Lobes short, blunt, spreading or bent down. Bracts present underneath the calyx. *C. glomerata:* Flowers $\frac{1}{6}$–$\frac{1}{5}$ inch, in dense masses. Lobes lanceolate, rather blunt, spreading or rarely bent down.

THE BLUEBELL FAMILY (CAMPANULACEAE)

Many plants, naturally, are called bluebells: many plants have bell-shaped flowers colored blue. But the name has been attached by botanists to one such group of plants. It was for these plants that Leonhard Fuchs in the sixteenth century coined the name *Campanula*, from the Latin *campana*, a "bell."

* There may be a few more. I have been unable to determine the status of some species.

THE BLUEBELLS (CAMPANULA)

Some bluebells live up to their name by having a bell-shaped corolla, the teeth relatively short. Other species, however, have a more deeply cleft corolla; in the first, below, the petals are joined only at the base and the lobes spread widely. All but one of our species do have a blue corolla. The flowers are generally in a raceme. The stamens have broad, thin stalks. The ovary is three-chambered, and the style bears a three-lobed stigma. The capsule opens by pores on the sides, with small "lids" which roll up.

I. *Species whose style projects beyond the corolla (as viewed from the side).*

C. AMERICANA (1–7 feet) has lanceolate or ovate
blades, toothed, tapering to their stalk. The spreading corolla-lobes are light blue, with a pale ring at the joined base; there is no proper tube or bell. The style grows downward, the tip turning up. The lower flowers are in the axils of foliage leaves; the upper form a raceme.

June to September: in woods and thickets and on roadsides in Kansas and Oklahoma. *Plate 190.*

C. scouleri (4–16 inches) grows mostly west of our range, but is found (rarely) east of the Cascade summits. The lower leaves have an ovate, toothed blade; the upper narrower. The several flowers are on slender stalks in a raceme. The corolla is pale blue, $\frac{1}{3}$–$\frac{1}{2}$ inch long, the lobes as long as or longer than the tube.

II. *Species whose style does not project beyond the corolla.*

HAREBELL, BLUEBELLS-OF-SCOTLAND, C. ROTUN-
DIFOLIA (4–20 inches), is slender and much branched, the bells hanging from the tips of branches. It has round-bladed ("rotund") leaves only at the base; they soon disappear; a few with narrower blades are above them, and also disappear; most of the leaves are very narrow.

June to September: on rock ledges and in meadows and woods throughout Canada and southward to Nebraska, Colorado, and California. *Plate 190.* Very variable in stature, length of leaves, etc.; a white-flowered form is known. The "Scotland" of the name should not conceal the worldwide distribution of the species. In England, bluebells usually means the abundant and beautiful *Endymion* in the lily family. The hare is a witch animal, so the harebell has magical properties. However, it appears that the English bluebell was originally named harebell, completing the confusion.

C. SCABRELLA has several stems, up to 5 inches tall.
The leaves are without teeth and rather narrow.

The flowers stand singly at the tips of stems; and there may be a few in the axils of upper leaves. The corolla is $\frac{1}{4}$–$\frac{1}{2}$ inch long, the lobes about equal to the tube.

June to August: in rocky places at high altitudes in central Idaho and western Montana; and in the Cascade Mountains from Washington southward through Oregon.

C. PARRYI (up to 10 inches) has most leaves with
scarcely any stalk, the upper narrow, all with few or no teeth; the upper 1–2 inches long. The flowers are generally single at the tips of stems; there may also be a few in the upper axils. The corolla is $\frac{1}{3}$–$\frac{3}{5}$ inch long.

July and August: in moist meadows and other open places in the Wenatchee Mountains of Washington, and from central and northern Idaho and adjacent Montana to Utah. *Plate 190.*

C. UNIFLORA (scarcely over 4 inches) has leaves with-
out teeth, those at the base $\frac{1}{2}$–1 inch long, widest in the outer half, tapering to the stalk. The flowers stand singly at the tips of the almost leafless stems, the corolla $\frac{1}{4}$–$\frac{1}{2}$ inch long, the lobes as long as or longer than the tube.

July and August: in rocky and grassy places at high altitudes from Montana to Colorado, and Utah. *Plate 190.*

MARSH BLUEBELL, C. ULIGINOSA (8–24 inches),
has narrow leaves, mostly without teeth, up to 3 inches long. The flowers are at the ends of mostly leafless branches. The corolla is about $\frac{1}{2}$ inch long.

June to August: in wet places from Canada southward to Nebraska.

C. aparinoides, also called marsh bluebell, is our only species regularly white-flowered. The stem is rough on the angles, as are the toothed edges and midrib of the lanceolate or narrower leaves. Some leaves may be nearly 2 inches long. The flowers are mostly single at the tips of partly leafless branches. The corolla is $\frac{1}{5}$–$\frac{1}{3}$ inch long.

June to August: in meadows and on wet shores from North Dakota to Nebraska and possibly in Colorado.

C. rapunculoides (2–4 feet) is a handsome species from Europe, naturalized along roads, etc., and becoming a weed at least in North Dakota. It has a tall raceme of deep blue flowers $\frac{3}{5}$–1$\frac{2}{5}$ inches long, pointing slightly downwards. Another European found in North Dakota is *C. glomerata* (1–2 feet), with flowers lacking stalks and clustered in the upper axils. The leaves have basal lobes which extend on either side of the stem.

GITHOPSIS

We have one species of *Githopsis*.

G. SPECULARIOIDES (2–6 inches) is gray with minute bristles. The leaves do not exceed $\frac{1}{4}$ inch, the lower ovate, the upper wedge-shaped; they may have a few teeth. The flowers are borne singly at the tips, or some scattered along the stems. The calyx is deeply cleft, with narrow, sharp-pointed lobes, less than an inch long. The corolla is blue or white, in one form shorter than the calyx, in another longer than the calyx.

May and June: in dry open places from southern Washington to California. Several species of *Githopsis* have been described; rarely collected and little understood. There is a tendency now to regard them all as varieties of the above species.

HETEROCODON

There is only one species of *Heterocodon*.

H. RARIFLORUM has very slender, rather weak stems, 2–12 inches long, with few or no branches. The leaves do not exceed $\frac{1}{3}$ inch; they have roundish, toothed blades, no stalks. The flowers are borne singly opposite small leaves (bracts). The base of the flower is bristly. A corolla may be lacking; when present it is $\frac{1}{8}$–$\frac{1}{4}$ inch long.

June to August: in moist open ground at low altitudes from Washington to California and eastward to Idaho, Wyoming, and Nevada.

TRIODANIS

The American genus *Triodanis* was long included in the European genus *Specularia;* it was first recognized as distinct by the brilliant and eccentric botanist Constantine Rafinesque-Schmalz. They are small plants, commonly unbranched, the leaves (except perhaps the lowest) lacking stalks, their edges generally scalloped. The flowers are several in each of the upper axils; but commonly only one matures; and there may be a single flower at the tip. The corolla has five spreading lobes and a short tube. The lower flowers do not open, the corolla being rudimentary; the calyx of these may have only three or four lobes.

All our species grow on the high plains east of the mountains; one (the first below) is throughout our range.

T. PERFOLIATA (commonly 1–2 feet) has leaves up to about $1\frac{1}{4}$ inches long which nearly surround the stem; they have wavy, bristly margins.

May to August: in various situations but not in deserts or wet places, almost throughout the United States; and introduced into tropical America, and Europe. *Plate 190*. This was known to Linnaeus in 1753, who placed it in *Campanula*.

T. leptocarpa (4–20 inches): Leaves generally lanceolate or elliptic, mostly $\frac{3}{5}$–$1\frac{2}{5}$ inches. Corolla blue-violet, about $\frac{1}{3}$ inch. From Mont and ND to Colo and Okla.

T. BIFLORA (1–3 feet) is generally coarsely hairy on its lower stem, rough above. The leaves are elliptic or ovate, mostly $\frac{1}{2}$–1 inch long. The flowers are lavender.

April to June: in disturbed soil (as after burns) in Kansas and Oklahoma.

T. holzingeri (1–2 feet): Bristly or coarsely hairy. Leaves elliptic, or wider toward the end, blunt, $\frac{3}{5}$–1 inch. From Wyo to Colo and Kan. *Plate 191*. *T. lamprosperma* (1–2 feet) resembles *T. perfoliata*. In woods in Kansas.

PLATE 190

Campanula rotundifolia   *J. Smith*

Evolvulus nuttallianus   *Henze*

Cuscuta gronovii   *Rickett*

Campanula uniflora   *Lomax*

Cuscuta salina   *Myrick*

Campanula americana   *Justice*

Campanula parryi   *Roberts*

Triodanis perfoliata   *Johnson*

The complete Index to Parts One, Two and Three
is to be found at the end of Part Three

P A C I F I C   O C E A N

C A N

N

ROCKY

MOUNTAINS

WASHINGTON

Mt Olympus △
Mt Rainier △
Mt Hood △
△ Mt Adams
Columbia R.

OREGON

IDAHO

MONTANA

NORTH DAKOTA

Bitter Root Mountains

Big Horn Mts

WYOMING

SOUTH DAKOTA

Black
Hills

Bad Lands

Cascade Range

Coast Ranges

Siskiyou Mts
Mt Shasta △
Sacramento

△ Mt Lassen

L. Tahoe

Great
Basin

UNITED

NEVADA

Great
Salt Lake

Wasatch Mts

Uinta Mts

UTAH

NEBRASKA

△ Long's Peak

COLORADO

Arkansas R.

KANS

Sierra Nevada 4,510

San Joaquin

CALIFORNIA

South Coast Ranges

△ Mt Whitney
Death Valley

Mojave Desert

Colorado R.

Grand Canyon

Channel
Islands

Colorado
Desert

ARIZONA

NEW MEXICO

OKLA

BAJA CALIFORNIA

Rio Grande

T E X A

Edwards
Plateau

M E X I C O

Rio Grande

DISCARDED